ENERGY AND THE NATURAL HERITAGE

THE NATURAL HERITAGE OF SCOTLAND

Periodically, since it was founded in 1992, Scottish Natural Heritage has organized or jointly organized a conference which has focused on a particular aspect of Scotland's natural heritage. The papers read at the conferences, after a process of refereeing and editing, have been brought together as a book. The fourteen titles already published in this series are listed below (No. 6 was not based on a conference).

This is the fifteenth book in the series.

ENERGY AND THE NATURAL HERITAGE

Edited by Colin A. Galbraith and John M. Baxter

SCOTTISH
NATURAL
HERITAGE

EDINBURGH: TSO SCOTLAND

First published in 2008 by The Stationery Office Limited
71 Lothian Road, Edinburgh, EH3 9AZ

Applications for reproduction should be made to Scottish Natural Heritage,
Great Glen House, Leachkin Road, Inverness, IV3 8NW

British Library Cataloguing in Publication Data
A catalogue record for this book is available from the British Library

ISBN 011 497341 4
ISBN 978 011 497341 4

The views expressed in the chapters of this book do not necessarily represent views of the editors or the organizations that supported the conference and this publication.

Cover image: Studio 9 (Scotland) Ltd.

ACKNOWLEDGEMENTS

The production of this book has been a team effort involving a great many people. We are especially grateful to the authors of the various chapters who have collectively produced the unique source of information presented here. Each chapter has been scrutinized by a number of independent reviewers, and we are grateful to them for their assistance. Thanks are due also to the various photographers who have allowed us to use their excellent pictures to illustrate this book.

The original conference, organized by Scottish Natural Heritage, involved the work of many people, however, the valuable organizational work by Helen Forster, Jo Newman, Marion Whitelaw and Iain Colquhoun deserves special mention. The conference was held at the Festival Theatre in Pitlochry. We thank all the staff of the theatre for their helpful and friendly support that made the event such a success.

Finally, we thank The Stationery Office for their support in the production of this book. Special thanks are due to Ron Wilson and Jon Dalrymple for their patience and expert advice and assistance.

CONTENTS

CONTRIBUTORS

B. Band, Scottish Natural Heritage, Battleby, Redgorton, Perth, PH1 3EW.

C. Bean, Scottish Natural Heritage, Caspian House, Clydebank Business Park, Clydebank, G81 2NR.

C. Beck, Highland Birchwoods, Littleburn, Munlochy, Ross-shire, IV8 8NN.

I. Bryden, Institute for Energy Systems, University of Edinburgh, Kings Buildings, Edinburgh, EH9 3JL.

Y.E. Bushby, Scottish Centre for Carbon Storage, School of Geosciences, University of Edinburgh, EH9 3JW.

D. Cameron, The North Harris Trust, The Old Hostel, Tarbert, Isle of Harris, HS3 3BG.

L. Campbell, Scottish Natural Heritage, 16/17 Rubislaw Terrace, Aberdeen, AB10 1XE.

R. Clift, Director of the Centre for Environmental Strategy, University of Surrey, Guildford, Surrey, GU2 7XH.

T. Cooper, Nuclear Energy Association, First Floor, Whitehall House, 41 Whitehall, London SW1A 2BY.

V. Copley, Natural England, Slepe Farm, Arne, Wareham, Dorset, BH20 5BN.

A.M. Coupar, Scottish Natural Heritage, Great Glen House, Leachkin Road, Inverness, IV3 8NW.

Z. Crutchfield, Joint Nature Conservation Committee, Dunnet House, 7 Thistle Place, Abderdeen, AB10 1UZ.

A.J. Downie, SEPA, Clearwater House, Heriot-Watt Research Park, Avenue North, Riccarton, Edinburgh, EH14 4AP.

P. Ekins, Professor of Energy and Environment Policy, University of London, King's College London, Department of Geography, Strand, London, WC2R 2LS.

L. Foubister, Aurora Environmental, 8 Garson Place, Stromness, Orkney, KW16 3EE.

S. Gair, Redgate Hill Cottage, Kippen, Stirling, FK8 3HS.

K.M. Geddes, MARECO Consultants Ltd, Brig O'Waithe, Stenness, Orkney, KW16 3EY.

S.M.V. Gilfillan, Scottish Centre for Carbon Storage, School of Geosciences, University of Edinburgh, EH9 3JW.

J.S. Gray, Marine Biodiversity Research Programme, Department of Biology, University of Oslo, Pb 1066 Blindern, 0316 Oslo, Norway.

T. Hart, Birchfield, Kings Road, Beith, Ayrshire, KA15 2BN.

R.S. Haszeldine, Scottish Centre for Carbon Storage, School of Geosciences, University of Edinburgh, EH9 3JW.

P. Hutchinson, Scottish Natural Heritage, Battleby, Redgorton, Perth, PH1 3EW.

T. Käberger, International Institute for Industrial Environmental Economics, Lund University, PO Box 196, SE-221 00 Lund, Sweden.

T. Langford, Centre for Environmental Sciences, School of Civil Engineering and the Environment, University of Southampton, Southampton, SO17 1BJ.

C. Lumsden, School of Geography and Geosciences, University of St Andrews, St Andrews, Fife, KY16 9AL.

J. McManus, School of Geography and Geosciences, University of St Andrews, St Andrews, Fife, KY16 9AL.

J. McSorley, Greenpeace UK, Canonbury Villas, Islington, London, N1 2PN.

K. Mills, 3 Priestley Wharf, Holt Street, Aston Science Park, Birmingham, B7 4BN.

C. Mitchell, Scottish Natural Heritage, Battleby, Redgorton, Perth, PH1 3EW.

J. Norris, EMEC Ltd, Old Academy, Back Road, Stromness, Orkney, KW16 3AW.

J. Sprent, 32 Birkhill Avenue, Wormit, Fife, DD6 8PW.

F. Strachan, Highland Birchwoods, Littleburn, Munlochy, Ross-shire, IV8 8NN.

F. Thin, Scottish Natural Heritage, Great Glen House, Leachkin Road, Inverness, IV3 8NW.

J. Thomson, Scottish Natural Heritage, Caspian House, Clydebank Business Park, Clydebank, G81 2NR.

I. Todd, Sunnyside, Ruthven, Huntly, Aberdeenshire, AB54 4TA.

K.C. Walker, Scottish Agricultural College Craidstone, Bucksburn, Aberdeen, AB21 9YA.

C.R. Warren, School of Geography and Geosciences, University of St Andrews, St Andrews, Fife, KY16 9AL.

D.P. Whitfield, Natural Research, Banchory Business Centre, Burn O'Bennie Road, Banchory, Aberdeenshire, AB31 5ZU.

S. Wood, Countryside Council for Wales, Maes-y-Ffynnon, Ffordd Penrhos, Bangor, Gwynedd, LL57 2DW.

INTRODUCTION

Scotland's landscapes and wildlife have for long been recognized as valuable national assets, contributing to tourism and to the wider enjoyment of the outdoors. The appearance of our landscapes, and the varied assemblages of habitats and species found in Scotland are, however, undergoing relatively rapid change, as the impacts of climate change begin to take effect. The need to understand such changes globally has led to a greater recognition that wildlife, habitats, and the processes that ensure ecosystem functioning, all contribute to our well-being and will be key in maintaining the capacity for sustainable development in the future. Services such as clean air, clean water, timber production and productive soils, can no longer be taken for granted and are rightly becoming viewed as assets that require the clear management, and in many cases, the conservation, of ecosystems to ensure their continued supply.

Along with the developing problems associated with climate change and the need to reduce the emissions of greenhouse gases, CO_2 in particular, comes the continually increasing demand for energy worldwide. Scotland is no different from many other countries in this regard and has the twin pressures of reducing emissions whilst meeting future demands for energy. Perhaps Scotland does, however, differ from many other developed countries in that it still retains large areas of semi-natural habitat: areas that have been altered by man, but that still hold spectacular wildlife and habitats, and that in many cases retain a feeling of "wildness", something that appeals to many people in an increasingly crowded and developed Europe. The challenge therefore is to maintain Scotland's environment by managing areas such as the uplands, seas, coasts and rivers in a way that ensures their effective functioning, whilst exploiting energy sources in these areas to meet current and future demands. It is apparent also that the conservation of energy, reducing use, developing energy saving means of transport and designing buildings to increase energy efficiency, should all form part of any future climate change adaptation plan. In addition, technological advances mean that the sequestration of carbon at an industrial scale becomes a more realistic prospect, and could have a key role in Scotland, especially given our history of oil exploration and large-scale industrial processes.

Looking to the future, Scotland has some key challenges to overcome to ensure continuity of energy supply. Technology in relation to energy generation is a rapidly developing field and Scotland is well placed to capitalize on recent innovations. In relation to renewable energy, the Government has recently announced proposals to cut CO_2 emissions by 80% by 2050 with an interim target of 50% by 2020. For these ambitions to be met will require a significant increase in renewable energy generation in the years to come. We are already seeing significant development of wind power generation on land and offshore. Similarly tidal power, perhaps especially tidal-stream, offers real potential for the future. The use of biomass crops as an energy source at a commercial scale is a recent innovation, yet the principles involved are ancient! Clearly modern solutions alter the production efficiency but the underlying practice is the same. The full value of biomass to the Scottish energy budget has yet to be realized but again the potential is clear to see. Similarly the role of fossil fuels in future energy production has to be fully evaluated. Looking more widely, the key debate relates to the role of nuclear power, not just in a Scottish context but internationally. Clearly in the debate to evaluate all of these sources, cost and the level of emissions will be important considerations, however, the use, or otherwise of nuclear power is also an issue of principle to many people. This should, however, be seen in context as the long-term and persistent pollution by excessive CO_2 emissions is just as insidious if not as emotive. The debate is likely to be long and heated.

No matter how the energy requirements of the country are met, by energy conservation or by increased generation, it is obvious that there will be continuing pressure on the environment and particular problems, requiring difficult trade-offs and contentious decisions will arise. Resolving these issues will not be easy or simple, yet there are opportunities for Scotland to lead the field internationally; not just from a technological viewpoint but also by demonstrating that it is possible to meet national energy needs in a way that maintains and even enhances the environment; a national resource on which so much of our well being and future prosperity depends. This win-win outcome will require close dialogue and collaboration between all the parties involved in planning and delivering future activities, and will need courageous decisions to be taken.

This book considers all these issues in depth, with chapters written by leading figures in the "energy and environment" field. It is based on a conference organized by SNH in November 2004; with the chapters being updated to consider recent advances and developments. A chapter on carbon capture and storage has been added to the original papers presented at the conference, as have a number of shorter "case studies" presented originally as "posters" at the conference.

As the debate on energy generation and its various impacts on the environment continue, we hope that the information in this book helps guide future activities and that it manages to shed a little light in dark places, and helps to take some of the heat out of future discussions!

Colin A Galbraith and John M Baxter

Edinburgh

December 2007

PART 1:
Scottish Energy Use

Grangemouth oil refinery and petrochemical complex on the River Forth with Longannet coal-fired power station in background © Patricia and Angus MacDonald/SNH

PART 1:

Scottish Energy Use

This introductory chapter from Janet Sprent *et al.* outlines the current state of play in relation to energy use. They stress that if CO_2 concentrations are to be reduced then we must change both our patterns of energy use and energy supply.

Focusing on some key examples they highlight the role that the aviation industry has in contributing to climate-forcing emissions and that short-haul flights can be particularly bad in this regard. In relation to energy generation, they note that biomass has the potential to make a significant contribution over the coming years, especially if it is used for heat or combined heat and power generation. Within Scotland the overall value of this technology has still to be fully explored; this chapter considers the production and environmental issues involved.

The Flow Country - Caithness and Sutherland, a vulnerable, massive carbon store © Steve Moore/SNH

1 Climate Change: The Need to Alter Our Patterns of Energy Generation and Use

Janet Sprent - *32 Birkhill Avenue, Wormit, Fife DD6 8PW.*

Roland Clift - *Director of the Centre for Environmental Strategy, University of Surrey, Guildford, Surrey GU2 7XH.*

Paul Ekins - *Present address: Professor of Energy and Environment Policy, University of London, King's College London, Department of Geography, Strand, London, WC2R 2LS.*
Formerly Head of Environment Group, Policy Studies Institute, 50 Hanson Street, London W1W 6UP.

Summary

1. If CO_2 emissions are to be reduced we must change both our energy use and our energy supply.
2. Aviation contributes an increasing proportion of climate-forcing emissions and its growth should be curtailed.
3. Short haul flights are particularly bad for the environment and should be replaced where possible by rail transport. This could also reduce the need for some airport expansion.
4. Biomass has the potential to make a significant contribution to energy production and reducing the use of fossil fuels.
5. Biomass should be used for heat only or combined heat and power generation, as well as co-firing with coal or gas.
6. Farmers and generators need a proper supply chain and start-up funding.
7. A form of renewable heat incentive (similar to the renewable electricity incentive) is essential if renewable heat generation is to be competitive.
8. Off-site blending should be allowed when biomass is co-fired with coal.

1.1 Introduction

In 2000, the Royal Commission on Environental Pollution (RCEP) published its 22nd report '*Energy – the Changing Climate*' (RCEP, 2000) in which it recommended that the UK cut its CO_2 emissions by 60% by 2050. This was subsequently accepted by the Government in its Energy White Paper '*Our Energy Future – creating a low carbon economy*' (Department of Trade and Industry, 2003). The two main strands to implementing this

Sprent, J., Clift, R. & Ekins, P. (2008). Climate Change: the Need to Alter Our Patterns of Energy Generation and Use. In *Energy and the Natural Heritage*, ed. by C.A. Galbraith and J.M. Baxter. TSO Scotland, Edinburgh. pp. 5-16 policy have been to reduce energy demand and to look for alternatives to the use of fossil fuel. The RCEP (2000) developed four energy scenarios to show how achievable is the target, including the possibilities of sequestering CO_2 in geological strata, a topic that is considered in Chapter 10 of this volume. There are several ways in which the demand for energy may be reduced, including making buildings (Chapter 7) and industry more energy-efficient. Considerable progress has been made in both of these areas. However, one area that has been badly neglected is transport, particularly aviation, which has been forecast to grow at more than 4% per annum for the foreseeable future (Department for Transport, 2002). The RCEP felt sufficiently strongly about this to publish a Special Report in 2002, 'The Environmental Effects of Civil Aircraft in Flight' (RCEP, 2002). It is this special report and its aftermath that will be the subject of the first part of this chapter. The second part will be devoted to a discussion of the potential of biomass for reducing the use of fossil fuel, another topic singled out for attention by the RCEP.

1.2 The consequences of unrestricted growth in aviation

This section concentrates on civil aircraft, since more comprehensive data are readily available for these and, arguably, it is easier to suggest possible solutions. However, it should not be forgotten that military aircraft also have a significant climate-change effect, associated with burning of fossil fuel. In the early 1990s it was estimated that they consumed as much fuel as about one third of the commercial fleet (Barrat, 1991). Further, because they fly both sub- and supersonically, their emissions, which include other climate-changing pollutants such as oxides of nitrogen, may have a disproportionately large effect (RCEP, 2002). In respect of civil aircraft, the RCEP calculated that, if the Government objective to reduce CO_2 emissions from other sectors were achieved, the proportion of climate forcing accounted for by the projected growth in aircraft movements would rise to be more than half the total by 2050. The findings of the RCEP for civil aircraft, which criticize some aspects of Government policy, have been largely endorsed by the cross-party House of Commons Environmental Audit Committee (EAC) (Select Committee on Environmental Audit, 2004).

The Sustainable Development Commission (2004) commissioned a critique of the Air Transport White Paper that also supported the RCEP's findings and made a number of recommendations, including the following: "we call on the Government to take measures to ensure that the aviation industry is taxed according to the environmental costs it imposes as externalities on others (with adequate compensation for those most directly affected)".

1.2.1 Air freight

In the civil arena, there has been rapid growth in both freight and passenger traffic. For some years the two were combined in that large passenger planes carried freight when they had excess space in their holds. By 2001, a third of all freight entering or leaving the UK by air was carried in cargo-only aircraft (CAA, 2001). To cater for the projected increases, the Department for Transport has suggested that it may be necessary to develop airports that are largely devoted to air freight (Department for Transport, 2002), and indeed such facilities are being developed quietly, for example at Manston in North Kent. Apart from the rapid growth in express parcel services, a significant portion of air freight consists of perishable foods, such as vegetables and fruit. The environmental impacts of air transport typically dominate all other impacts from the supply chain (Sim *et al.*, 2007). Because of

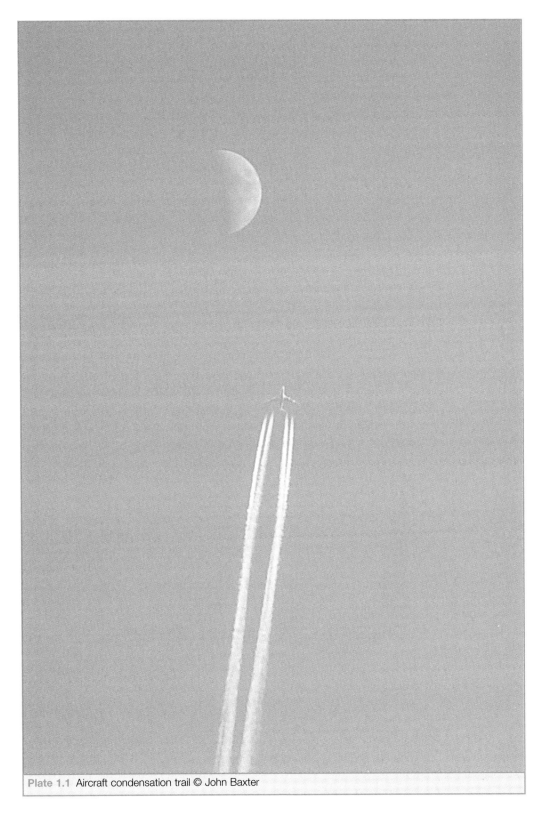

Plate 1.1 Aircraft condensation trail © John Baxter

the relatively low cost of air transport, discussed below, the use of properly controlled transport by sea seems to have been side-lined. It is known that it is possible to transport tropical fruit such as pineapples, and salad items such as lettuce, in good condition on journeys of up to four weeks (JIS personal observations in the Antarctic), as long as handling is minimized and temperatures are strictly controlled. For the same reason, there is no incentive to use improved storage to extend the availability of 'fresh' seasonal produce. It is likely that it will need strong economic drivers to slow down the growth in demand for express parcel services.

1.2.2 Passenger transport

The Government projects that demand for passenger transport at UK airports will double from its present level of around 250 million per year to about 500 million by 2030 (Department for Transport, 2003). These figures are being used to plan airport developments, which the Government argues are necessary to keep the UK competitive with its European neighbours. Although there are vociferous lobby groups associated with particular airports, for example Stansted (Stop Stansted Expansion, 2006), rather less public concern has been shown for the climate-change effects of these increases. Indeed, one of the motivations for the RCEP's 2002 study was the need to point out that a property of aircraft is that they fly!

In its 2002 report, the RCEP drew on a comprehensive study by the Intergovernmental Panel on Climate Change (IPCC, 1999) to show how the contribution to climate change of emissions from aircraft in flight is likely to increase markedly. There is not enough technical change in prospect to offset the projected growth in emissions, and the only means of curbing emissions therefore seems to be to curb the growth in the number of flights, especially the number of short haul flights, which particularly aggravate climate change. This is because of

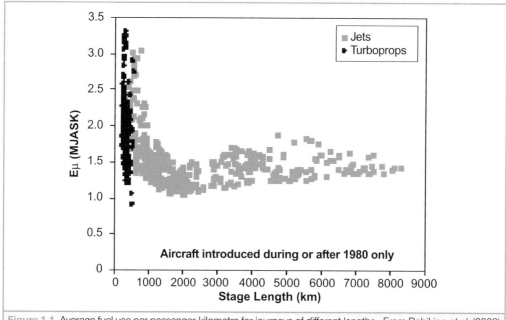

Figure 1.1 Average fuel use per passenger-kilometre for journeys of different lengths. From Babikian *et al.* (2002)

the relationship between the fuel used per passenger nautical mile and the distance flown: short-haul flights use a disproportionate amount of fuel in taxiing, take-off, initial climb and landing. Very long haul flights are also bad because of the amount of fuel used in getting large amounts of fuel airborne, and there is thus an optimum distance in terms of fuel used per passenger-km (see Figure 1.1: the ordinate is a measure of fuel use per passenger-km). The most efficient stage length (the term used in the industry) is about 2000 km. The scatter for very short stage lengths arises, of course, because fuel used then depends on traffic patterns and whether the aircraft is held in a 'holding pattern'. Fuel usage obviously goes up sharply below about 1000 km, a distance corresponding roughly to London to Copenhagen or Munich, or Brussels to Belfast or Gothenburg. All UK domestic flights and those to the nearer parts of Europe are thus particularly bad in terms of climate forcing, and traffic congestion makes them even worse. Gases emitted by jet aircraft plus the condensation trails which are such obvious features of clear skies (particularly over NW Scotland, where many great circle routes between Europe and North America pass close to the navigation beacon at Stornoway) and possibly cirrus cloud seeded by the trails, all combine to contribute about three times the climate forcing caused by the CO_2 emitted by all civil aircraft movements. Thus any form of surface transport, even by car, is preferable in terms of climate change.

However, rail travel and marine transport are, in environmental terms, the best way of transporting large numbers of people and freight. The RCEP argued that investment would be better spent on rail services both to replace short-haul flights for internal travel and to connect people to 'hub' airports, as is the case for cities such as Frankfurt in Europe. If this were to be done, much of the expansion of existing airports would not be necessary. There are various ways in which the demand for flights could be reduced, including taxing aircraft fuel (at present neither aircraft nor marine fuel is taxed), levying a charge on emissions from aircraft, passenger levies, and even rationing flights per person per year. Taxing fuel for international flights is against the terms of the 1944 Chicago Convention, although the EU is now considering the imposition of such a tax within Europe, as well as emission charges and the inclusion of aviation in the EU Emissions Trading Scheme, which started on 1st January, 2005.

One of the policy concerns about increasing the price of air travel is that it would remove from low-income groups the opportunity given to them by low-cost airlines to take holidays that have previously been denied them. However, in 2004, the CAA's Economic Regulator Group (CAAERG) published an extensive analysis of flights taken to and from England and Wales in 2003, as part of their ongoing remit to provide statistics "that enable airlines, airports and other users to respond to demand". One of their most interesting results was that a large proportion of low-cost flights are made by members of the higher socio-economic groups, rather than the lower. One might well ask how enabling relatively high spenders to take short breaks outside the UK helps the UK economy. Further, the majority of those travelling to airports do so by car, taxi or minicab, rather than by public transport, even when this is available. Table 1.1 gives some of the data from this survey for those airports in England and Wales with the largest numbers of passengers. Clearly there are large variations, but the data for Stansted, which is the home of many low-cost flights, illustrate the points particularly well.

Unfortunately the CAAERG did not collect such detailed data for Scottish airports. However, the Scottish Government (formerly known as the Scottish Executive) publishes

Table 1.1A Socio-economic group of UK Passenger by journey purpose 2003

| Socio-economic Group (%) | Business | | | | |
	Birmingham	Gatwick	Heathrow	Manchester	Stansted
A/B	52.2	53.1	65.9	67.3	48.0
C1	43.8	42.5	30.5	27.7	47.5
C2	2.9	3.8	3.1	4.6	3.8
D/E	1.2	0.7	0.5	0.4	0.7
Total	100.0	100.0	100.0	100.0	100.0
Total Passengers ('000s)	1431	2778	9228	2678	2137

| Socio-economic Group (%) | Leisure | | | | |
	Birmingham	Gatwick	Heathrow	Manchester	Stansted
A/B	22.1	33.0	39.8	30.1	33.5
C1	35.0	37.0	42.2	32.5	47.0
C2	19.3	22.9	11.2	27.6	11.8
D/E	23.6	7.1	6.8	9.9	7.8
Total	100.0	100.0	100.0	100.0	100.0
Total Passengers ('000s)	5,783	17,260	14,913	13,110	9,034

Table 1.1B Modes of transport used to reach survey airports. Percentage of total passengers (business and leisure combined).

Mode of Transport	Birmingham	Gatwick	Heathrow	Manchester	Stansted
Private car	52.7	50.5	35.9	57.5	49.8
Hire/taxi/minicab	24.2	17.1	28.4	31.6	11.2
Rail/tube	0.8	25.0	22.9	6.7	28.5
Bus/coach	21.5	7.3	12.6	3.6	10.2
Other	0.8	0.1	0.2	0.6	0.3

regular transport statistics (Scottish Executive, 2004) and these include some data for 2003. They show that in Scotland, as elsewhere in the UK, passenger numbers are increasing rapidly and that most of the flights from Scottish airports are short haul. Of the total, 95% of passengers pass through Glasgow (8.1 million in 2003), Edinburgh (7.7 million), Aberdeen (2.5 million) and Prestwick (1.9 million, mainly low-cost airlines). It must be remembered that Scotland has a long tradition of air transport and that flights are a lifeline for the

Highlands and Islands, especially when bad weather prevents transport by ferry. However, flights to the Highlands and Islands are only a small proportion of the total. For example, of the 2.5 million passengers passing through Aberdeen, only 39,000 went to Kirkwall and 61,200 to Sumburgh, two of the major routes from Aberdeen to the islands.

1.3 Biomass production and combustion as a way of reducing use of fossil fuel

In its Energy Report (RCEP, 2000), the RCEP devoted a whole chapter to alternatives to fossil fuels. A number of these alternatives, including wave and tidal power, wind power and nuclear energy, are considered in other chapters of this volume and are being actively pursued. The RCEP felt that insufficient attention was being given to use of biomass and it therefore produced a Limited Report on '*Biomass as a Renewable Energy Source*' in 2004 (RCEP, 2004). (although the use of biofuels for transport, another topic considered elsewhere in this volume, was not covered).

1.3.1 RCEP (2004)

Because of time constraints, the RCEP only considered plant biomass although many of the same considerations apply to other forms such as chicken litter waste (see also RCEP, 2000).

Plants may be grown specifically for use in energy production: examples include short rotation coppices (SRC) with woody plants such as willow, and grasses such as *Miscanthus* sp.. Except for a few cases, for example willow plantations being developed by Scottish Coal in Lanarkshire, specially grown crops are unlikely to be a major source of biomass energy for Scotland in the near future (Towers *et al.*, 2004). In parts of the UK there are many forest trees not being harvested because of lack of markets, and these could be used for energy production. Co-products from agriculture (for example straw from cereals and oil-seed crops) and forestry (for example thinnings, bark and sawdust from sawmills) can also be used. An extensive analysis of the availability of woodfuel resources in the UK has been carried out

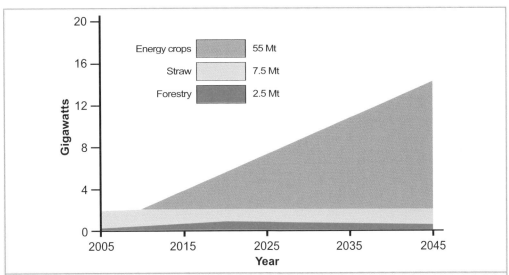

Figure 1.2 Possible scenario for the generation of 16 GW of energy from forestry, straw and energy crops. From RCEP (2004)

by the Forestry Commission (McKay, 2003). In addition, there are often local sources, such as prunings from municipal parks that can and have been used for energy production. These various sources of biomass are sufficient to form the basis for the development of an industry that could contribute up to 12% (16 GW) of the UK's energy needs by 2050 (Figure 1.2).

One of the major disadvantages of current large scale energy generation from fossil fuel, with the notable exception of some combined heat and power (CHP) plants using natural gas, is that only electricity is produced. Heat associated with this electricity generation is wasted, a phenomenon most obviously shown by the presence of large cooling towers. However, most users of energy consume more in the form of heat than electricity (Table 1.2),

Table 1.2 Fossil fuel used for heating and electricity in different operations. From RCEP (2004)

Operation	Units	Space heating & hot water	Electricity
Hospitals	kWh/bed	25,740	7,000
Universities	kWh/fte*	4,200	1,710
Factories	kWh/m²	245	47**
Local Government Offices	kWh/m²	95	39
Commercial Offices	kWh/m²	147	95
Retail	kWh/m²	185	275
Hotels	kWh/bedroom	13,620	6,387
Schools/FE***	kWh/pupil	2,583	372
Leisure Centres	MWh	2,350	65

*   full time equivalent student

**   excluding process electricity

***   further education

which underlines the waste of energy as heat from current power generation. Biomass can act as a unique renewable form of heat, has the potential benefit of providing both heat and power, and uses technology that is available and proven and, indeed, is being used in much of the rest of Europe.

However, there are a number of barriers to the use of biomass for heat, or combined heat and power, which need to be addressed. Firstly, matching supply and demand. This is a problem that varies in extent with the magnitude of the operation: small-scale heat-only plants, serving one or a few houses, need a reliable source of fuel such as wood chips, obtained relatively locally to reduce transport costs. In some cases, such as West Dean College in West Sussex, the heating system is fuelled by material from the estate's forestry enterprise that is unmarketable or is from thinnings (RCEP, 2004). The capital costs of heat-only plant are relatively small, whereas capital costs for combined heat and power and for the hot-water pipework of district heating schemes are higher, although fuel costs should still be relatively low. If surplus electricity is to be fed into the grid, then suitable connections must be in place. In Scottish terms, heat-only and CHP plants from biomass are particularly well suited to areas that are distant from grid connections or from piped gas supplies.

In the longer term, if biomass is to contribute significantly to energy generation (see Figure 1.2), an appreciable area of land must be planted with energy crops. At present, some of this can come from set-aside land, in which case the farmer may get a subsidy. However, larger scale changing over from traditional crops to ones that may have a long rotation (20 years) means that farmers need a guaranteed market for their product, as well as start-up grants. Electricity generators may qualify for Renewables Obligation Certificates (ROCs) reflecting the amount of biomass they use. The RCEP recommended that where biomass is co-fired in a predominantly fossil-fuel fired power station, the issue of ROCs should be conditional upon a contract with the supplying farmer for a period long enough to provide sufficient confidence to plant such long-term crops. This should also time-limit the undesirable practice of importing biomass (such as palm waste from Malaysia), the transport of which significantly reduces the net environmental benefit that co-firing delivers.

There are other supply-chain problems associated with co-firing. When co-fired in coal-fired power stations, biomass must be blended with coal before being fed into the furnaces. OfGem's (The Office of Gas and Electricity Markets) present interpretation of the regulations is that to qualify for ROCs, the blending must be carried out on-site, which significantly increases the cost of co-firing to generators and has therefore reduced the use of biomass for co-firing.

Secondly, the market for biomass heating and combined heat and power applications needs to be developed. Surprisingly few building contractors even think of using anything other than gas or electricity from the grid to provide central heating and other needs of housing or public buildings. It should be mandatory for all planning to include consideration of use of biomass for CHP. There are good precedents: Leicester City, for example, has been providing district heating for over 50 years, initially fuelled by coal. Their new plant will be fuelled by woodchips, 70% of which will be obtained from within a 10 mile radius of the city centre and the rest from municipal arisings within the city boundaries (which also saves money that would have been spent on land-fill tax). Further details of this and other schemes can be found in RCEP (2004). Both the market and the supply chain would be further developed if a Renewable Heat Obligation, along the lines of the Renewables Obligation for electricity that is already in place, was introduced.

Third, government policy in this area is currently very fragmented, with too many different government departments involved. Planning comes under the Department for Communities and Local Government (formerly the Office of the Deputy Prime Minister (ODP)), agriculture and forestry (i.e. growing biomass) is the responsibility of Department of Environment, Food and Rural Affairs (Defra) and power generation that of the Department of Trade and Industry (DTI). In addition to these bodies, devolved administrations have responsibility for different parts of the system. For example, in England there is a Woodland Grant Scheme, part of the England Rural Development Programme, whereas in Scotland there is the Scottish Forestry Grants Scheme. However, there are now signs of a move towards a more coordinated approach to biomass utilization, such as the introduction of Defra's Biomass Infrastructure Scheme and their Strategy for Non-Food Crops. On 15th October, 2004, the Government announced the formation of a Biomass Task Force to generate a 'green power surge' by addressing these and other issues in relation to biomass. The Task Force's one-year study of biomass has been led by Sir Ben Gill, ex-President of the National Farmers' Union, with John Roberts, Chief Executive of United Utilities, and Nick Hartley of OXERA Consulting.

1.4 Natural heritage aspects of the use of biomass

Other chapters will consider the natural heritage aspects of renewables such as wind farms. In Scotland these can be particularly sensitive when much of the energy generated goes into the grid and then south of the border. Similar concerns could arise over increased use of biomass for energy.

1.4.1 Landscape issues

The public, especially in Scotland, is very sensitive to some landscape issues, for example the widespread dislike of monocultures of sitka spruce on uplands. It is possible that these trees could be used for biomass, but the economics in terms of infrastructure, in particular transport costs, may preclude this. For the same reason, large scale planting of trees for biomass is more likely to be at lower altitudes, and the feasibility of using managed mixed woodland should be investigated. This could have amenity benefits and also encourage biodiversity (see below). SRC grown on arable land generates a crop that may be several metres high; grasses for biomass are shorter (2-3m), but still above the level of traditional arable crops such as cereals. If growth of energy crops is to become a major feature of the UK energy system, then this whole issue needs to be subject to proper Strategic Environmental Assessment (SEA), and major energy crop developments should be subject to environmental impact assessment, perhaps carried out through the planning system. Advice on good practice is available: for example the Forestry Commission has produced guidelines on the planting of SRC, particularly willow, to minimize the impact on the landscape (Forestry Commission, 2001). At all stages, the involvement of local communities in the planning process, and their acceptance of it, will be crucial if energy crops are to be grown and the associated technologies for their use are to be installed on a wide scale (RCEP, 2004). In the case of small scale local heating systems, the plant involved may be fitted into a building typically the size of a domestic garage (as seen for example in the Fyne Homes unit at Lochgilphead, Argyll). Larger scale plant needs to be sited carefully, particularly with respect to location of chimney stacks.

1.4.2 Biodiversity and pollution issues

The farming industry is getting increasingly involved in environmental issues, particularly in protecting and enhancing biodiversity, for which there are various incentives (e.g. set-aside) and producer-led initiatives such as LEAF (Linking Environment and Farming). The revised EU Common Agricultural Policy which came into effect in January 2005 represents a move towards defining the environmental role of farming. The Game Conservancy Trust and others have carried out a series of research studies to examine the effects of SRC on biodiversity (e.g. Sage and Tucker, 1997). SRC can support a wider range of biodiversity than, for example, winter wheat. In particular many invertebrates and small mammals flourish and these in turn provide food for a variety of birds. As SRC can tolerate a higher level of insect damage than crops for the food market, pesticide and herbicide usage can be reduced. More weed species are found and these also act as a food source for birds. Properly sited and managed, energy crops can have amenity value for bird watchers and others interested in wildlife.

Biomass crops use nutrients and water, and this has caused some concern, but these concerns should be considered in relation to requirements of alternative crops, and in the case of water, other needs, such as for domestic water supplies. It is important to take into

Plate 1.2 Willow coppice - Edge of a field of established short-rotation coppice showing the willow (centre-right) adjacent to the field hedge (left). © Phil Baarda

account the overall use of plants such as willow when considering their potential for biomass. Now that it is illegal to dump sewage sludge at sea, trials have been conducted on its use to provide fertilizer and water for biomass crops: results are very encouraging in terms of plant growth and cost-effectiveness as a way of sequestering pollutants (Johansson, 2003). Because willow, in particular, is good at extracting heavy metals such as cadmium from soil, it can also be used for bioremediation, provided that care is given to the disposal of the fly ash from subsequent burning of the crop.

Any form of incineration produces gases that may be harmful, and these must at least comply with pollution control standards. Since there are wide variations in the mineral content of different biomass species grown on different types of soil, these should be dealt with on a site-by-site basis. In the incineration plant, some gases, such as nitrogen oxides, can be removed by wet or dry scrubbing, leaving two kinds of ash. Bottom ash from the combustion chamber itself has various possible uses, depending on its composition; these range from a useful P and K fertilizer to a construction aggregate for use in breezeblock production. Heavy metals such as cadmium, mercury and lead are concentrated in the fly ash, which is collected from the gas cleaning system along with any sorbent material used. Thus the pollutants are concentrated in the fly ash, for disposal in managed land-fill. These processes and problems are dealt with in detail in RCEP (2004).

1.5 Final comments and acknowledgements

We have concentrated here on some aspects of the problems of aviation and biomass, drawing heavily on recent publications of the RCEP, of which all the authors of this paper are members. However, this chapter is written in our personal capacities and we have taken this opportunity to include material that was not available when the RCEP's reports were written. In addition to the references given below, we recommend readers to visit the websites of major players such as the CAA, Defra, Forestry Commission and SEERAD. We thank John Baxter for adding some additional material to help bridge the gap between the conference date and publication of this volume.

References

Barrat, M. (1991). Aircraft Pollution: Environmental Impacts and Future Solutions. *Research paper by World Wildlife Fund, Geneva.*

Babikian, R., Lukachko, S. P. and Waitz, I. A. (2002). Historical Fuel Efficiency Characteristics of Regional Aircraft from Technological, Operational, and Cost Perspectives, *Journal of Air Transport Management.* **8**: No. 6, 389-400.

CAA. (2001). International and Domestic Freight 2001.

CAAERG. (2004). *2003 Passenger Survey Report.*

Department of Trade and Industry. (2003). Energy White Paper: Our Energy Future – creating a low carbon economy http://www.dti.gov.uk/energy/energy-policy/energy-white-paper/page21223.html; accessed 05 August 2006.

Department for Transport (DfT). (2002). The Future Development of Air Transport in the United Kingdom. A National Consultation.

Department for Transport. (2003). *The Future of Air Transport,* Cm 6046, December 2003.

Forestry Commission. (2001). *Short Rotation Coppice in the Landscape,* Forestry Commission.

IPCC. (1999). *Aviation and the Global Atmosphere,* Cambridge University Press, Cambridge.

McKay, H. (2003). *Woodfuel resource in Britain,* Forestry Commission.

Johansson, E. (2003). Personal communication obtained during a visit of JIS and RC to Ena Kraft, AB, Sweden.

RCEP. (2000). Energy – the Changing Climate. *22nd Report of the Royal Commission on Environmental Pollution* Stationery Office Ltd., Norwich.

RCEP. (2002). The Environmental Effects of Civil Aircraft in Flight. *Special Report of the Royal Commission on Environmental Pollution* Stationery Office Ltd., Norwich.

RCEP. (2004). Biomass as a Renewable Energy Source. *Limited Report by the Royal Commission on Environmental Pollution* Stationery Office Ltd., Norwich.

Sage, R.B. and Tucker, K. (1997). Invertebrates in the canopy of willow and short rotation coppices. *Annals of Applied Biology.* **49**: 105-111.

Scottish Executive. (2004). Transport Statistics No 23:2004 edition. see also http://www.scotland.gov.uk/stats/bulletins/360/00360a-03.asp

Select Committee on Environmental Audit. (2004). http://www.publications.parliament.uk/pa/cm200304/cmselect/cmenvaud/623/62303.htm; accessed 05 Agust 2006.

Sim, S., Barry, M., Clift, R. and McLaren, S. (2007). The relative importance of transport in determining an appropriate sustainability strategy for food sourcing: a case study of fresh produce supply chains. *The International Journal of Life Cycle Assessment* http://www.scientificjournals.com/sj/lca/Abstract/ArtikelId/8696

Stop Stansted Expansion. (2006). http://www.stopstanstedexpansion.com/news.html; accessed 05 August 2006

Sustainable Development Commission. (2004). UK Air Transport White Paper (The Future of Air Transport'. Analysis and Report to the Sustainable Development Commission. http://www.sd-commission.org.uk/

Towers, W., Birnie, R.V., Walker, K. and Howes, P. (2004). *Energy from Crops, Timber and Agricultural Residues.* Report to SEERAD.

PART 2:
Legacy of the Past

Laggan dam © Lorne Gill/SNH

PART 2:

Legacy of the Past

Scotland has a long history of technological innovation and of heavy manufacturing industries that required large amounts of energy to power development. This part reviews the key developments over recent times and considers the social and environmental implications of energy production. A series of innovations have allowed previous generations to exploit fossil fuel reserves, notably of coal, providing a reliable and relatively cheap source of energy. The provision of coal must have transformed the lives of many and the consequent availability of electricity, again made possible by technological innovation, has led to perhaps the biggest single improvement in the quality of life of the population. John McManus reviews the evolution of the coal industry in Scotland in the following chapter and notes the contribution it has made to society in Scotland over the years.

The development of hydropower, primarily during the 1950s and 1960s marked a key period in the expansion of power generation capacity in Scotland. The recognition that renewable sources of energy could be developed in this way, and that Scotland had the capacity to generate a significant percentage of its electricity by this means was important. These developments have given us a legacy of renewable power generating capacity that will surely help meet new and challenging CO_2 reduction targets. No development of this nature comes cost free, however, and the chapter by Terry Langford reviews the environmental issues involved.

The development of the nuclear industry, again over the 1950s and '60s changed the dynamic of how the UK might meet its increasing requirements for energy. Nuclear offers a technology, essentially free from carbon emissions, albeit with other environmental issues to be considered. The chapter by Jean McSorley considers the issues involved, noting that many are of international importance as well as being significant nationally.

The chapter by John Gray, looks at the implications of the oil and gas industry for the environment. Clearly, the oil and gas industries remain an important part of the economies of Scotland and the UK, hence ensuring environmentally benign forms of extraction for both oil and gas is important. By drawing from examples in Norway the chapter explores how monitoring in the marine environment can help evaluate any changes detected. Recent work in mapping the seabed, and in studying the habitats found there, has begun to show us just how important and fragile many of these habitats are.

Finally, in this part, Tom Hart outlines the complex relationships between the economy, energy and transport, and reviews future scenarios for transport for the next 20 to 30 years in light of the current situation of ever increasing emissions from this sector. He explores the impact of both the Micawber Approach and the Precautionary Approach to the problem and concludes that it is only through the latter that the transport sector can contribute to easing the problems of climate change with greater emphasis placed on energy conservation, travel restraints and more sustainable settlement patterns.

The following chapters demonstrate the key role that energy generation has played in the past and how many of our current approaches and attitudes to environmental issues have been shaped by earlier developments and arguments. The challenge now is to learn from the past to help ensure a better and more sustainable future.

2 Impacts of Coal Mining and Abandonment

John McManus - *School of Geography and Geosciences University of St Andrews KY16 9AL.*

Summary

1. The coal-bearing rocks of Scotland lie principally within the Midland Valley. Five phases of exploitation reflect changes of extraction methods or of waste disposal methods.

2. The Romans in Scotland used coal, and documents show its use in the 11th century. Until 1550 coal for domestic heating and saltings was from coastal outcrops, or valley side exposures. Waste production was minimal.

3. Between 1550 and 1750 shallow depth bell pits and room and stoop workings were introduced, but shaft depth was limited to 40-50m by groundwater. Men were hewers and their families carried coals to the surface, with wastes remaining below ground.

4. The demand for coal to power industry increased during the Industrial Revolution after 1750. Steam-driven water pumps and use of pit ponies were innovations. After steel wire replaced ropes and the lifting of coals to the surface became mechanized, women and children were banned from working underground and transferred to sorting the coals at the surface. Waste disposal created the first bings; longwall excavation and reduced backfill by wastes on abandonment led to increased mining-induced subsidence. Canals spread across the country to carry the coals to ports and smelters.

5. Deep mining output soared to 5.5 million tons per annum by 1900. Bing growth mirrored the underground activity, although backfilling by wastes limited subsidence. In coastal mines the redd was released to the foreshore.

6. Following Nationalization in 1947 progressive closure of the deep mines reflected increasingly difficult geological conditions and the removal of bings began. Today virtually all mining is opencast, with excavated sites 'restored' to largely agricultural use; short-lived, isolated opencasts are tolerable, but surrounding villages with simultaneous landscape devastation is not acceptable.

2.1 Introduction

Distributed across the Midland Valley of Scotland from the Firth of Clyde to the North Sea, most coal bearing rocks in Scotland are of the Carboniferous period, but younger, Jurassic, coals are present in the Brora area of Sutherland. The story of coal exploitation links

McManus, J. (2008). Impacts of Coal Mining and Abandonment. In *Energy and the Natural Heritage*, ed. by C.A. Galbraith and J.M. Baxter. TSO Scotland, Edinburgh. pp. 21-32 technological advance, social history and international economics. The ability of miners to penetrate ever deeper into the earth was accompanied by problems of disposing of extracted but unwanted materials. The evolution of the industry will be addressed as a series of temporally linked changes, few of which created landscape features.

2.2 Pre-1500

During the Roman occupation of Britain, coals in the Forth and Clyde valleys were exploited by troops on the Antonine Wall (Montgomery, 1994) but the documented history of coal winning in Scotland began in the 12th century, when King Malcolm IV (1153-65) and King David I affirmed their right to a tithe of the coals recovered. In 1202 William de Vipont granted a tithe of his coals to the monks of Holyrood. Two decades later Seyer de Quinci granted the monks of Newbattle Abbey a coal works near Tranent (McKechnie and Macgregor, 1958) and a charter dated 1291 permitted the monks of Dunfermline Abbey, to work the coals for their own use, 'but not for sale to others' (Cunningham, 1913). In 1294 the monks of Paisley Abbey were given rights to dig sea-coal; by this time coal was being used for heating monasteries, castles and by the general population. The first Clean Air Act, passed in 1306, banned the use of coal for domestic purposes in London in the belief that the smoke and fumes were dangerous to health.

Coals were also used at this time for the boiling of sea water in salt-pans, at places such as Prestonpans, Kennetpans, Grangepans but also at many other coastal sites. At Wemyss, in Fife, estate records show salt production in 1428 (Moodie, 2002). Between 6 and 16 tons of coal were needed to produce one ton of salt (Duckham, 1970; Brotchie, 1998). The first coal heughs or excavations were recorded at Crossraguel Abbey, at Kirkoswald, in Ayrshire in 1415 in connection with coal working at Dailly (McKechnie and Macgregor, 1958). By the mid-15th century most of the shallow near surface coal heughs were nearing exhaustion. Ash began to accumulate around the salt pans, and was disposed of directly into the sea.

At this stage the mining industry began to develop, extending the quarrying of individual coal seams from their outcrops, along valley sides or at the coast into the hillsides or cliffs. The coals were removed and any waste material was deposited near the mouth of

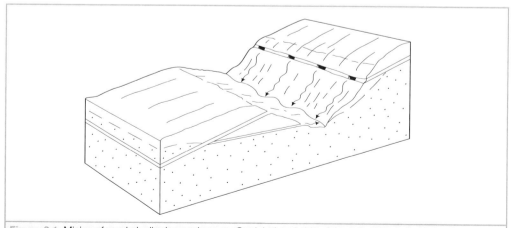

Figure 2.1 Mining of regularly dipping coal seam. On right hand side of the valley the seam drains freely to the air. On the left side the water is drained by a 'day level' tunnel. Dotted symbol marks the water-saturated rocks. Dark inlets on the valley outcrops are 'ingauin e'es'.

the opening. Once the coals were removed the roof was supported on wooden props or fallen rocks displaced as they were undercut. Penetration beneath the hillsides was commonly accompanied by the mine encountering the groundwater, the drainage of which became a major issue. Where the seams sloped upwards away from the valley side outcrop, the waters would drain under gravity, and extraction of the coal could continue unhindered. However, where the seams were inclined downwards from the outcrop, unless an alternative means of removal of the water could be devised, the mining would be severely limited. The construction of a tunnel (the day level) sloping upwards from the river bank to intersect with the workings or shafts lowered the level of the groundwater, producing a 'free zone' which enabled working to continue for a period. Mines driven directly from surface along the coal seam were later known in some areas as 'ingauin e'es' (Figure 2.1).

The lasting landscape features from such workings are difficult to recognize, for they consist of limited quantities of fill on the lower slopes of hillsides, albeit often below a sharp increase in the slope across the outcrop of the worked seam, but even here landsliding after abandonment was common, so the superficial manifestations of the workings are generally minimal and difficult to detect. The quantities of waste carried from the workings were small as most of the 'goaf' (rock fragments) and small coals were retained within the mine to prevent or limit roof fall. All transport of material to the surface was by human labour and unnecessary energy expenditure was to be avoided. In general only 'great coals' (coarse blocks) were carried to the surface.

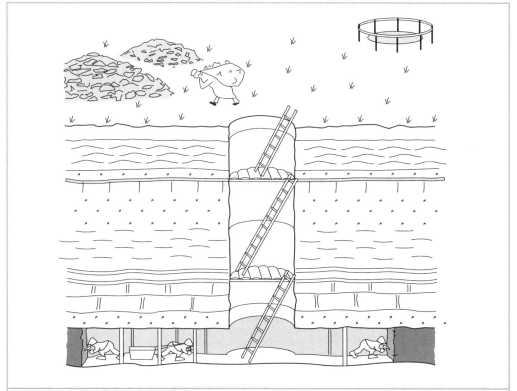

Figure 2.2 Deep bell pit working with ladders and platforms for access. Wastes were deposited to the left as extraction worked to the right. Woman carries coals to the 'hill'. Note nearby abandoned shaft top.

Where the seams lay at no great depth, the extraction of coal was made possible by sinking short vertical shafts to the seam. The coals were removed from the base of each shaft, from which the workings extended for short distances from the shaft base, broadening along the coal seam, and giving rise to their name as 'bell pits' (Figure 2.2). Later the workings extended radially for over 50 m. In many cases the shafts penetrated more than one layer of coal and simultaneous working at two or more levels was possible. The coals were pulled to the base of the shaft in tubs by putters (children or women), and physically carried up the 15-25m to the surface by bearers (usually women) ascending sequences of ladders or stairs. The use of bell-pits continued well into the 18th century, when accounting records from the Banfield Coalbook (1749-1761; Melville, 1793) show that in that one field near Ceres in Fife, new shafts 40-50m deep were sunk every six months or so. Often the adjacent workings were connected to earlier excavations.

Abandoned shafts were often filled with wastes from the new shafts as they were constructed, but the presence of many shallow pits in the landscape above former bell-pit workings testify to the fact that the back-filling was far from total. Little waste beyond an occasional piece of rock within the light coals would have been brought to the surface, lest the load be rejected and the hewer effectively fined by surface quality control personnel. Where outcrop extraction continued, the wastes were still deposited locally, and in the First Statistical Account of Dysart, Muirhead (1792) refers to a 'continuous line of waste visible for three miles along the crop'. Thus, their landscape impact remained for several centuries after outcrop working ceased.

2.3 1550-1750

At the start of the 16th century no mines were large or highly productive (McKechnie and Macgregor, 1958); by the end of that century most outcropping coal had been worked out,

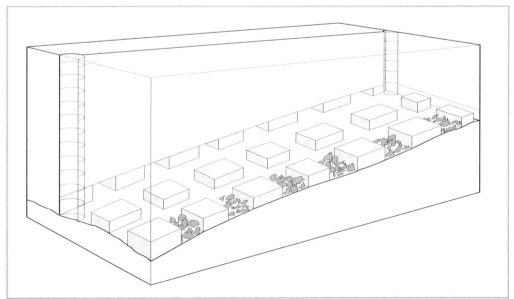

Figure 2.3 Room and stoop workings on an inclined coal seam. Deep Pit and Bye Pit shafts are shown. Wastes are stored in abandoned rooms.

as at Balgonie (Brodie, 1978). During this period 'room and stoop' working was introduced to Scotland (Figure 2.3); in this system the first of two shafts (the deep pit) reached the lowest level to be worked on the seam: from its base a horizontal mine or road was constructed along the strike within the coal seam, and a second shaft was driven up the dip. A second shaft (the bye pit) was formed at a high point of the workings, linking to this second road. From the lower level road the colliers worked up the slope, extracting rooms 3m-5m square between which were left 2m-4m square pillars to support the roof. At best about two thirds of the coals were removed (Duckham, 1970), the remainder being left in the supports. Waste material was packed into abandoned rooms, helping to minimize subsidence.

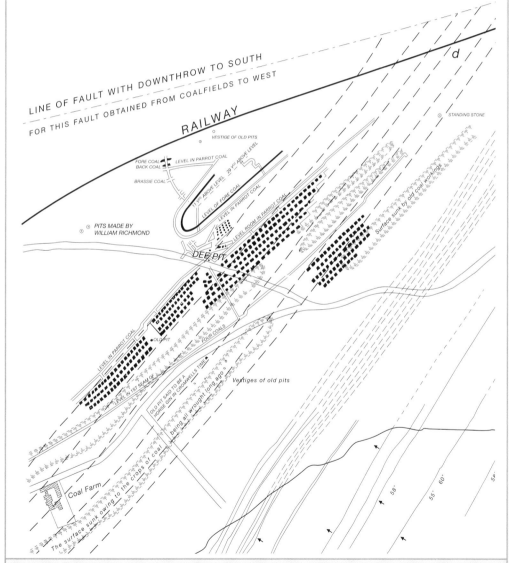

Figure 2.4 Extract from map by Hogg in Galloway (1885) showing distribution of rooms (black squares), and the levels used to drain waters in the Parrot Coal and the First of the Four Coal seams, draining towards an engine to the west of Coal Farm, St Monans. The sea outfall from the pumps was wrongly marked as a 'Mineral Well'.

Evidence of abandoned shallow depth room and stoop workings is seen in many areas, as on slopes south of Markinch, Fife. Systems of deep and bye pits, levels and associated workings along the southern margins of the former Pittenweem Coalfield, in south-east Fife, are shown on the 1785 map of Hogg (Martin, 1999), a site where Galloway (1885) estimated that 70% of the coal remained in the ground (Figure 2.4).

By the late 16th century, water was the principal problem for the mine owners, and mechanical pumps introduced to drain water from mine workings permitted extraction to greater depths. One form was the 'Egyptian Wheel' (sakhia) pump, whereby a horse follows a circular path around a central axle driving a chain of buckets to scoop and discharge the water into a drainage channel. Sir George Bruce opened a shaft at Dunimarle (near Culross) and linked it to an artificially created island, dubbed the Moat Mine, by excavating beneath the Forth. Drained by horse power, it was overwhelmed during a major storm shortly after being visited in 1617 by King James I who briefly believed himself to have been kidnapped when he emerged on the island (Montgomery, 1994). At Wemyss, in south Fife, a similar horse gin with a chain of buckets was used in 1622 to drain water from workings extending 40m below sea level under the Forth (Moodie, 2002). Water- or wind-powered drainage followed, and many lades or diverted stream systems produced in the mid-17th century survive today, although no longer providing power for industry. The water powered systems could not work in dry or freezing conditions while the wind powered systems could operate only during windy weather and therefore lacked reliability.

The introduction of steam-powered pumps by Savery (1698) and Newcomen (1705), revolutionized the industry. First recorded in Scotland in 1720 at Elphinstone, Stirlingshire and in 1725 in Midlothian, these early steam pumps used coals to raise the steam, but were rather unreliable.

Until the start of the 18th century little waste was produced from the mines - only marketable material was carried to the surface and the wastes were retained below ground. The creation of stream diversions or lades to power the waterwheels and surface subsidence above shallow workings were manifestations of the industry. Many of the early subsidence hollows remain visible today.

2.4 1750-1850

The coal industry in Scotland was transformed after 1750, when the first impact of the industrial revolution was felt. By then average annual coal consumption was between 0.5 and 0.75 tons per head of population (Duckham, 1970). The development of iron smelting using coke at the Carron Ironworks led to greatly increased demand for coal, and many new mines were created.

James Watt (1763) greatly improved on the Newcomen steam engine by developing a double acting cylinder system that enabled a shaft to be rotated continually; flywheels on the shaft could be used to drive machinery such as pumps and winding wheels. Steam engines were introduced at the Kinneil Colliery (West Lothian) in 1768, primarily for use in pumping, and in 1784 they became used as winding engines. With mechanized haulage of coals to the surface the mine roadways below ground were enlarged, wooden rails were installed, and pit ponies below ground hauled coal tubs to the shaft foot. Later subsidiary steam powered winding machines at depth permitted haulage along the main access routes from remote parts of the mine.

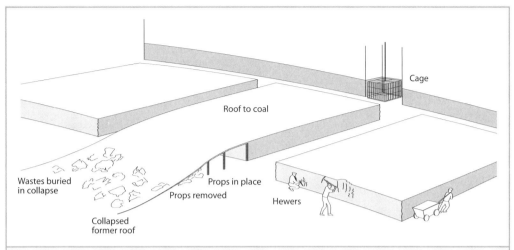

Figure 2.5 Longwall mining in which the entire coal seam is removed systematically. Roof support props are taken down and moved forward as extraction progresses, allowing the overlying rocks to collapse behind the active workings. Coals are transported to shafts along well defined roadways using wheeled tubs.

At this time longwall exploitation became widely used (Figure 2.5). In this method two tunnels 100-200m apart are driven into the coal seam from a shaft access road, and a tunnel is formed to link them. One side of this tunnel is the longwall working face: the coal is removed from this face as it is caused to retreat towards the shaft access road. The coals are removed to the normally much larger access tunnels, which are firmly supported by coal and rock walls or props. The area within which the miners work is supported on pit props which are moved forward as the face advances; any wastes are packed into the abandoned areas, and as the face retreats the excavated sector is allowed to collapse behind the workings. By this method it is also possible to work the thinner seams in the succession, and a longwall working may equally advance between two tunnels. The economics of such workings are greatly superior to the room and stoop method. However, because the entire seam thickness is extracted, there is commonly greater damage to the land surface above the workings if shallow.

A second technique was used, horizon mining, in which the coal seams were approached by constructing horizontal access roads driven from the shafts to intersect the coal seams. In collieries using this method several horizons could be worked simultaneously, with the roads driven at different levels, including the lowest to be worked in the field (Figure 2.6). The actual coals were then worked as longwall or room and stoop as appropriate. An early example of this form of working at Halbeath, Fife, is given by Payne (1982). During the early phases of both forms of mine development, substantial quantities of wastes were produced to accumulate as the earliest "bings" ('bing' is Swedish for heap).

The increased use of 'fire engines' as the steam driven powered systems were known, enabled the winding wheels to lift the coals to the surface. Hemp ropes were replaced by steel wires for haulage in 1829 and transport of materials to the surface was greatly accelerated - and with greater safety, as the elasticity of the wire was much less than that of the hemp ropes.

Duckham (1970) concluded that the annual coal supply in Scotland reached 1.55 million tons in 1800, a substantial increase over the 0.475 million tons produced in 1700.

Coal dust, of little commercial value was regarded as waste and accumulated on the surface near the mine. Transport of the raised coals to the consumer was hindered by a poor and often dangerous road system, and water was a preferred option if industry did not develop near the coalfields. The era of canal building to provide transport for industrial materials had arrived, a prime example being the Forth and Clyde Canal across central Scotland, completed in 1790. A system of wooden-railed wagon ways along which horses drew tubs to the harbours is known to have been operated at Pittenweem in 1770 (Martin, 1999). Turnpike road development began in the mid-18th century, the network reaching completion towards the end of that century. MacAdam constructed the roads with 20cms of rock aggregate to provide a secure surface; only much later, in 1867, was the surface first bonded with asphalt to form "tar MacAdam". Although the coal mining itself was having little impact on the landscape the associated infra-structure was starting to cause substantial changes. By the early 19th century reliable road and canal systems were in place, and waste bings were sprouting around the larger collieries.

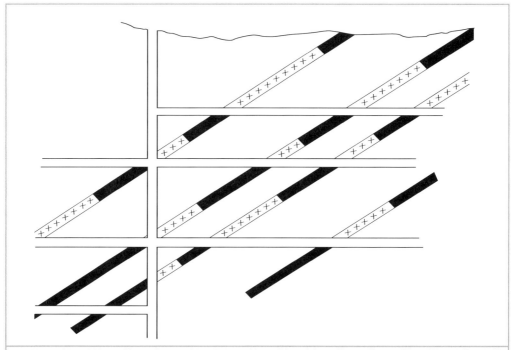

Figure 2.6 A pattern of horizon mining in which roadways are drived horizontally at different depths and the coals extracted by room and stoop or longwall methods from above the roadway levels, Coals removed are indicated by + symbol

2.5 1850-1947

By 1851 the era of steam driven transport by railway had begun, and the country would soon be criss-crossed by railway networks, many initially built to transport minerals to their markets, and later used by passengers. Linear embankments and cuttings marked the routes taken by the railways, with bridges appearing across valleys. Quite major landscape changes were happening as a result of the needs of the coal mining industry.

It was not until 1897 that mine abandonment plans were required to be prepared to provide an accurate plan of the mine headings, pillars of coal remaining, position and dip of the seam and depth of shaft. Until that time miners not infrequently and unexpectedly broke into former workings, often flooded, with dire consequences. The idea of boring ahead to locate flooded workings came much later.

With the widespread adoption of mechanized extraction techniques the era of 'modern mining' had arrived, and the peak of Scottish coal production was recorded in 1913 when 43.2 million tons were produced. With the advance of mining methods came the production of increasing quantities of waste materials carried to the surface for disposal in bings where previous methods of winning coals by room and stoop or longwall methods kept the workings almost entirely within the seams themselves. Beyond the material excavated from the shafts any wastes were from fallen roofs, risen pavements or access tunnels, and much of this material was left within the abandoned rooms or longwall workings. The mechanized cutters produced usable coals but also generated dust, which was transported to the surface along the conveyors. Seams containing thin internal layers of sandstone or shales were removed completely and the rocks were separated at the surface sorting tables.

The peak period for the building of bings was between 1870 and 1920. Mining wastes consist of two main components: (a) rock excavated during shaft sinking and construction of underground roadways, and (b) solids, including dust, separated during cleaning at the pit head. The first material is important in the early stages of colliery development and accumulates at the base of the bing, but the second group of materials, derived during production, dominate the bulk of the structure. Most of the latter is of shale with minor sandstone, limestone, mudstone and coal. Constructed either by aerial tipping or released from wagons on rails, the bings had either a conical form or were linear ridges up to 50m

Plate 2.1 Coal bing – Dalmellington in the Doon valley where coal had been mined for over 200 years before the last pit closed in 1978. Lorne Gill / SNH

in height, the tipped material sliding down the sides of the structure under gravity, forming a loosely textured mass at its angle of repose.

2.6 After 1947

After World War II the mining industry was in a state of decline when Nationalization took place. Many mines were no longer economic. Closures after Vesting Day 1947, were accompanied by plans for opening new deep mines to replace lost production. The deep mines continued to operate in diminishing numbers as geological problems, explosions, fires or flooding were encountered. However, the bings remained.

The shale debris on the bings, subject to rain-induced weathering, commonly reverted to clays within 20 years of disposal (Down, 1975). Soil erosion, gullying, and mass creep when wet characterized the wastes, their unstable nature being revealed in the tragic collapse of wastes at Aberfan in 1966. This disaster resulted in a reappraisal of the Scottish bings, with most structures lowered to form plateaux less than 15m in height within the former colliery grounds (Bradshaw and Chadwick, 1980). Often attempts were made to make the replacements fit into the landscapes, creating ridges and hollows (Kent, 1986). Some bings provided material for the new motorway system, and across central Scotland many of the former bings have been converted to agricultural use, playing fields, parkland or golf courses.

Many mines in coastal locations disposed of their wastes directly into the sea, building promontories or shore terraces covering beaches and other coastal features. The Wellesley colliery at Methil, Fife, buried the site of the original Buckhaven village to accommodate its bing, having already reclaimed foreshore to create railway marshalling yards and dockside facilities. The redd from the bing buried the former harbour and 'silver sands beach', a significant tourist attraction of the area. The wastes continued west towards a bing from the Michael colliery. With the closure of the Wellesley colliery and cessation of supply of wastes from the bing, the former deposits are being removed by the sea: the harbour has reappeared at Buckhaven, the beach is reappearing and coastal erosion is starting to attack cliff-lines now several metres below their former level due to mining-induced subsidence (Saiu and McManus, 1998).

Opencast mining characterizes the winning of coal today: as part of the licensing requirements the soils and unwanted overburden are removed from above the coals and retained to be replaced when the coals have been excavated. Whilst most opencast excavations are no more than 20m deep, at Westfield, Fife an entire coal basin was excavated, forming a hole over 250m in depth. The scar of reworked ground and abandoned water pool await eventual use as a waste disposal site.

During the period of working, opencasting is destructive, and after restoration the land is in a substantially altered condition. The former, often poorly drained soils with characteristic habitats of bogland, moorland or heaths and woodland, are replaced by well-drained soils adapted for agricultural use. In this way the landscape of Central Scotland has been altered substantially since the 1940s. The greatest changes in area covered by quarries and opencast mining noted by Mackey *et al.* (1998) were to be found in Strathclyde, a rise from 18 km^2 to 59 km^2 between the 1940s and 1980s; in Lothian the area had almost doubled (to 15 km^2) in the same period. In 1965 open cast working in Scotland produced 0,75 million tons of coal, and peaked at 19 million tons in 1991-92 (Friends of the Earth, 1999). In 1999 there were 32 opencast workings in Scotland, with an average duration of excavation of 4.5 years. Normally only one such operation takes place in an area at any one time, but in Lanarkshire entire communities are blighted by long term open casting at multiple sites in the surrounding neighbourhood. This cannot be acceptable either to people or the natural system.

References

Allan, R.L., Dickinson, G., Dickinson, J.H., Duncan, H.J, Murphy, K.J, Pulford, I.D., Rogerson, R. and Watson, K. (1997). The natural heritage interest of bings (waste tips) in Scotland : inventory and review. Scottish Natural Heritage Review No 48, SNH Perth, 74pp.

Bradshaw, A.D. and Chadwick, M.J.(1980). *The restoration of land*. Blackwell Scientific Publications, Oxford.

Brodie, W.C.R. (1978-80). Introduction to the Rothes Papers. *Proceedings of the Society of Antiquaries of Scotland*. **110**: 404-431.

Brotchie, A.W. (1988). *The Wemyss Private railway*. The Oakwood Press.

Cunnungham, A.S. (1913). *Mining in the Kingdom of Fife* (2nd edition) Romanes and Son, Edinburgh. Minerals Planning Guidance. MPG3 Opencast Coal Mining.11pp.

Down, C.G. (1975). Soil development on colliery waste tips in relation to age: 1. Introduction and physical factors. *Journal of Applied Ecology*. **12**: 613-622.

Duckham, Baron F. (1970). *A History of the Scottish Coal Industry. Vol.1 1750-1815* David and Charles, Newton Abbot, 387pp.

Friends of the Earth, Scotland. (1999). Opencast coal mining in Scotland : the hole story. 8pp. Edinburgh.

Galloway, W. (1885). Report on the Pittenweem Coalfield. W.Lewis, Cardiff. 7pp. and maps.

Goodwin, R. (1959). Some physical and social factors in the evolution of a mining landscape. *Scottish Geographical Magazine*. **75**: 3-17.

Halliday, R.S. (1990). *The disappearing Scottish Colliery*. Scottish Academic Press, Edinburgh, 199pp.

Hutton, G. (1999). *Fife: the Mining Kingdom*. Stanlake Publishing, Ochiltree, Ayrshire. 112pp.

Kent, M. (1986). Visibility analysis of mining and waste tipping sites – a review. *Landscape and Urban Planning*. **13**: 101-110.

Mackey, E.C., Shewry, M.C. and Tudor, G.J. (1998). Land Cover Change : Scotland from the 1940s to the 1980s. Scottish Natural Heritage, HMSO, Edinburgh, 263pp.

McKechnie, J. and Macgregor, M. (1958). A short history of the Scottish Coal-mining Industry. National Coal Board, Scottish Division, 116pp.

Martin, C. (1999). *The 18th century industrial landscape between St Monans and Pittenweem: a cartographic and archaeological study*. In The salt and coal industries of St Monans, Fife in the 18th and 19th centuries Ed. by P.Yeoman Tayside and Fife Archaeological Committee, Glenrothes, 42-66.

Melville, J. (1793). *The Banfield Coal Book*, Unpublished account. Cupar, Fife Library.

Montgomery, G. (1994). *A mining chronicle*. Newcraighall Heritage Society, Musselburgh, 328pp.

Moodie, D.M. (2002). *A dark and dismal strife*. Dauv. Miner Publications, Grantully, Perthshire, 599pp.

Muir, A. (1958). *The Fife Coal Company. A short history*. The Fife Coal Company Ltd, Leven. 133pp.

Muirhead, G. (1792). Statistical Account of Scotland. *Dysart*. **12:** 502-504.

Payne, P.L. (1982). *The Halbeath Colliey and Saltworks, 1785-91*. In Business , Banking, and Urban History, Ed. by A.Slaven and D.H.Aldcroft Scottish Academic Press, Edinburgh, 1-33.

Richards, I.G., Palmer, J.P. and Barratt, P.A. (1993). *The reclamation of former coal mines and steelworks*. Elsevier, London. 718pp.

Siau, E.M. and McManus, J. (1998). Impacts of coal mining on coastal stability in Fife. Coastal defence and Earth Science Conservation. Ed. by J.Hooke *Geological Society of London*, pp.58-66.

Opencast coal workings at Glenbuck, east of Muirkirk with windfarm in distance © P & A Macdonald/SNH

3 Hydroelectricity Development and the Environment: The Formative Years

Terry Langford – *Visiting Professor, Centre for Environmental Sciences, School of Civil Engineering and the Environment, University of Southampton, Highfield, Southampton SO17 1BJ.*

Summary

1. A reliable source of electricity has been one of the major forces in the economic progress of the developed regions of the world.
2. The many socio-economic benefits have been accompanied by various degrees of environmental penalties.
3. In regions such as Scotland, dams and hydroelectric power generation have brought prosperity but have also intruded into remote wild lands and affected river flows and connectivity, sometimes to the detriment of the flora and fauna and to fisheries.
4. Remarkably, some of the impacts have not been as great as predicted but there is a continuing need to control and monitor future developments that might affect wilderness areas and the wilder rivers.
5. This chapter takes a general look at the early history of power development, its impacts, and the lessons to be learned from this period.

3.1 Introduction

A safe, secure and relatively cheap supply of electricity has been one of the more recent positive factors in improving the survival of *Homo sapiens* and the quality of life of individuals and communities in developed regions of the world. Water power has been used for driving machinery for several thousand years in various parts of the world and for at least 1000 years mills operating for various industrial and agricultural activities have existed in Britain (Haslam, 1991). It was, therefore, logical that early electricity generators which needed rotary motion to operate, would be driven by the already tried and trusted resource of falling water. Thus the first domestic electric lighting in Britain, at Sir William Armstrong's house, Cragside in Northumberland, was supplied by a 6hp generator driven by the small stream that ran through the estate, although steam-driven generators had been used to power lighthouses in Britain before this (Electricity Council, 1973; Hannah, 1979; Langford, 1983). The first public supply in the UK was installed in Godalming in Surrey in 1881 with generators driven by the River Wey and the first in Scotland was at Greenock

Langford, T. (2008). Hydroelectricity Development and the Environment: The Formative Years. In *Energy and the Natural Heritage*, ed. by C.A. Galbraith and J.M. Baxter. TSO Scotland, Edinburgh. pp. 33-42 in 1885 (Payne, 1988). In 1890, the monks of St Benedict's Abbey at Fort Augustus installed an 18kw hydroelectricity generator to supply the abbey and the local population. The first of the larger schemes in Scotland was the Foyers installation which began construction in 1895 to supply power for aluminium production and had an early capacity of about 25-26 MW. At the same time, there were small steam-driven plants in operation but they did not cause the same scale of concern either as obstacles to migrating fish or as destructive landscape features. After 1900, hydrogeneration increased throughout the Scottish Highlands, though there was only 200 MW of installed capacity by 1945. The major acceleration in demand and in hydroelectricity production occurred from the 1940s to the 1960s (Birkett, 1979).

Although it is easy with hindsight to disapprove of the environmental impacts of the industry during the expansion phase, the ingenuity, imagination and confidence of the engineers who designed the schemes must be admired. Further, the successes would not have been achieved without the courage, determination and tenacity of the front-line workforce, albeit not always well behaved, in work that was difficult, dirty and dangerous (Payne, 1988; Miller, 2002). There were, however, environmental and human costs, some of which we may still be experiencing and these are the subject of this chapter. It will not be possible to give more than a brief overview here and the reader is referred to the bibliography for more details.

3.2 Some environmental concerns

Almost from the outset, proposals for hydroelectricity schemes met resistance (Payne, 1988). The main opposition came from vested interests such as coal owners, mining unions, land-owners, local authorities who coveted the water plus sporting and commercial tourist organizations. Fisheries and amenity concerns were also heavily involved. The main environmental concerns centred around the effects of dams and flow changes on salmon, effects on scenery and topography and later the intrusion into the more remote lands by roads, dams, transmission lines and the artefacts of the industry. Inundation of land, forest and rivers was also of concern. For example, the effects of the Foyers Aluminium power developments in the late 1890s on the tourism value of the Foyers Falls were considered a major reason for opposing the developments. Evidence to the Cooper Committee about the total effects of hydropower schemes in the 1940s suggested scenarios which in the event, have not emerged. For example, Edward Keeling, MP for Twickenham predicted that *"huge white dams … wide stretches of rotting vegetation and slimy mud … and blackened skeletons of trees … projecting above the ooze"* (Payne, 1988) would replace the dramatic natural scenery in the Highlands. Although such phenomena did not occur in Scotland for various reasons, the impoundment of rivers for power and navigation in other parts of the world have produced disastrous ecological and topographical impacts and continue to do so (Ackermann *et al.*, 1973; Langford, 1983; Pearce, 1992; Reisner, 1993; Heat-Moon, 2001).

The human dimension of schemes was scarcely considered for the more sparsely populated parts of Scotland in the early days, the concentration being on the benefits of electricity to the more populated areas. Indeed, the proposals for the Glen Affric scheme almost arrogantly discounted any human effects because of the low number of houses and people who lived and worked in the glen. However, a number of schemes were rejected at first in both the lowlands and the highlands, though once there were assurances that the power generated would be mostly for the benefit of Scottish communities and industrial development, some of the main opposition faded (Miller, 2002). The environmental concerns led eventually to a considerable research and development programme on many aspects of both the terrestrial and aquatic effects of schemes which continue today.

3.3 Power developments in context

Migratory fish throughout the world have always had to face natural obstacles. Waterfalls, land-slips, rockfalls and massive dams of fallen trees have been natural features of rivers and many were removed or by-passed by human activity over thousands of years. Further, because of the thousands of water-mills that existed in Britain many miles of stream and river had been blocked by dams and weirs for many centuries before the onset of hydropower (Haslam, 1991) (Figure 3.1). In Scotland, most villages and towns possessed at least one mill and often many more. Wool towns like Hawick had over 20 mills and the Water of Leith through Edinburgh drove 16 mills in 23 miles during the early 19th century. Most of these mills also produced some kind of polluting discharge, for example, paper mills, fulling mills, tannery mills, corn mills, snuff mills, mills for iron and steel industries among others. Thus migratory fish were both impeded and often killed by these mills and

Figure 3.1 Mill structures have blocked streams for centuries. © Terry Langford.

the streams rendered chemically unsuitable for their survival and spawning. The difference between the mill-dams and the larger hydroelectricity dams was scale, notably the height and the initial impenetrability of the obstacle but the hydroschemes used no chemicals and produced no toxic wastes in the process.

Before 1900, there were probably more tracks into the remote areas than in recent years but these were mainly for stalking, walking, agricultural or peat transport and made a fairly light impact on the land (Carver and Wrightham, 2003; Scottish Natural Heritage, 2004). The development of hydroelectric power was the first of the new land-uses to make a significant impact on the more remote *'wild'* areas of Scotland but the major impacts occurred after 1945. Land use and the intrusion by large numbers of workers, their accommodations, large machinery, roads, pipelines, tunnelling and use of explosives was different in principle and on a vastly larger scale than anything seen previously. The huge scars on the landscape from such land disturbance, albeit some temporary, were hardly tolerable to many people (Miller, 2002). Local businesses may have benefitted from the workers but small communities felt swamped and threatened by large numbers of men with little to occupy them between working hours. There were thus both environmental and social impacts that divided opinion as the schemes were developed.

3.4   Aquatic impacts

There are two principal types of hydroelectric power station. The 'run-of-river' station utilizes the hydrostatic head and unidirectional flow of water from an impounded river or loch outflow to drive the turbines, and a succession of such stations may be installed along a river system (Figure 3.2). Variations include controlled lochs and water transfers from other catchments. The majority of hydropower in Scotland comes from run-of-river sites. The 'pumped-storage' power station uses water falling from a high source to a lower source, usually lakes or reservoirs, to generate electricity. The water is then pumped back to the higher source at times of low power demand and reused as needed. The major pumped-storage scheme is on Loch Awe. All types include some form of dam or lake by-pass and may affect migratory or resident fish (Langford, 1983).

Figure 3.2 Hydroelectric dam at Faskally, Pitlochry © Lorne Gill / SNH

The need for research into the effective passage of fish through passes and the effects of impoundment and diversion of rivers in Scotland led eventually to the creation of the Freshwater Fisheries Laboratory at Faskally near Pitlochry from which much research into the effects of hydroschemes has originated (Struthers, 1996; Stephen, undated). Fish counters were also installed at many dams, funded and partly operated by the Hydroelectricity Boards and the data from these have led to improvements in the migration and survival of the fisheries. The potential physical, chemical and biological effects of hydroelectricity generation are outlined by Langford (1983) and the temperature effects by Langford (1990). Fortunately, in Scotland, the naturally low water temperature regimes and the oligotrophic (mineral-poor) waters preclude major temperature or chemical effects that might occur in highly stratified, warmer, more eutrophic waters, though Summers (*pers. comm.*) has suggested that low-level (hypolimnial) outlets may cool water temperatures downstream at some dam sites to the possible detriment of hatching times of salmon eggs.

The research and monitoring has produced large amounts of both practical and fundamental information on the ecology of migratory salmonids and resident species, data on effects of river, fishery and power station management, fish stocking, uses of fish ladders and lifts and the effects of passage through turbines by smolts. These results are presented in a series of reports, a selection listed in the bibliography here. The studies include information on:

- Potential delays of smolt migration by up to a year through some lochs.
- Up to 70% predation on smolts by various predators through one impounded loch.
- Successful entry and passage of adults through various types of fish passes.
- Improved numbers of migrating smolts and adults after stocking rivers with eyed ova or parr.
- Various survival and mechanical damage rates on smolts passing through turbines and methods of reducing damage by operational management.
- Long-term records of numbers of adults passing through fish passes which indicate little change over up to 40 years after the dams were completed (Struthers, 1996).
- No consistent decline in rod-caught salmon from Scottish rivers since 1950 despite annual fluctuations (Figure 3.3).

Radio tags have been used to track potential predators and novel techniques such as balloon tags combined with radio tags have been used to measure damage and survival rates through turbines at different load factors (Stephen, undated). Clearly there are effects of hydrogeneration on migratory fishes but the extent from the natural state is mostly unknown as data were not collected before most dams and stations were completed. However, two main points emerge from the post-completion studies, namely:

- There are still healthy runs of migratory salmonids through most rivers used for hydroelectricity generation, though some may be a result of stock augmentation.
- Despite decline since 1991, there is no trend in numbers that can be correlated with hydrogeneration.

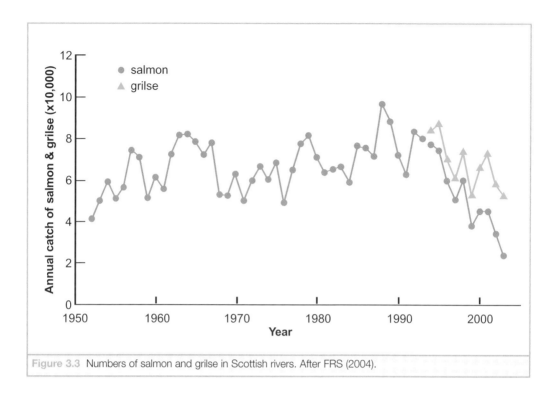

Figure 3.3 Numbers of salmon and grilse in Scottish rivers. After FRS (2004).

It is notable that while fixed engine and net catches of salmon in Scotland have declined consistently since 1950, rod catches have not (Fisheries Research Services, 2004). There are, of course, other impacts that have affected migratory fish including sea-captures, forestry, acidification, poaching, drought, illegal fishing and poor farm practices so it is impossible to consider any factor in isolation.

There are clear indications that the numbers of fish passing through one dam reach are not related to the numbers passing further upstream as fish may be naturally diverted to preferred spawning streams. An example is shown by the data for the Pitlochry dam and the Clunie dam upstream where only about 10% of the fish passing through the lower dam pass through the upper dam. The reason is that most fish select to spawn in the River Tilt which joins the system between the two dams (Figure 3.4). Many studies are still in progress at a number of sites and these involve both adult fish passage and screening of smolts from intakes. It is generally agreed that although behavioural screening is effective, the most effective method for keeping smolts from intakes is properly cleaned and maintained physical screens and deflectors.

There is no doubt that impounding rivers and lochs and using them for power generation has significant impacts on the ecology of the waters. The simple process of turning a flowing river into a static loch will change the ecology completely upstream of a dam (Langford, 1983). Further, the use of the water creates a drawdown zone around a loch. This zone does not usually develop an aquatic fauna and can cause difficulties for fish that might spawn there when water levels fall. It is also unsightly. In some cases, however, it may become colonized by terrestrial plants and invertebrates which are exploited as food by fish as water levels rise again.

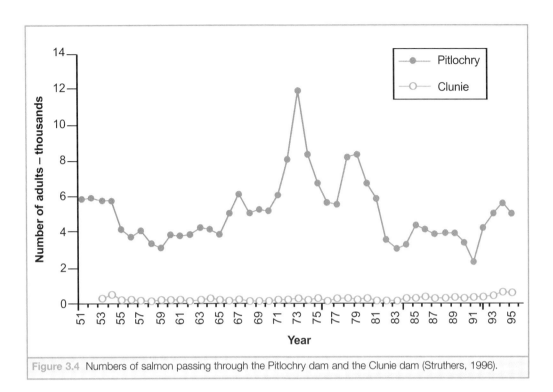

Figure 3.4 Numbers of salmon passing through the Pitlochry dam and the Clunie dam (Struthers, 1996).

Ranked against other forms of power generation hydropower has caused far more significant changes. Throughout the world *'there is no doubt at all that as far as the electricity industry is concerned the major alterations in the ecology of natural water bodies have come from … river dams, diversions, and lake control … rather than from nuclear, coal or oil-fired generating stations …. Hydro-electric power is not "clean power" in the ecological sense … it has been responsible for massive and dramatic ecological changes in most rivers of the world …. Whether any (specific) hydro-electricity scheme is totally harmful or not depends on the … situation'* (Langford, 1983). However, despite the development of hydroelectricity throughout Scotland, some 47% of upland rivers and 28% of lowland rivers were considered to be pristine at the end of the 20th century.

3.5 Topography and wild lands

Removing and blasting away large volumes of soil and rock, for example 36,000 cubic yards and 56,000 cubic yards respectively for the Sloy dam, created scars in many of Scotland's glens. The installation of metal pipelines of unprecedented diameters (weighing a total of 3500 tons for the Sloy scheme) over miles of hillside and the drilling and blasting of tunnels (180,000 tons of rock removed for Sloy) were huge disturbances in previously unspoiled and remote country (Payne, 1988). In some 20 years, the North of Scotland Hydro-electricity Board alone built 56 dams, 54 main power stations, 600km of road, 350km of rock tunnel and 350km of aqueducts and installed some 35,000km of overhead cable (Figure 3.5). The impacts on the landscape were huge, both in intensity and in extent. Sensitivities were recognized and protection of many sites was managed through controls of water levels, architectural treatments and landscaping. This was not universal. Rivers were dried out in

39

Figure 3.5   High-voltage electricity pylons, East Lothian © Colin Galbraith

places and transmission lines were carried through remote country such as Corryairack and later through Kinlochhourn to Skye.

There are still aesthetically poor drawdown zones in some of the more remote controlled lochs and there was, in the early days, less attention to topographical sensitivities in such areas. Indeed, some of the construction roads remain as active erosion scars today. Even so, economic and political pressures eventually led to the slow-down in developments. The later and more recent proposals such as the pumped-storage scheme under Ben Lomond, the run-of-river scheme south of Loch Maree and the Sheildaig scheme in Wester Ross have run into very substantial opposition mainly based on the increasing concern for the protection of wild and remote areas. The emotional impetus of harnessing nature is now challenged by arguments for the value of untrammelled natural processes. For example, the relatively modest Sheildaig scheme drew over 800 letters of objection, many based on issues of landscape and the aesthetic and ecological value of wild land.

The measurement of what constitutes wild and remote land is an essential part of the arguments and the areas so classified can vary based on which measurement is used (Carver and Wrightham, 2003; Scottish Natural Heritage, 2004). Whilst remote or wild land in Scotland is still owned and often used for some sporting or other economic purposes, its distance from easy access points makes it special both in human and ecological terms. It should not be regarded, however, as 'economically sterile' but more as an asset in its own right. Hydroelectric developments are not the only intrusions. New and improved roads from the time of General Wade to the present have eased access for many more people to remote areas. Forestry, tourism, sport and recreation, even marine fish-farming have intruded such that the areas more than 8km remote from roads and access points have substantially reduced. Such areas need special protection.

3.6 Conclusions and the future

It is clear that hydroelectricity generation has had considerable impacts on the lands and waters throughout Scotland and provided many benefits to the human populations. It is also clear that an electricity supply is essential to modern living. The balance is to provide electricity with minimal impact on the environment and this has to be through some carefully valued judgements of the economic need and the environmental disturbance. Birkett (1979), for example, suggested that the Highlands could be developed further to produce up to an additional 1000MW.

There is now a focus on the amenity values and the aesthetic qualities of wild lands, freely-flowing rivers and naturally replenished lochs. These will need to be protected more in the future unless political and economic pressures supersede the requirement for such protection. Large scale wind-power developments are the new fashion in renewable energy and will be until the subsidy given to such developments is terminated. However, now the landscape and visual impacts of large numbers of massive machines, many of which may be proposed in the wild and remote areas, are recognized, these may have a limited life and distribution. Their infrastructure of access roads and transmission lines is also intrusive. Clearly there must be a future for a mixture of power developments in which the present and possibly low-impact future hydroschemes will have their place but thermal, particularly nuclear, generation is probably the only way forward for the provision of large scale electricity supply for the UK as a whole.

As in any new industry, early hydroelectricity development paid relatively little attention to its overall environmental impact because of its commercial and socio-economic advantages. In more recent years, the values of environment and socio-economics have reached a more balanced state. Both are of great importance, especially to regions such as Scotland or Wales with their remote, wild, mountainous beauty and sparse human populations, all of which need special services and special protection for the future.

Acknowledgements

My thanks to Scottish Natural Heritage for the invitation to contribute to the Conference and this publication. Also, thanks to Jean Langford for literature research, compiling the bibliography and copy editing the MS. I am also grateful to Dr. Andrew Turnpenny at the Jacobs-Babtie Environmental Laboratory at Fawley, Hampshire for access to his collection of publications and to the Fisheries Research Station at Faskally for library access and assistance. Finally, my thanks to Robert Aitken, Independent Consultant based in Edinburgh who generously supplied me with information, advice and photographs.

References

Ackermann, W.C., White, G.F. and Worthington, E.B. (Eds). (1973). Man-made lakes: their problems and environmental effects. *Geophysical Monographs*. **17**. American Geophysical Union, Washington D.C.

Birkett, D.G. (1979). Review of potential hydro-electric developments in the Scottish Highlands. *Electronics and Power*. **May**: 339-347.

Carver, S. and Wrightham, M. (2003). *Assessment of historic trends in the extent of wild land in Scotland: a pilot study*. Scottish Natural Heritage Commissioned Report No. 012 (ROAME No. F02NC11A). Scottish Natural Heritage, Perth.

Electricity Council. (1973). *Electricity supply in Great Britain. A Chronology: Organisation and development* (2 vols). Electricity Council, London.

Fisheries Research Services. (2004). *Scottish salmon and sea trout catches, 2003*. Fisheries Series No. Fis/2004/1 September 2004. Scottish Executive, Environment and Rural Affairs Department, Edinburgh.

Hannah, L. (1979). *Electricity before nationalisation*. London: Macmillan Press.

Haslam, S.M. (1991). *The Historic River: rivers and culture down the ages*. Cambridge,UK: University of Cambridge Press.

Heat-Moon, W.L. (2001). *A voyage across America*. London: Pimlico.

Langford, T.E. (1983). *Electricity generation and the ecology of natural waters*. Liverpool University Press, Liverpool.

Langford, T.E. (1990). *Ecological Effects of Thermal Discharges*. Elsevier Applied Science, London and New York.

Miller, J. (2002). *The dam builders*. Birlinn Ltd., Edinburgh.

Payne, P.L. (1988). *The Hydro*. Aberdeen University Press, Aberdeen.

Pearce, F. (1992). *The Dammed*. The Bodley Head, London.

Reisner, M. (1993). *Cadillac Desert*. Viking Penguin Inc. New York.

Scottish Natural Heritage. (2004). *Wildness in Scotland's Countryside*. Scottish Natural Heritage, Perth.

Stephen, A. (undated). *Scottish and Southern Energy plc Hydro Generation Fisheries progress Report 1997-2001*. Scottish and Southern Energy Hydro Generation, Pitlochry, Perthshire.

Struthers, G. (1996). *Hydro-electric development in Scotland and its effects on fish*. Scottish Hydro-Electric.

4 The Everlasting Legacy: Nuclear Power and Scotland

Jean McSorley - *Greenpeace UK, Canonbury Villas, London N1 2PN.*

(With acknowledgement to **Pete Roche***, consultant to Greenpeace.)*

Summary

1. The nuclear power industry in Scotland will leave a legacy of low, intermediate and high level wastes to be dealt with. The exact extent of the waste problem, in terms of the volume of waste and final determination of the type, is not yet known as the Committee on Radioactive Waste Management is still examining the full inventory of the UK's nuclear waste legacy.

2. No final disposal method or site has yet been found for the UK's nuclear waste and it may be that Scotland will be chosen to host a site for some of the wastes which have arisen from activities within Scotland or from other parts of the UK.

3. In addition to existing wastes, reactors operating at Torness and Hunterston B will continue to create spent nuclear fuel that will be sent to Sellafield for reprocessing. Radioactive materials from reprocessing at Sellafield contaminate Scottish waters and fisheries as a result of the daily discharges from the site.

4. The major fraction of radioactive contamination in Scottish waters is due to Sellafield, where the extremely hot and radioactive high level waste that results from the reprocessing of spent fuel from Scotland is also stored. Through this circuitous route, Scotland's use of nuclear power has contributed to the country's overall burden of radioactive contamination.

4.1 Introduction

If a new-build programme for ten reactors takes place, then the amount of spent nuclear fuel that will have to be managed in the UK will be treble the current holdings (CoRWM, 2004a, b). It is not likely this spent fuel will be reprocessed. The nuclear industry has indicated that it expects to keep spent fuel on site at new builds for up to 100 years. Any proposal for new build in Scotland would thus have to take into account both long term storage of spent fuel and possible disposal in Scotland.

McSorley, J. (2008). The Everlasting Legacy: Nuclear Power and Scotland. In *Energy and the Natural Heritage*, ed. by C.A. Galbraith and J.M. Baxter. TSO Scotland, Edinburgh. pp. 43-52

In terms of natural heritage impact, Scotland's nuclear programme and its infrastructure requirements is not perceived, by some, to have had a significant visual impact (although in Caithness the extensive Dounreay site has a very visual impact on its surroundings). However, current facilities may remain part of the landscape for the next 100 years, depending on the speed at which Government, agencies and companies concerned decide on dismantling them – thus becoming a long term legacy.

Other parts of the legacy of the use of nuclear power in Scotland are to be found in the waste tailing dumps at mine sites in Australia, Canada, the US and Namibia, all of which supply or have supplied uranium to reactors in the UK. Other wastes, not in Scotland but which arise from supplying fuel for Scottish plants, are at uranium enrichment plants such as Capenhurst (Cheshire) and fuel fabrication plants (Springfields, Lancashire).

4.2 Dounreay, Caithness: fast reactor and nuclear research site

The main facilities at this site are:

- Dounreay Fast Reactor (closed).
- Prototype Fast Reactor (closed).
- Fast Reactor Reprocessing Plant (closed).
- Materials Test Reactor and MTR Reprocessing Plant (both closed).

The principal wastes include:

- liquid High Level Waste (HLW) from reprocessing fast reactor spent fuel;
- Intermediate Level Waste (ILW), the main components of which are contaminated and irradiated redundant scrap items; waste resulting from research reactor reprocessing, and the contents of the ILW shaft;
- Low Level Waste (LLW), the main components of which are general trash from routine operations and contaminated soil from decommissioning projects.

The Dounreay Site Restoration Plan (DSRP) (UKAEA, 2000) identified the requirement for approximately 1500 activities which will be needed to complete the decommissioning of the site, including the construction of up to 20 major facilities over the next 15 to 20 years. In readiness for becoming a contractor to the Nuclear Decommissioning Authority (NDA) in April 2005, the United Kingdom Atomic Energy Authority (UKAEA) upgraded the DSRP and renamed it as the Life Cycle Base Line.

4.2.1 Dounreay Fast Reactor (DFR) breeder fuel elements

There are around 44 tonnes of this fuel on the Dounreay site (UKAEA, 2000). Approximately 32 tonnes have yet to be removed from the reactor vessel and the remaining 12 tonnes are in the form of cut fuel elements, fuel pieces and debris (UKAEA, 2000) i.e. spent fuel, which is currently not classified as waste, and so does not appear in the Nirex Waste Inventory as High Level Waste.

The UKAEA is seeking to build a fuel treatment facility at Dounreay and expects it to be operational by 2007, but if this plan fails it may go for an earlier option which would involve 'passivating' the metallic fuel for encapsulation as waste. This would be subject to consultation with the NDA after it takes over the running of the site. The UKAEA has had discussions with British Nuclear Fuels plc (BNFL) over the treatment and transport of the breeder fuel and a preliminary contract has been signed under which BNFL is carrying out technical reviews of processing and transport (HSE, 2001).

4.2.2 Plutonium Contaminated Material (PCM)

The UKAEA's reference strategy is to transfer this category of Intermediate Level Waste to Sellafield for supercompaction, over-packing into stainless steel drums, and cementation in the Sellafield Waste Treatment Complex. The Authority assumes this transfer will take place after 2010. However, it has identified the need for a fallback strategy, which is to construct a new PCM supercompaction facility at Dounreay, with storage of the wastes at Dounreay after treatment.

4.2.3 Low Level Waste (LLW)

Considerable quantities of LLW will be produced at Dounreay mainly as a result of decommissioning activities (see Table 4.1). Disposal of new material at Dounreay has now ceased because the original disposal trenches are nearly full, and significant quantities of LLW are consequently currently in interim storage. UKAEA is undertaking a Best Practicable Environmental Option (BPEO) Study into long term management to establish a way forward (HSE, 2001), but it has also applied to SEPA to transport some LLW to Drigg near Sellafield as an interim solution (HSE, 2001). This means either a train-load every month or a lorry-load every fortnight for the next five to 10 years.

The Radioactive Waste Management Advisory Committee (RWMAC) has noted - *"It is not clear at present ... whether a post-closure safety case can be made for the facility ... if the retention of waste in the pits is not sustainable, this will have implications for the provision of future facilities at Dounreay or elsewhere".* Cumbria County Council has sought to stop further imports of LLW into Cumbria for disposal at Drigg, so the UKAEA plan to empty the LLW pits and transfer the historic arisings of LLW elsewhere may not happen, and the BPEO study will need to address this possibility.

4.2.4 Prototype Fast Reactor (PFR) fuels

Despite the announcement on 18th July 2001 by the Energy Minister at the time, Brian Wilson, that there would be no further reprocessing at Dounreay, the option of reprocessing this fuel at the Thermal Oxide Reprocessing Plant (THORP) at Sellafield has not been ruled out. It will apparently be some time before firm proposals emerge for the management of PFR fuel: Mr Wilson stated that:

"No clear preference emerged from [the] UKAEA's assessment of the options, or the public consultation".

This seems odd, given the overwhelming opposition in Scotland and the neighbouring Nordic countries to reprocessing of spent fuel in favour of storage. All the local authorities in the Highlands and Islands as well as the Scottish Nuclear Free Local Authorities (NFLAs), environmental groups and the Liberal and Scottish National Party parties favour long-term storage over reprocessing. Nordic countries whose coasts and fisheries have been contaminated by discharges from Sellafield and Dounreay have also rejected reprocessing in favour of storage. The environment movement has recommended that the UKAEA should

Table 4.1

Dounreay Summary: Waste Volumes after conditioning and packaging m³. (HLW - High Level Waste; ILW - Intermediate Level Waste; LLW - Low Level Waste)

Dounreay	Stocks at 01.04.01 (Operational & Decom)	Future Arisings including from Decommissioning	Total
HLW	31.2	0	31.2
ILW	6638.9	3542.7	10181.6
LLW	7842.4	70945.0	78787.4

Chapelcross Summary: Waste Volumes after conditioning and packaging.

Chapelcross	Stocks at 01.04.01 (Operational & Decom)	Future Arisings including from Decommissioning	Total
ILW	156.4	10673.8	10830.2
LLW	106.4	36547.6	36654.0

Hunterston A	Stocks at 01.04.01 (Operational & Decom)	Future Arisings including from Decommissioning	Total
ILW	3648.6	4773.3	8421.9
LLW	164.2	43435.8	43600.0

Hunterston B Summary
Waste Volumes after conditioning and packaging.

Hunterston B	Stocks at 01.04.01 (Operational & Decom)	Future Arisings including from Decommissioning	Total
ILW	1848.8	7132.5	8981.3
LLW	Presumed sent to Drigg so none on site.	12947.2	12947.2

Torness (m³)	Stocks at 01.04.01	Predicted Future Arisings 2001-2029	Total	Decommissioning Waste expected to arise 2020-2039 [Stage 2]	Decommissioning Waste expected to arise 2100+ [Stage 3]
ILW	191.9	465.8	657.7		2863.2
LLW	2.3	1153.1	1155.4	600.0	10797.4
ILW (when conditioned)	232.8	555.4	788.2		3435.8
LLW (when conditioned)	4.7	780.0	784.7	187.4	12746.2
ILW (when packaged)	531.5	1261.1	1792.6		6585.4
LLW (when packaged)	14.1	1097.9	1112.0	235.1	14905.7

Torness Summary
Waste Volumes after conditioning and packaging.

Torness (m3)	Stocks at 01.04.01 (Operational & Decom)	Future Arisings including from Decommissioning	Total
ILW	531.5	7846.5	8378
LLW	14.1	16238.7	16252.8

concentrate on developing above-ground, on-site, retrievable storage systems capable of being monitored for this and all other forms of radioactive waste on the site.

4.2.5 Other areas of concern

The UKAEA had proposed building a vitrification plant sometime between 2007 – 2011 to turn the liquid HLW on site into glass blocks. The proposal is for this facility to come into operation in 2012 as it is crucial to the reduction of the hazard potential of the Dounreay site. The Nuclear Installations Inspectorate (NII) has said it would "welcome an acceleration to this timescale". RWMAC has agreed with the NII and said the current arrangements rank highly as a potential risk because of the hazard posed by the radioactivity and mobility of the liquid HLW. RWMAC has suggested that it ought to be possible to bring forward the timetable.

UKAEA has said, however, that the PFR 'raffinate' or liquid waste has now had a minimum of 10 years to cool and no longer generates a significant level of heat, and as such, it can now be reclassified as ILW. It is now consulting on a proposal to immobilize this waste in cement rather than by vitrification. While the advantage of this method is that this highly dangerous waste will be solidified much sooner, there must also be a question mark about whether a cement based waste will achieve the necessary containment over the long term compared with vitrified (glass-based) waste.

4.2.6 Other major Dounreay waste management legacy facilities or issues

The Dounreay shaft (containing solid ILW)

The Dounreay shaft has had ILW dumped in it, and this now has to be retrieved and re-packaged. It was originally excavated to allow the vertical removal of spoil during

Plate 4.1 Dounreay, Caithness: Fast Reactor and Nuclear Research Site © ukaea

construction of the Dounreay effluent discharge system and was later authorized for the disposal of ILW.

The UK Atomic Energy Authority (UKAEA) recently announced it will launch the cleanup programme for the 65-metre-deep ILW shaft near an eroding cliff edge at Dounreay. It is estimated the work in total will cost between £215- 355 million and could be completed in 10 to 15 years (Nucleonics Week, 2004).

Approximately £16 million will be spent on putting a 10-metre wide band of rock around the vertical shaft, which is unlined for most of its depth. The ILW shaft, first licensed in 1959, experienced a violent explosion in May 1977 when two kilograms of sodium and potassium reacted with water. The ignition of hydrogen gas blew off the concrete roof slab and expelled an unquantified amount of solid waste, much of which was simply dumped back down the shaft during an emergency cleanup operation. Expert groups have linked the shaft to highly radioactive particles that have appeared on local beaches (see below), and it has been said that remedial steps should be taken over a "relatively short time-scale" given the danger of encroachment by the sea. RWMAC has warned that by 2020 such coastal erosion might already start to cause problems in retrieving waste from the shaft.

Reports by the UKAEA in 1998 on the "Dounreay Shaft Inventory" noted difficulty in compiling accurate waste receipts at the shaft. The report estimated the maximum fissile content of the shaft as up to 4 kg of plutonium and 98.5 kg uranium-235 in the 1,165 kg total uranium, which the UKAEA described as "upper bound figures." The figures included the assumption that 15% of the Dounreay Fast Reactor MUF (material unaccounted for) and 22 kg of uranium-235 from the Dounreay Fuel Cycle Area's MUF are contained in the shaft.

The current UKAEA plans are for waste retrieval occurring sometime between 2014 and 2019, but this timing is now under review. The recent announcement means that shaft decommissioning is beginning four years earlier than previously planned.

The Dounreay particles

About the size of a grain of sand, these are radioactive metal fragments which are almost certainly derived from research reactor spent fuel which was reprocessed on site. They have been found for many years on the site itself and the Dounreay foreshore that is inaccessible to the public. However, since the late 1990s these have also been found on Sandside beach which, although privately owned, is accessible to the public. By 2004 around 50 particles had been found but this figure has since risen to around 100 in 2007. No-one is quite sure how these particles are continuing to arrive on the beach, although their presence may be linked to the explosion in 1977 in the waste shaft on site. The particles are of varying levels of radioactivity, but should an individual be unfortunate enough to swallow one of the most radioactive particles, it could burn through their gut. The particles on Sandside beach are removed when found during monitoring surveys, but the monitoring programme for the beach has been criticized as inadequate.

Overseas wastes

Dounreay holds residues resulting from commercial reprocessing contracts the UKAEA entered into with foreign operators of materials test reactors (MTRs) during the 1990s. The total volume of foreign ILW that is required to be conditioned would result in about 300 500 litre drums.

A condition of the contracts was that the waste separated from the reusable uranium would be returned to the country of origin. A recent consultation report has claimed that a 2008 start to the return of research reactor reprocessing residues from the UK to Australia, Germany, Belgium and Spain may be possible, but optimistic: the UKAEA believes such a timeframe is still feasible (Nuclear Fuel, 2004a). Before return can be achieved, a £16 million import/export facility will have to be constructed at Dounreay, and the foreign customers will need to have receipt facilities available. The UKAEA has said that there also needs to be licensed international transport casks for the transport duty (Nuclear Fuel, 2004b).

4.2.7 Conclusion

Operations at Dounreay have led to considerable contamination on and off site. The UKAEA is now solely devoted to decommissioning, and the "clean up the environment" movement has expressed its support for Dounreay to become a centre of excellence in decommissioning and above-ground dry storage of nuclear waste in a retrievable condition that can be monitored. It believes the UKAEA should get on with this task of decommissioning and maximizing the best waste storage plants and that it should drop plans to transfer its problems to Sellafield.

4.3 Chapelcross

This Magnox station with four reactors was opened in 1959 and closed in June 2004. Although originally established as part of the UK's 'civil' nuclear programme, the Government has since admitted that the reactors were used to produce tritium and plutonium for the UK nuclear weapons programme.

Magnox fuel element debris, which has a high hazard potential because it can cause a hydrogen explosion or fire, is stored in water tanks in the spent fuel storage ponds on site. Intermediate level wastes in the voids inside the reactor will result in more complex removal procedures and could lead to a significant delay in decommissioning. Recent reports show that there are some 40,000 spent fuel rods to be shipped out from the site – for reprocessing at Sellafield – between 2005 and 2007 (Sunday Herald, 2004) .

4.4 Hunterston

There is an operating Advanced Gas-cooled Reactor (AGR) (Hunterston B) and two closed Magnox Reactors (Hunterston A) on this site: the AGR opened in 1976 and is planned to run until 2011, while the two early Magnox reactors opened in 1964 and closed in 1989 and 1990. The Hunterston A site will be under the initial stages of decommissioning until 2010, with the whole process estimated to take 135 years. Recent NII reports have highlighted that the decommissioning programme has been moving very slowly.

A store is planned to deal with long term ILW on site: this may avoid incidents such as that during 2000 where radioactive materials were taken out of the site, and it probably went (accidentally) to a landfill site or a scrap yard. There are also safety problems with large amounts of combustible Magnox debris, and with AGR fuel debris placed in voids in the reactor structure, making future decommissioning more difficult as retrieval is not easy.

Recently it has been disclosed that an estimated 81,000 cubic metres of soil (equivalent to 900 double decker buses in volume) has been contaminated at the site as a result of spills from pipelines and contamination blown from open-air ponds holding spent nuclear fuel.

Plate 4.2 Hunterston Nuclear Power Station " Lorne Gill / SNH

British Nuclear Fuels (BNFL), which manages the site, said it was unaware of the extent of this contamination. The Nuclear Decommissioning Authority, the government body established to oversee the clean-up of nuclear installations, found the contamination is the result of historic leaks (Herald & Times, 2004). It is not clear if people living and working in and around nuclear facilities have been exposed to radioactive contamination as a result of the leaks.

4.5 Torness

This is an AGR reactor site only, with two reactors that began operation 1988 and which are planned to run until 2023. In the early 1990s Scottish Nuclear proposed building a dry store to house spent used fuel on site at Torness: this was an alternative to transporting this dangerous material across country to Sellafield for reprocessing. Environmental campaigners argued that the proposed dry store was preferable to reprocessing, partly because of the extent of contamination from reprocessing. However, following pressure from BNFL the plans for a dry store at Torness were dropped in 1995. Using voids in the reactor structure for fuel debris will, as with other AGR plants, make future decommissioning more difficult. Current storage facilities for resins, sludges and desiccants on the site have a limited capacity.

4.6 Contamination arising from Scotland's nuclear programme

The relevant monitoring and environment agencies measure the radiation exposure to the different communities around Scotland as a result of releases from the nuclear industry e.g. the local fishing community around Dounreay. Most of the contamination measured is due to Sellafield, not only at Chapelcross and Hunterston, but also Dounreay and Torness.

Exposure comes from working in contaminated areas, eating contaminated seafood or fish or contaminated produce. The half life of some of the radioisotopes found in Scottish waters and on land ranges from 312 days (Manganese-54) to 24,000 years (Plutonium-239).

For the most exposed group around Dounreay, estimated radiation exposures have historically been less than the legal maximum. For example, in 2000 it was estimated exposures were 0.02mSv - less than 1/20th of legal limit: this, however, is the maximum radiation dose proposed by UK Health and Safety Executive (HSE) as a 'basic safety objective' that would have to achieved for a greenfield site. The reason 0.02mSv was chosen is that this is the upper limit of acceptable risk to the individual from radiation exposures.

In 1988 Dounreay was embroiled in controversy when a follow-up report by the Committee on the Medical Aspects of Radiation in the Environment found a five-fold excess of childhood leukaemia around the Dounreay site. This report came after a ten-fold excess of childhood leukaemia was discovered around Sellafield. There is still debate over the exact cause of the high incidence of childhood leukaemia around both sites – which were Britain's largest dischargers of nuclear waste (this still remains the case for Sellafield) although discharges from Dounreay have reduced significantly since the site effectively stopped operating. Although there is division over the question of whether both plants caused or contributed to the excess of leukaemia in the surrounding populations, it is accepted that exposure to radiation is one of only two acknowledged causes of childhood leukaemia.

4.7 Disposal

Although a Dounreay spokesman is on the record as saying 'Our aim is to remove as much of the material from the site as possible to allow it to be decommissioned', this plan is yet to be put into operation. Cumbria County Council has formally objected to Dounreay wastes going to Sellafield; similarly NIREX (formerly an industry body, now independent) has admitted that it may be 25-40 years before there is a nuclear waste dump for the UK's legacy wastes (if such a plan is ever accepted). In the meantime all nuclear sites in Scotland – including military and civil research sites – will be expected to keep waste on site in stores until a repository is found. This is partly because the industry is keen to avoid having to move waste to a site for storage and then to move it a second time for disposal.

References

CoRWM. (2004a). *Preliminary Report on the Inventory,* CoRWM document. No. 542.

CoRWM. (2004b). '*Options for long term management of high active solid radioactive waste in the United Kingdom.*' CoRWM. document. No. 749.

Herald & Times. (1 Nov. 2004). Nuclear Industry urged to come clean over leaks.

Health and Safety Executive. (2001). Safety Audit of Dounreay 1998: Final Report

Nuclear Fuel. (2004). *UKAEA hopeful, but realistic, about shipping waste by 2008* Vol. 29. No. 8.

Nucleonics Week. (2004). UKAEA to begin difficult clean up at Dounreay's cliffrside ILW shaft. Vol. 45. Iss. 45.

Sunday Herald. (31 Oct., 2004). Exposed: scandle of nuclear leaks at Scots plant.

UKAEA. (2000). Dounreay Site Restoration Plan. Vols. 1 – 8.

Brent Alpha Platform in the northern North Sea © Shell Photographic Services

5 How Norway has Managed the Environmental Effects of the Norwegian Oil and Gas Industry in the Vicinity of Oil Platforms

John S. Gray – *Marine Biodiversity Reseach Programme, Department of Biology, University of Oslo, Pb 1066 Blindern, 0316 Oslo Norway.*

Summary

1. In the early days of exploitation of the oil and gas resources on Norway's continental shelf there was little control over environmental impacts. The oil companies expected effects of their activities to fall within a 1 km radius around platforms.

2. In the late 1980s data started appearing that suggested that effects were over much larger areas. These findings were disputed but subsequent studies showed that a more realistic figure of the area affected was a 3 km radius giving roughly ten times the area affected from that predicted by the companies.

3. The Norwegian environmental authorities reacted by imposing restrictions on discharges of oil-based drilling cuttings and in 1993 a total ban was introduced. Expensive field-by-field monitoring has now been replaced by regional monitoring which not only save costs but is also more efficient in obtaining a better overview of the environmental conditions along the whole Norwegian continental shelf.

5.1 Introduction

One of the most unfortunate scientific predictions ever made must be that of the Norwegian Geological Survey who in 1958 in a report to the Norwegian Foreign Department stated, *"One can exclude the possibility that coal, oil or sulphur can be found on the Norwegian continental shelf."* Fortunately for the economy of Norway this prediction was wrong and Norway is now the world's third largest oil and gas exporting country!

The oil and gas adventure started when Phillips became the first company to seek permission to explore for oil in 1962. However, at that time the Norwegian government had not claimed jurisdiction over the resources on the continental shelf, and it was not until

Gray, J.S. (2008). How Norway has Managed the Environmental Effects of the Norwegian Oil and Gas Industry in the Vicinity of Oil Platforms. In *Energy and the Natural Heritage*, ed. by C.A. Galbraith and J.M. Baxter. TSO Scotland, Edinburgh. pp. 53-62

1965 that permission was first given for exploration to begin. Then in 1969, two days before Christmas, oil was found at the Ekofisk field and the oil adventure had begun. At first exploration was restricted to south of latitude 62° N and it was only in 1980 that drilling north of this latitude was permitted. In the last few years a new phase has begun with exploration for oil and gas now taking place at depths of 1,500m in the Vøring plateau, much different from the shallow 70m at Ekofisk.

Exploratory drilling involves the use of a number of chemicals, including lubricating oils and the use of materials which are used to maintain the pressure whilst drilling and removing drilled rock cuttings. The drilling muds are usually composed of barite, but since this material is derived from natural deposits it comprises a number of additional elements notably small amounts of other heavy metals. In the mid to late 1970s the use of oil-based drilling muds increased rapidly due to their technical superiority over water-based muds when drilling difficult and non-vertical wells. In the early days of exploration, the material reaching the surface (drilling muds which could not be recycled and drilling cuttings), were discharged into the sea. In the early 1960s it was felt that the composition and amounts of these wastes were unlikely to lead to detrimental environmental effects. For the Ekofisk field, Phillips produced an Environmental Impact Assessment (EIA) in 1968 that was presented to the relevant Norwegian authority, the State Pollution Control Authority (Statens Forurensningstilsyn): this predicted that the species diversity of the benthic organisms inhabiting the seabed would be affected to a maximum of a 1 km radius from the drilling platform. Extensive discharge of oil-based muds on cuttings to the North Sea bottom occurred from 1965 onwards, and in 1985 the Paris Commission Working Group on Oil Pollution compiled a list of 'agreed facts' on the impact of oil-based muds. They also concluded that the effects of oil and gas exploration and production activities in general on benthic organisms was confined to less than 1 km from the discharge source, with a few exceptional cases reaching to 2 km.

5.2 Development of environmental control procedures

From 1973 the Norwegian authorities required all the companies exploring on the continental shelf to submit annual reports on the environmental conditions in the areas being explored. The companies engaged a variety of consulting companies to do this work; all of the monitoring work was paid for directly by the companies with no State subsidies. The first monitoring was done at Ekofisk in 1973, and first at Statfjord (a survey of possible chemical contamination only) in 1978. The State Pollution Control Authority (SFT) received these reports and yet they were not reviewed or analysed.

Our analyses of the monitoring reports showed that quality control left much to be desired. In the worst case a survey one year had revealed more than 300 species of benthic organisms whereas a survey of the same area five years later reported only 26. Pollution was not the cause, quality control was simply non-existent. Similar examples were found with the chemical analyses. The SFT responded by setting up an expert group in 1986 with the primary objective of assessing the quality of the reports. An initial analysis of the data from several surveys at the Statfjord field (Reiersen *et al.,* 1988), suggested that there were biological effects over much greater areas than that predicted in the companies' EIAs. This paper received an extremely hostile reception from the oil companies and when printed,

Plate 5.1 Oil Production Platform in the North Sea © John Baxter

(without the authors' knowledge), had a disclaimer added to the first page suggesting that the results were not to be trusted!

Simultaneously an initiative was taken by SFT to establish common guidelines as to how the monitoring should be done. Guidelines were developed by the expert group based on a two day scientific workshop held in 1987, and were subsequently discussed in an open forum with the oil companies. Table 5.1 shows the development of the programme. Sampling methods for both biology and chemistry were standardized as were analysis methods, including statistical analysis, largely based on the best practices already used by the

Table 5.1 Development of Environmental Programme

1970-1985	Annual reports submitted by companies to State Pollution Control Board (SFT)
1985	Expert group established, (2 biologists 2 chemists), to review reports
1988	Official Guidelines for Monitoring Methods established and adopted by OSPARCOM
1990	Norwegian Guidelines made mandatory for Norwegian offshore monitoring. Revised version in 1997
1993	Norwegian Guidelines adopted by OSPARCOM
1995	Regional monitoring began

Table 5.2 Monitoring Programme established in 1989

| A fixed network of stations is established at each field on 4 radii (at 0°, 90°, 180° and 270°) and at logarithmically increasing distances (250m, 500m, 1000m, 2000m, 4000m) from the structure |
| For all fields during drilling: annual chemical surveys covering sediment particle size, heavy metals and hydrocarbons, once every 3 years biological surveys of macrofauna retained on a 1 mm sieve |
| For oil fields during production: as during drilling |
| For gas fields during production: surveys once every 6 years |

scientific community and the oil companies. In 1988 the Guidelines were adopted by the Paris Commission for general application, and in 1990 they were made mandatory for monitoring around Norwegian fields. The basic outline of the monitoring programme is shown in Table 5.2.

One important aspect of the Norwegian system is that once the reports are received by SFT they are in the public domain and open to scrutiny by interested scientists, the green movement or members of the public.

5.3 Reassessment of environmental effects

By use of the expert group SFT had established annual reviews of all the reports submitted as well as the production of annual summary reports on the environmental condition around the Norwegian offshore installations. At this time new statistical methods for examining effects on benthic organisms had been developed and were being applied. Gray *et al.* (1990) published an analysis of the Ekofisk data submitted to SFT. It was clearly apparent to the expert group that effects on the benthos covered much larger areas than that predicted in the mid 1960s by the oil companies, (3 km^2 at each drilling or production platform where drilling muds and cuttings were discharged) and by the 'agreed facts' of the Paris Commission Working Group (1985). By integrating comparable data from several surveys Bakke *et al.* (1990) also found that some of the more common benthic invertebrates around North Sea oil and gas fields were decimated in abundance at oil concentrations which could be expected as far out as 10 km or more from the drilling discharge points, thus supporting the conclusions from Reiersen *et al.* (1988). The findings of Gray *et al.* (1990) aroused controversy since it was argued, notably by the oil companies and by the British environmental authorities, that no effects on fish or fish food had been found. The effects were merely on 'worms and snails'.

The response of the Norwegian authorities was that the effects were unacceptable because they covered ca. 10 times the area predicted by the oil companies' EIAs. This is an important aspect that is not generally appreciated. The criterion used by the authorities is the prediction made by the EIA; if instead one asks the question "Are there effects on fish or food for fish?", then the one cannot use the monitoring data obtained but have to make value judgements; since value judgements are subjective there is room for constant argument. Testing for compliance with environmental criteria should not be left to subjective appraisal, and it is thus essential that EIAs make quantitative predictions which can then be tested using objective statistical methods.

Figure 5. 1 shows how the principles of monitoring can be established (Gray and Jensen, 1993). This example was developed to protect the environment when building the Great Belt Bridge in Denmark, and was highly successfully in controlling the environmental effects of constructing the enormous Øresund Link between Copenhagen, Denmark and Malmö, Sweden. A Control Panel was constituted which comprised all stakeholders, the environmental authorities, the experts and the green movements. They examined the EIA and defined the terms 'acceptable' and 'unacceptable' environmental effects in relation to the area likely to be affected by the construction. For example, for the Øresund Link the Danish environmental authorities determined that acceptable effects were a 25% reduction in the areas of mussel and seagrasses within 3 km of the line of the link for up to five years. Outside this area no effects should occur. Having clear guidelines the experts devised a monitoring programme to detect this level of change. The link was constructed with few environmental effects, and is now used as a model example of environmentally-friendly construction.

With the development of the environmental programme for the Norwegian continental shelf, finding that the effects were greater than predicted in the EIA, the authorities enacted legislation in 1991. This restricted the maximum amounts of oil that could be discharged with cuttings to 60 g kg^{-1} up to 1st January 1993; after 1st January 1993 discharge of oil-contaminated cuttings was prohibited. That this legislation was justified was apparent after Olsgard and Gray (1995) analysed much of the data then available on the effects of oil and gas exploration on the Norwegian continental shelf and found that the Ekofisk result of effects on benthic organisms to a radius of 3 km (i.e. ca. 30 km^2) at a single field was a general one. Figure 5.2 shows the historical development of effects at the Gyda field (1987

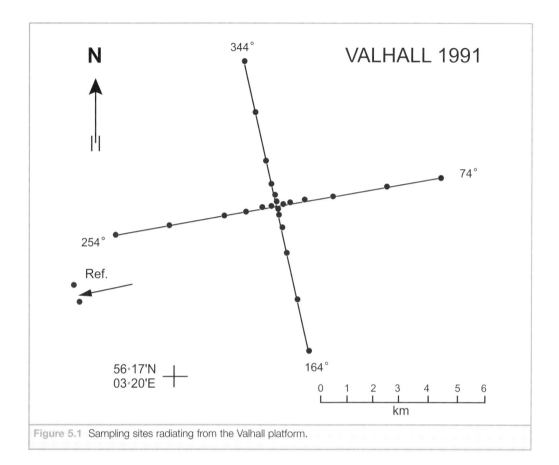

N

344°

VALHALL 1991

74°

254°

Ref.

56°17'N
03°20'E

164°

0   1   2   3   4   5   6
km

Figure 5.1 Sampling sites radiating from the Valhall platform.

was the baseline survey). Three years later effects were marked and after six years effects were found in an area similar to that at Ekofisk.

The response of the oil companies was to invest in new technology that led to no discharges of oil-based drilling muds and cuttings in the Norwegian sector by 1993. The technologies included re-injection down bore holes, retaining material and disposing on shore, development of new drilling procedures, as well as introducing synthetic drilling fluids (based on esters, ethers, olefins, etc.) with comparable technical performance to that of oil based mud. Since 1993 there has been a rapidly increasing use of these synthetic muds in the Norwegian sector and oil-based drilling muds could only be used in the Norwegian sector in very special circumstances under licences issued by SFT.

Now that water-based and later generation synthetic drilling fluids are used, effects are much less extensive than with oil-based fluids. Figure 5.3 shows a survey at the Tordis field conducted in 1995 (Gjøs *et al.*, 1996). Drilling took place between 1987 and 1989 and the area has received Barite-4054 tonnes, Novadril (polyalphaolefin)-160 tonnes, Finagreen (ester based)-2.6 tonnes, and the following accidental spills: ethylene glycol-1,500l, Novadril fluid-7.3 tonnes, oil-1.4 tonnes. The extent of effects six years after discharge began is far less than at Gyda (see Figure 5.2) and even those affected areas have high numbers of species and show, at most, very slight effects. Thus the legislation and follow-up by the companies has led to a dramatic reduction in pollution levels.

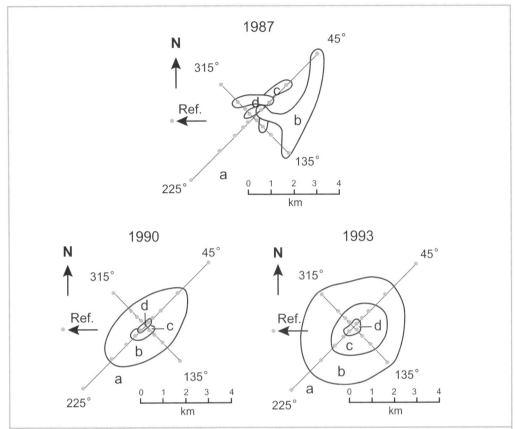

Fig 5.2 Development of effects of pollution on benthos at Gyda oil field. a – unpolluted, b – slightly polluted, c – moderately polluted, d – severely polluted.

The problem with the monitoring system, however, was that it required each company to investigate each field every three years. As new marginal fields were developed the sampling design for close fields led to overlap of sampling stations. Often different consultancy companies were involved in adjacent surveys that were costly and led to inefficient analyses as methods, although similar (as required by the Guidelines), were not identical. There were still differences in the quality of the reports submitted. Since control stations were 10 km away these were often not appropriate as controls having different depths and sediment types or were influenced by new neighbouring fields. The Expert group recommended to SFT that the Guidelines, although working well and giving reliable data, had become obsolete in terms of sampling design and strategy. Revision was needed and regional monitoring was suggested.

5.4 Regional monitoring introduced in 1995

The whole of the Norwegian continental shelf is divided into 11 regions, of which only six have oil exploration or production. Monitoring is now required at a regional level rather than by each company investigating its own sites. Each regional survey is required to be done by a single consulting company; the oil companies through their national organization (OLF) develop the proposal and agree on joint financing. The proposal is then put up for

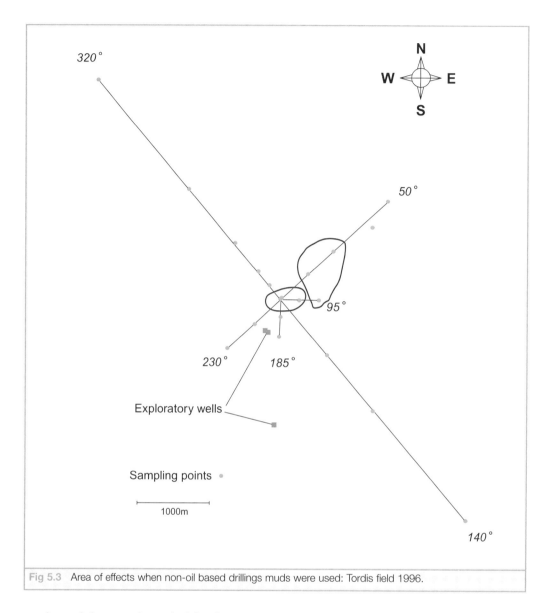

Fig 5.3   Area of effects when non-oil based drillings muds were used: Tordis field 1996.

tender and the consultants bid for the contract. Since the requirements are for large surveys, only two consulting companies now have the resources and national accreditation, and are pre-qualified to submit tenders. Both are highly regarded both by the oil companies and the experts who review their reports.

The sampling sites cover all the oil fields and, in addition, a number of general reference sites to provide data for long-term changes such as those induced by climate change. Each year two regions are covered so that within three years the whole continental shelf from 56° to 68°N is covered, which is the area that had been drilled to the end of 1998. The first whole shelf survey has been completed and we are beginning the second cycle.

The companies are extremely pleased with the new monitoring system since they save on average NOK 15 million per company per year through a coordinated and more efficient system. Equipment is purchased centrally and standard containers are now available with the gear needed stored centrally. With fewer companies involved, it is far easier to examine trends in distribution patterns of fauna across the whole shelf and this provides knowledge of zoogeography and long-term changes which were not possible previously. The new regional monitoring has thus led to excellent collaboration between oil companies, scientists and consultants, and shows that the scepticism of the 1960s has changed to a fruitful and profitable liaison which has led to protection of the marine environment and a mutually beneficial data collecting system.

References

Bakke, T., Gray, J. S. and Reiersen, L. O. (1990). Monitoring in the vicinity of oil and gas platforms: Environmental status in the Norwegian Sector in 1987±1989. In Proceedings of the 1st International Symposium on Oil and Gas Exploration and Production Waste Management Practices. US EPA, 623 pp.

Gjøs, N., Nølan, S.A. and Jensen, T. (1996). Environmental monitoring survey Tordis 1995. Sintef Applied Chemistry, Report No. STF27F95036, 134 pp.

Gray, J.S., Clarke, K.R., Warwick, R.M. and Hobbs, G. (1990). Detection of initial effects of pollution on marine benthos: an example from the Ekofisk and Eldfisk oilfields, N. Sea. *Marine Ecology Progress Series.* **66**: 285-299.

Gray, J.S. and Jensen, K. (1993). Feedback monitoring: A new way of protecting the marine enviroment. *Trends in Ecology and Evolution.* **8**: 267-268.

Gray, J.S., Bakke, T., Beck, H-J. and Nilssen, I. (1999). Managing the environmental effects of the Norwegian oil and gas industry: from conflict to consensus. *Marine Pollution Bulletin.* **38**: 525-530.

Olsgard, F. and Gray, J.S. (1995). A comprehensive analysis of the effects of offshore oil and gas expoloration and production on the benthic communities of the Norwegian continental shelf. *Marine Ecology Progress Series.* **122**: 277-306.

Paris Commission. (1985). Guidelines for Monitoring Methods to be used in the Vicinity of Platforms in the North Sea. Chameleon, London, 28 pp, ISBN-0946956200.

Reiersen, L. O., Gray, J. S., Palmork, K. H. and Lange, R. (1988). Monitoring in the vicinity of oil and gas platforms: results from the Norwegian sector of the North Sea and recommended methods for forthcoming surveillance. In *Drilling Wastes*, eds. F. R. Engelhardt, J. P. Ray, and A.H. Gillam, pp. 91-117. Elsevier, London.

Solving ever increasing traffic conjestion is part of the carbon management challenge © Colin Galbraith

6 Energy, Transport and Impacts on the Scottish Environment

Tom Hart – *Birchfield, Kings Road, Beith, Ayrshire KA15 2BN.*

Summary

1. After outlining the complex relationships between the economy, energy, transport and the range of environmental concerns, this chapter reviews scenarios for future relationships between transport, the economy and the environment with particular reference to the next 20 to 30 years.

2. It compares the impact of a Micawber Approach (something will turn up to solve present problems) and a Precautionary Approach. It concludes that only the latter is capable of allowing the transport sector to become a contributor to the easing of problems of climate change.

3. At present, the transport sector is increasing emissions, aided by high growth in air transport. However, a combination of policy change, technical change and altered lifestyle preferences offers scope to cut emissions and ensure less demand for movement, in ways jointly strengthening the Scottish economy and both environmental and social justice objectives.

4. In conclusion, emphasis is placed on greater energy conservation (reinforced by modal shifts away from cars and domestic UK air travel), travel restraint aided by pricing, fiscal and regulatory measures, an early review of mega projects and stronger use of applied land use planning policies to encourage more sustainable settlement patterns and sustainable tourism. More meaningful consultation, backed by relevant information, is sought on transport options before final decisions.

6.1 Starting points

The principal theme examined in this chapter is whether the transport sector is the main obstacle to large cuts in CO_2 emissions over the years to 2050. Is transport also a source of increased environmental concerns or can it play a much larger role in cutting emissions without creating major new environmental problems as part of the CO_2 solution? In considering this theme, however, we must be clear that environmental and social concerns cover a considerably wider range than the climate change issue. Some environmental concerns can increase energy use rather than cut it – two examples are the impacts of catalytic converters in cutting exhaust pollutants at the expense of reduced fuel efficiency

Hart, T. (2008). Energy, Transport and Impacts on the Scottish Environment. In *Energy and the Natural Heritage*, ed. by C.A. Galbraith and J.M. Baxter. TSO Scotland, Edinburgh. pp. 63-78

Tom Hart is a former chair, and continuing committee member of the Scottish Transport Studies Group, and also a Board Member of Transform Scotland, the campaigning group for sustainable transport. He is a retired lecturer in Economic and Social History. The views expressed in this chapter are personal.

and the Disability Discrimination Act in reducing seats per train to give room for wheelchair accessible toilets (not required for air travel). Environmental concerns about transport noise levels, safety and sheer volumes of movement (including too much walking and cycling in highly sensitive areas) are also largely separable from energy issues.

We have to recognize that, within the environmental area, there is a need for balance between differing objectives. The 'natural environment' is a misnomer since our physical environment is heavily influenced by human interventions over many centuries, some of which now offer highly regarded heritage while others have had adverse impacts on humans and on the habitats of plants and animals.

Wider political objectives also embrace economic growth and complex issues of equity and environmental justice within Scotland and the UK, and with respect to narrowing the large differences in income levels and in energy use between rich and poor countries. Discussion of these issues is often fudged or postponed – and not helped by uncertainties about the reliability of existing information and future forecasts. There are considerable tensions between political rhetoric on the importance of sustainable development and on substantial moves away from non-renewable energy (with former Prime Minister Tony Blair reinforcing this rhetoric in his speech on 14th September, 2004) and contrasts in actual policies and perceived attitudes which have watered-down the urgency for early action in the context of short-term threats to economic growth and electoral success. As regards the Scottish Government, its rhetoric on sustainable development has been even stronger than that of the UK. In practice, it has moved forward on sustainable development indicators including the aspiration, unique in the devolved governments of the UK, to stabilize road traffic. The restatement of economic strategy (announced on 11th November 2004) emphasized the importance for the economy and for social justice of sustainable development strategies ensuring better use of resources and less waste.

6.2 Information issues

Information issues affect both current data and future forecasts. On one interpretation, *Scottish Transport Statistics* shows an encouraging cut between 1993 and 2003 of 20% in petrol and derv deliveries despite a 15% rise in road vehicle kilometres and a 26% rise in vehicle ownership. This implies an impressive gain in fuel efficiency yet checks with DTI have revealed considerable caveats about the reliability of road fuel delivery data. Turning to forecasts, the Forth Estuary Transportation Authority (FETA) in a consultation document concluded that its most expensive option for tackling Forth crossing problems would be the least effective in reducing demand for road vehicle movement (FETA, 2005) This option was the least effective in reducing total energy demand arising from Forth crossings. There is an urgent need, utilizing *Scottish Transport Appraisal Guidance* (STAG), for further development of option analysis in relation to economic impacts and to the range of environmental and energy impacts. This is essential to raise public awareness of realistic choices before informed decisions. A significant aspect of current research is ongoing work in relation to evaluating quality of life in the context that present methods of calculating real incomes per head may not make sufficient allowance for the quarrying of resources and some decline in quality of life eroding apparent gains from higher income.

6.3 The importance of global action

Without action by other countries, the sum total of potential Scottish Government action to influence the impacts on Scotland of global climate change will hardly be noticed

Plate 6.1 Forth road and rail bridges looking northwards to Fife © P&A Macdonald / SNH

(though action within Scotland has greater scope to offer more localized or regional environmental benefits). The Scottish Government needs to plan to minimize the adverse impacts of climate change already in the pipeline.

Nevertheless, Scotland and the UK can still provide a lead for other countries – encouraging them to be more proactive on the global agenda but also offering the benefits of Scottish expertise in the renewable energy and energy conservation sectors with growing prospects in world markets. This process can also see Scottish business gaining from being leaders in conservation and in value-added – including sustainable tourism - not requiring large energy inputs, i.e. greater convergence and complementarity in economic and environmental objectives.

6.4 Why pick on transport as a special theme?

The reason for paying special attention to transport is that, compared to other sectors, transport related CO_2 emissions are still rising despite cuts in other sectors of the economy. Gains from fuel efficiency have been more than cancelled out by growth in energy intensive (and often environmentally intrusive) movement. Here, it is opportune to revisit the 1999 Report (part funded by SNH) on *Transport Policy Options for a Sustainable Scotland 2000-2020* (Hart and Doar, 1999). This found that, in 1995, Scottish transport accounted for around 32% of carbon emissions in Scotland compared to 27% from industry, 24% from the domestic sector and 17% from services. The Report then examined a scenario embracing a *Business as Usual* approach to transport within an overall goal of cuts of about one-third in Scottish CO_2 emissions by 2020. The estimated outcome was a rise of around 40% in Scottish road vehicle miles and in CO_2 emissions from transport by 2020 with the weight of CO_2 cuts

Plate 6.2 Petrol station forecourt with petrol, diesel and LPG pumps © John Baxter

falling entirely on other sectors of the economy. Such cuts were considered unrealistic, leading to rejection of this scenario . The case for such rejection is reinforced when account is taken of the rapid growth in external air services and of the energy absorbed in vehicle and transport construction and related recycling.

Without policy changes, the *Aviation White Paper* (Department for Transport, 2003) stated that aviation alone by 2030 could contribute 25% of CO_2 emissions attributable to the UK. This compares with a 1980s' air travel contribution of no more than 3%. In the Scottish context, the high level of Anglo-Scottish travel by air along with overseas travel could raise the Scottish transport share of CO_2 emissions by over 50% by 2030 with this percentage still rising over the years to 2050 – contrasting sharply with the government aspiration for a 60% cut in total CO_2 emissions by 2050. This sharp rise in transport's absolute use of energy and in its share of emissions is in no way a convincing or safe scenario – other actions are required to resolve the conflict between transport and sustainable development. Using the (*Business as usual*) Scenario 1 of limited policy change and low oil prices, Hart and Doar (1999) concluded that transport internal to Scotland could experience a rise of 40% in CO_2 emissions by 2020, mainly due to higher levels of road traffic. Adding in Anglo-Scottish and overseas air travel as postulated in the high growth forecast of the Aviation White Paper could lead to a 300% rise in energy consumption in Scottish related air travel by 2030 and even more by 2050 – so what can be done?

6.5 Two divergent responses

The Micawber Approach - something will turn up to allow expanding energy use and conventional economic growth without significant damage to the environment (possibly even gains depending on definitions of environment) – assumes that there will be dynamic technical responses including more efficient energy use and a revival of nuclear power.

The Precautionary Approach - takes the view that public policy should be more cautious except where there is strong evidence of the ability of technical change, conservation and policy change to ease energy problems without adverse environmental impacts – suggests there is no requirement for revival of nuclear power, especially so in Scotland where there is

Table 6.1 Summary of some of the prospects for technical change and their environmental impact.

Technical Change	Environmental Impact
Energy conservation through change in building, vehicle and engine design	Mainly positive unless efficiency gains lead to rise in total energy demand, including demand for intrusive movement
Energy conservation through changes in land use policy and working practice	Settlement patterns and changing work practices (aided by IT) can allow increases in living closer to work and increases in working at home – people also closer to other facilities – can enhance sustainable tourism and leisure
Alternative fuels	
– nuclear	Very limited CO_2 emissions but major issues relating to environmental acceptability, development costs and the sourcing and transport of hazardous materials and residues – requirements for grid upgrades and other associated provision for final use via electricity
Other alternatives	
– batteries	Still require chemical inputs, recharging from mains – can cut local pollution/noise but give significant environmental (and economic) problems if scale of use was to rise
– hydrogen fuel cells	Major problem is still the energy cost of producing the hydrogen plus an added fire risk – can eliminate localized pollution from exhausts
– wind, wave, tidal, solar, hydro	Can give rise to localized landscape intrusion plus habitat/marine issues and requirements for grid upgrades through sensitive areas (or more expensive underground or under sea provision)
– biomass (crop fuels)	Can absorb CO_2 created but can raise landscape, habitat and some transport issues – also possible competition with land for food supply and leisure/recreation
CO_2 storage	Still at exploration stage – possibility of leaks

a wide range of alternative sources with potential to replace the existing Hunterston and Torness plants due for closure within 25 years.

These responses are examined below.

6.6 The Micawber approach

This should not be dismissed out of hand. Environmentalists can be at fault in failing to appreciate the ability of human ingenuity to overcome problems without creating new ones – yet they are on stronger ground in arguing for the importance of policy change linked with technical change and changing perceptions of what people want to see in their lives and those of future generations (Table 6.1).

All of these technical issues also involve the questions of the feasible scale of application and the opportunity costs i.e. comparison of alternative uses of proposed funding. For example, wind power has significant installation costs relative to the quantity and reliability of energy gained – it is arguable that better results could come from some switch of funding to wave/tidal power and to improve the efficiency of coal-fired power stations while cutting total emissions (including sulphur). Rising energy prices, fiscal policy and regulatory policy will influence actual change – as will changes in transport pricing and in practical awareness of differing options for business and individuals. With continuing increase in real incomes, technical change alone does not guarantee reduced energy demand or reduction in travel demand. Technical change lowering costs may boost demand if there is a high desire to travel – hence Mr Micawber's potential revisiting of nuclear power if Scotland and the UK is to even approach the aim of a 60% cut in CO_2 by 2050, while allowing oil use (or new fuels) to become more concentrated on aviation.

6.7 The precautionary approach

The essence of this approach is to adjust policy, pricing and regulatory activity to provide greater use of both carrots and sticks to expand renewables, cut energy demand and introduce a sharper focus on restraining demand for energy intensive and intrusive movement. Policy is used to encourage appropriate technical change and changes in personal and business behaviour.   Results are observed before any decisions are taken on major transport investments which could further increase demand, particularly for travel by air and by car. Such a policy can also provide cuts in congestion aiding the reliability of business and personal travel while increasing the access opportunities of those without cars. It can find room for some exceptions such as a more generous approach to easing island access through some improvement in air services and cuts in island air fares – but at the same time, it would dampen down present trends to encourage expansion in longer flights and in short scenic flights and air taxis adding to noise and intrusion in sensitive areas.

Hart and Doar (1999) also included two additional scenarios featuring greater use of policy changes in conjunction with technical change to restrain energy use and encourage energy conservation. Scenario 2 focused on a greater degree of modal shift away from cars to public transport, walking and cycling (plus some rise in car-sharing at peaks) while Scenario 3 placed more emphasis on *reducing the need for movement*.   In these scenarios, transport made greater contributions to CO_2 cuts than Scenario 1 with Scenario 3 achieving transport CO_2 cuts almost as great as prospects in other sectors of the economy. These scenarios did not explore the emerging issue of much higher growth in air travel to and from

Plate 6.3 Train with coal bing in background © Lorne Gill/SNH

Scotland. In this area, it is hard to see any absolute cut in overseas air travel, but there are opportunities for shifts from Anglo-Scottish flights to high-speed rail. Some growth in direct overseas flights to and from Scotland will replace flights via English international hub airports. Scotland may still see a 100% rise in direct international air travel over the next 30 years – but this would be well below the forecasts in the Aviation White Paper. Runway and terminal space for such flights could be released by major shifts within Britain from domestic air travel to high-speed rail.

Hart and Doar (1999) concluded that a combination of policy and technical change, reinforced by greater environmental awareness, could cut CO_2 emissions from all sectors by 35% by 2020 with transport achieving a cut of some 27% under Scenario 3. This scenario included some gains in fuel efficiency also aided by modal shift and improved load factors. It estimated a cut of some 23% in road vehicle miles but a rise in personal movement within Scotland of 9% between 2000 and 2020.

Reviewing these estimates, two points emerge:

a) insufficient allowance was made for gains in fuel efficiency and shifts towards acceptable alternative fuels; and
b) there is a need for scenarios to include external movement to and from Scotland.

These features may balance out, i.e. a 27% cut in CO_2 emissions from internal transport between 2000 and 2020 looks achievable if road vehicle kilometres stay around present levels (with further cuts in emissions between 2020 and 2050 as a changing vehicle population becomes more efficient) - but with such gains being balanced by a constrained rise in overseas air travel to and from Scotland (allowing overall CO_2 targets to be met).

With this level of improvement by 2020, even on a precautionary view it should prove possible to deliver a 60% saving on 1990 CO_2 emissions by 2050. In terms of impacts on more localized environments in Scotland, policies encouraging existing trends towards road vehicle km stabilization (and cuts in some areas) offer substantial advantages in reducing intrusion and lowering existing noise levels (as more and more vehicles incorporate new technology and observe lower speed limits). Health and other social benefits also flow from shifts to walking, cycling and public transport while shifts to these modes allow urban areas and rural areas the advantages of some rise in personal movement without the considerable disadvantages of too many moving and parked vehicles on routes and at locations unable to absorb them without environmental strain. Both the economy and society would gain from a much reduced need for major road investment and the removal of any need for new parallel runways at either Edinburgh or Glasgow airports. There would be some requirements for extra rail, bus and path/cycleway investment and maintenance but with relatively few problems of adverse environmental impact. With selected works, including more extensive and enforced bus priorities, the road network can handle a continuing rise in bus movement. Similarly, existing railways, given extra rolling stock and selected investment to raise track capacity, that improve interchanges and extend the network, are well placed to handle 3 to 5 times the present volume of usage, giving net economic and environmental benefit in the years to 2050.

One area of controversy which arises is in relation to Greenbelt Policy and policy for transport, energy and the environment. This is currently under review and is being influenced by the argument that, given limits to brown-field potential and objections to crammed cities with little greenspace, some selective relaxation of greenbelts around cities may be preferable to a continuation of present strategies accepting too readily a rise in longer-distance commuting, often by car. There are prospects for shifting such longer distance travel to improved public transport yet the net impact of an outward shift of population can be a bigger rise in car use than in public transport. City extension plans merit examination as they can aid, not only public transport modal share, but also a rise in walking and cycling as part of normal travel – rather than a distinct leisure activity.

6.8 Conclusions

Would the economy suffer or would it gain because of improved incorporation of environmental benefits in economic assessments in future scenarios to be considered before final choices?

Hart and Doar (1999) drawing on the Standing Advisory Committee on Trunk Road Assessment (SACTRA) Reports on *Transport and the Economy*, (Interim Report in 1998 with Final Report in 1999) argued that reduced road traffic (and more cautious attitudes to air travel) could help the Scottish economy and at the same time produce benefits for social inclusion and for a range of environmental concerns – of which the need for absolute cuts in CO_2 was only one concern, though a major one.

This view was reflected in the *Scottish Economic Report* (Scottish Executive, 2000) which saw strictly selective transport issues as being important for the economy. These included reduced congestion and improved external links but the main motive factors in growth were seen as lying elsewhere in the economy – notably in relation to skills, knowledge and value added. The SACTRA report and other economic evidence e.g. from Japan – has drawn attention to the fact that the transport intensity of economies has been decreasing. Internal movement has been growing less rapidly than rates of economic growth with weakening evidence of further transport investment being a key driver of growth. Energy and environmental policies favour fairly concentrated rather than dispersed towns and cities with investment shifts towards public transport and, more controversially, towards external links. Future road investment is likely to focus on smaller schemes giving a high safety and environmental return and on a few projects allowing some rise in capacity linked with higher charges for use of busier sections of the network (many of which appear free at the point of use while public transport fares are up-front and higher). Real incentives for car-sharing have also been lacking.

This thinking ties in with the then Scottish Executive lead in announcing in 2002 an aim for road traffic stabilization over the next 20 years. Overall, Scotland is already close to this despite weaknesses in delivery. Road traffic growth on major roads has fallen from 8% a year in the early 1980s to an average of 2.4% a year between 1993 and 1998 and to 1.4% between 1998 and 2003 (Scottish Executive, 2004). Rail use has risen faster than car use since the mid 1990s while bus travel, after years of decline has risen since 2000.

Issues of delivery, notably in relation to public transport improvements and road pricing are now beginning to be tackled with more vigour but clearer links must be established between sustainable objectives and actual programmes and priorities for transport and related land use changes. There are some 'growth' hotspots but road traffic since the mid 1990s has grown more slowly than the economy and more slowly than the rise in car ownership. Air travel has risen most of all yet, in terms of freight movement and net tourism gain, a stable, sustainable economy is not compatible with the high levels of growth in the Aviation White Paper. Indeed, high-speed rail (including premium freight) offers potential for trips under 1000 miles while shipping – with low energy costs and other unit costs falling through the use of larger ships – is strengthening its primary role in international freight links and is also expanding in the shorter-distance sector raising some specific environmental issues for locations like Scapa Flow, Hunterston and Rosyth.

In the light of this evidence, Scotland stands to gain, not lose, from the precautionary approach. To a large extent, these gains can be joint for the economy and for the environment. It is time to ensure that such gains are maximized in the actual policies and programmes affecting our transport networks. Mega-projects require re-examination with more priority for immediate measures giving quick wins for the economy and the environment with demonstrable delivery of overall road traffic stabilization (and cuts in some areas) and a more realistic approach to air travel.

6.9 Key actions

1) An integrated mix of policy change and technical change offers substantial prospects for joint gains for the economy and the environment, including a much enlarged contribution from Scottish internal and external transport to cumulative cuts in CO_2 emissions.

2) Scenarios 2 and 3 in the 1999 Report on Sustainable Transport Options have proved robust and merit review and adjustment in the light of changing circumstances and policy aims since 1999. A revised Scenario between 2 and 3 seems best placed to advance economic, environmental and social aims.

3) Information provision and consultation on option scenarios should be improved as a better basis for national, regional and local strategies for delivery and monitoring. This approach is endorsed in STAG and in new requirements for Strategic Environmental Assessment (SEA) but requires a sharper focus to speed delivery of high-benefit programmes, abandon preparatory work on unacceptable projects and expand detailed evaluation of intermediate options prior to fuller consultation and decisions on preferred options.

4) Policy should place increased emphasis on energy conservation in both the transport and non-transport sectors with particular attention to greater use of fiscal policy to raise energy prices but with the proceeds earmarked for reductions in other taxes and a rise in funding supportive of energy conservation and the renewable sector.

5) Greater urgency should be attached to transport pricing reform raising prices paid by motorists at the point of use and especially at times of congestion and where more road capacity has been provided with net proceeds applied to fare reductions and improvements increasing the attractions of public transport, walking and cycling.

6) There should be a review of mega-transport projects in Scotland to ensure that they are cost-effective and compatible with sustainable development, energy and environmental strategies

7) Land use policy – including Greenbelt and greenspace strategy- should be reviewed to ensure that it gives full support to sustainable development, energy and environmental strategies.

November, 2005.

References

Department for Transport. (2003). *The Future of Air Transport.* The Aviation White Paper.

Department for Transport. (2007). *(October 2007) Towards a Sustainable Transport System: Supporting Economic Growth in a Low Carbon Economy.*

Department of Trade and Industry. (May 2007). *Energy White Paper.*

FETA. (2005). *Local Transport Strategy.*

Hart, T. and Doar, N. (Editors). (1999). *Transport Policy Options for a Sustainable Scotland : An Assessment of Three Policy Scenarios.* A Report by the Scottish Forum for Transport and the Environment.

IPPC. (2007). *Report from International panel on Climate Change.*

SACTRA. (1998). *Transport Investment, Transport Intensity & Economic Growth. Interim Report Scottish Transport Appraisal Guidance.* Interim report.

SACTRA. (1999). *Transport and the Economy.*

Scottish Executive. (2000). *The Way Forward : Framework for Economic Development in Scotland.*

Scottish Executive. (2003). *Scottish Transport Appraisal Guidance* (STAG).

Scottish Executive. (2004). *Scottish Transport Statistics,* No 23.

Scottish Executive. (December 2006). *National transport Strategy for Scotland and related modal strategies.*

Scottish Executive. (July 2007). *High Level Rail Output Specification (HLOS) for Scotland.*

Statements and actions by SNP Government since May 2007-12-04.

UK Government. (December 2006). *Stern and Eddington Reports* (relating respectively to overall Climate Change Issues and to Transport).

Energy, Transport and Impacts on the Scottish Environment

ADDENDUM (5 November 2007)

Changing evidence and attitudes since the chapter was first written in November 2004 leave the original arguments intact and, if anything, strengthen the growing convergence in economic, energy and environmental pressures for radical cuts in global CO_2 emissions and a reducing link between economic activity and the use of fossil fuels with rising costs and uncertain supply (see various references). Some implications of recent developments are outlined below.

UK aspirations for net cuts in total CO_2 emissions have gone beyond the previous aim of a 60% cut on 1990 levels by 2050. The Conservatives now favour an 80% cut while the new SNP administration in Scotland is also seeking this target for 2050 though it has dropped the original proposal for immediate action to ensure cuts of around 3% a year. But there are significant variations of view on how to achieve 80% cuts and on the extent and nature of the contribution required from transport.

Achieving overall CO_2 cuts

The present UK government, while seeing an important role for the more efficient use of energy (including the eco-towns suggested by Gordon Brown) and for the expansion of renewable sources, has placed more emphasis on the importance for national security and for the economy of a renewed expansion of nuclear power to replace existing gas, oil and coal sources. Such power can also be used to produce the hydrogen required for expanded use of fuel cells. Many politicians in Micawber fashion, see technical solutions as more attractive than changes in policy and environmental awareness which can have important and cumulative impacts on life styles. Influenced by the short-term electoral cycle, much political action, and inaction, still boosts energy-intensive mobility. Settlement patterns and low energy costs relative to income are seen as continuing to encourage both more dispersed living and increased mobility (including growth in longer-distance air travel). The UK Government expects environmental objections to nuclear power, intrusive wind farms, tidal barrages (as proposed for the Severn) and related power lines to be weakened by the relative advantages of secure and increasing power sources – though with the extra power required being less that rates of growth in the economy.

In Scotland, however, the evidence suggests that there is less justification for any expansion of nuclear power and, indeed, scope for its elimination. This view is influenced by the existing energy surplus, a much lower population than England and better access to renewable sources which can be used without controversial intrusion into sensitive landscape. Alternative sources and increased efficiency in energy use could – over a period of years – substitute both for the existing nuclear stations at Hunterston and Torness and for existing fossil fuel sources. The economic feasibility of this requires further investigation with the SNP showing continued intcrest in fossil-fuelled power stations (possibly making more use of controlled opencast working and new deeper mines on the Forth and where known reserves exist at Canonbie south of Langholm) but with a more rapid development of 'carbon sinks' related to power stations. However, BP plans for a North Sea carbon sink related to the Peterhead gas generating station have been aborted due to disagreements with the UK government.

The SNP is also seeking to complement the 'carbon sink' approach with a widening use of both electricity and direct power and heat from acceptable renewable sources. The previous Labour/Liberal administration put more stress on renewables than was the case in England yet experienced problems from a plethora of intrusive windfarm proposals and related plans for high pylons from Beauly to Denny. In addition, there have been attacks on the economic merits of windfarms and the scale of incentives to encourage their development. Prior to the elections of 3 May, 2007, new planning guidance outlined a more strategic approach to the location of major windfarms. Policy is also incorporating a mix of micro and larger generators across the renewable range from solar to wind (with a larger off-shore element), wave and tidal power plus some growth of biomass. Alternative pylon routes are being examined to reduce intrusion while the demand for much higher transmission capacity has been queried. Underground and undersea transmission has also been considered but involves much higher costs. Alternatively, renewable electrical power can be used close to its source to produce hydrogen for fuel cell engines, including uses in transport. But compressed hydrogen is a more explosive fuel that petrol, possibly raising more problems in being moved to areas of higher hydrogen demand than would arise from electrical transmission. Oil and oil substitutes will continue to be more heavily used in transport than in other sectors of the economy.

Though many issues remain to be settled, Scotland seems capable of meeting future energy demand at prices no higher than those prevailing elsewhere while reducing the nuclear share of output and minimizing conflicts between power generation and the environment. Commercial prices for energy are more likely to rise, rather than fall, from present levels, partly for reasons of world demand outpacing supply but also due to policy action to use prices and regulation – rather than only the carrot of subsidy – to encourage sustained advances in energy conservation and shifts to alternative fuels.

Transport's contribution to energy efficiency and CO_2 cuts

The *Stern Report* and the more recent *White Paper on Energy* both suggest that it is unlikely that transport will be an early contributor to CO_2 cuts. There is scope for considerable improvement in energy efficiency within transport – including air travel – yet, if increased efficiency leads to an increase in total annual distances travelled in, and to and from, Scotland, energy consumption in transport will continue to rise. CO_2 emissions will also rise due to the high dependence of transport on oil.

Extra movement and extra, or projected, congestion creates demand for extra capacity, itself encouraging traffic generation and greater problems of visual intrusion, noise, vibration and community disruption. Despite adoption by the SNP of an 80% cut by 2050, other aspects of SNP policy conflict with this objective. These include the lowering of road taxation (though this remains a UK reserved power), completion of bridge toll abolition, a new Forth crossing, upgrading to dual carriageway the A9 between Perth and Inverness and the A96 between Aberdeen and Inverness, cuts in public transport spending and continuation of the former administration's plans for the three lane urban M74 and a new dual carriageway Western Peripheral Road from Stonehaven to north of Aberdeen. The background papers alongside the UK *Climate Change Bill*, now to be followed by a Scottish Bill in 2008, take the view that pressure for CO_2 cuts in transport, and elsewhere in the British economy, will be eased through carbon trading allowing the UK to have lesser cuts by paying other countries to secure greater cuts. This raises ethical issues beyond the scope of this chapter yet there are grounds for questioning the assumption that transport will be one of the last sectors to see major cuts in CO_2.

The critical flaw in this assumption is that policies to aid economies and income levels will inevitably lead to broadly similar levels of economic growth and increased mobility with consequential adverse impacts on the environment and on social access which, at best, can be ameliorated rather than avoided. Yet advanced economies are already becoming less transport intensive. In contrast to the growth of electronic communications, physical movement by land and sea – measured by passenger kilometres and tonne kilometres – has been rising more slowly than rates of economic growth. This lessening of movement relative to economic growth has been especially noticeable for car vehicle kilometres.

Policy can encourage shifts from cars to better loaded trains, trams and buses needing less space and using less energy per passenger Km. There is also scope for improvement in car occupancy levels, especially at congested peaks where it is still common for over 80% of cars to have only one occupant. Given more encouragement in applied policies, car sharing and shifts to rail, tram, bus, walking and cycling can reduce, and even eliminate, demand for large additions to road capacity. Growth in car use in Scotland slowed to zero in 2005 despite economic growth rising to 2% while recent averages show car use growing at 35% to 45% of the level of economic growth. In contrast, rail use has been rising at more than twice the economic growth rate with buses showing potential for much improved performance if trip times and reliability are enhanced and fares reformed. Related benefits include less energy consumption, lower noise and emission levels and less land take. Rather than accept the argument that substantial cuts in surface transport CO_2 must be delayed, measures to continue an overall stabilization of road vehicle kilometres in Scotland over the next 20 years offer large economic and social benefits. Combining stabilization with vehicle and engine design innovations, cuts of 40% or more in road vehicle CO_2 emissions are deliverable by 2030. Further technical advances and modal shift could allow road transport to be almost carbon free by 2050 (DfT, 2007). This DfT Report however, differs from Scottish policy in being more reliant on technical advance to permit both growth in road vehicle kilometres and in aviation concurrently with large cuts in CO_2 emissions from surface transport. Though SNP policy shows some contradictions, it has retained the emphasis of the former coalition on promoting a sustainable economy and society through reduced growth in total surface movement with phased shifts from cars and lorries to rail and water-borne freight and to public transport, walking, cycling and a rise in car sharing.

The finalized *National Transport Strategy for Scotland*, (December 2006), retained the aspiration for stabilized road traffic and greater use of demand management (including differential road pricing) as part of a coherent economic, environmental and social strategy. Though overruled by Ministers, the Reporter at the urban M74 Public Inquiry also concluded on the evidence presented that this motorway would generate extra traffic, encourage shifts away from public transport and work against the stated government aims of delivering a sustainable and more inclusive economy.

Safety, local environmental issues and better maintenance still justify spending within the road sector but the alternative opportunities arising if funds are no longer devoted to higher road capacity offer strong grounds for a re-think of road spending and moves in the next five years to initial schemes for differential road pricing and higher parking charges to cut congestion and improve reliability. This approach offers significant economic benefits plus the direct social and environmental gains of stabilized or reduced road traffic (and lower speeds). A similar case can be made for reviewing major rail projects unless they have very clear advantages for modal shift or cutting operating costs. The SNP has rightly identified weaknesses in the expensive Edinburgh Airport Rail Link but similar thinking needs to be applied to Forth crossing options. The expectation of continued modal shift to rail and a mix of city trams and busways gives stronger grounds for enhanced spending on rail rolling stock, buses and essential works to improve trip times, perceived costs and comfort relative to cars. Though the SNP administration was forced to accept the initial Edinburgh tram scheme by a parliamentary vote, audit reports as well as political opinion favoured continuation of this project.

Equally, there is a need to deliver well-designed programmes and travel plans to encourage greater walking and cycling as a means of daily travel and a leisure activity contributing to health and reducing motorized movement. By excluding off-road walking and cycling, current data exaggerates the decline in walking and cycling. Some cities and rural tourism/leisure areas are showing strong growth – indeed growth so strong that there are risks to the environment unless spending on walkway maintenance and other remedial action is increased. The SNP has also identified opportunities to increase working from home.

Scottish geography and land-use planning policy has favoured settlement patterns more suited to public transport, walking and cycling than in England, yet there are still strong pressures for dispersal and decentralization which increase, rather than decrease, transport demand and energy consumption. Current policy is ambivalent. However, since 2005, Edinburgh City Council has promoted the case for finger type growth within 12 miles of the centre rather than a greater degree of longer-distance and often car-based commuting. The environmental issue here is how to balance the advantages of compact forms of city expansion against greenbelt encroachment. Two final issues require updated comment. These are the economic, energy and environmental impacts of air travel and prospects for transport electrification.

Aviation

Aviation continues to grow well above rates of economic growth but there is confused thinking about whether this is a result of economic growth (with rising real incomes allowing more people to travel more) or a cause of economic growth through better air services promoting business connectivity and allowing a spread of tourism. Energy concerns and the added adverse impacts on global warming of high-level aviation emissions are producing much debate between those who see aviation as a crucial contributor to economic growth able to buy into higher supplies of fossil fuel and those who see aviation mainly as an expanding leisure activity increasing CO_2 emissions and exacerbating the environmental problems of mass tourism, airport expansion and new runways. Since economic growth is more dependent on a wider range of factors and on cuts in energy and carbon intensity, aviation is a weaker driver of economic growth than many politicians consider.

Mainly due to the growth of long-haul flights, aviation contributed 87% of the continuing rise in UK CO_2 emissions attributable to transport in 2004-05, contrasting with other sectors delivering varying levels of absolute CO_2 decline. The absolute rise in aviation related CO_2 emissions in 2004-05 was 9.9%. Changing attitudes, greater sensitivity to green issues and an era of no frill low fare airlines past its peak suggests that public policy can now help both the economy and the environment by slowing the rate of aviation growth. Despite the Aunt Sally position of some aviation lobbyists that their opponents are seeking a total ban, this has never been seriously suggested. What is argued by those more critical of aviation is that, with an increasing shift from short-haul air links to higher-speed rail, existing runways have capacity to allow growth of long-haul traffic over the next 20 years while also allowing peripheral cities and islands to make greater use of air travel to improve their relative economic prospects e.g. greater use of Inverness Airport (and improved internal rail links) may actually reduce A9 traffic volumes north of Pitlochry while promoting the Highlands and Islands economy.

Alternative fuels and transport electrification

As previously outlined in Table 6.1, alternative and commercially attractive fuels offer no quick answer to reducing transport's dependence on oil. Their importance is only likely to become substantial after 2020 with early savings on CO_2 in transport being more dependent on constrained growth in road and air traffic in association with design improvements, higher load factors and fiscal/regulatory measures to raise efficiency in fuel use.

Nevertheless, the planned expansion of electricity from renewable sources in Scotland (and from coal fired generating stations associated with 'carbon sinks' and combined heat and power schemes) offers two particular opportunities. The first of these relates to rural transport and the second to public transport electrification. It is likely that rural areas with large sources of wind and wave power may be among the first to use local electricity to produce hydrogen for use as a local transport fuel. Due to the lack of on-street emissions (apart from water), wider use of hydrogen to power city buses, vans and 'city cars' is also a medium-term possibility.

The second opportunity relates to extension of the direct use of electricity in transport. In particular, electric trains and trams offer lower operating costs and a higher quality of service than alternative forms of traction, facilitating modal shifts from oil-reliant and energy intensive planes, cars, lorries and buses. Innovative train design is also lowering net electrical energy inputs per passenger km. Other benefits include lower noise levels and elimination of emissions at the point of use. Use of electricity does involve some energy loss in transmission and extra costs in providing electrical contact and sub-stations but these disadvantages are countered by lower overall costs and oil savings on principal corridors of movement. Energy policy and environmental policy are therefore strengthening the case for electrifying heavily used parts of the rail network and for further expansion of urban trams, in some cases sharing tracks with under-used railways or seeing such tracks converted to light rail or tram operation. On the whole, the visual intrusion of electric wiring is regarded as a minor downside more than countered by overall benefits and sensitive design.

Through studying alternative fuels for rail, DfT is now showing more interest in extended rail electrification and reduced use of diesel power on freight and through passenger trains which presently run on sections of route already electrified. In Scotland, the Rail Strategy published in December 2006 proposed to extend electrification to almost all lines in the Scottish Central Belt in conjunction with track and signalling work to

Plate 6.4 Heavy road freight has a significant impact on Scotland's roads © Lorne Gill/SNH

improve trip times on both electric and non-electric routes. This strategy was fleshed out in the High Level Rail Output Specification (HLOS) for Scotland in July 2007. Except for Fife, Central Belt electrification should be complete in 10 years with later extensions to Aberdeen and possibly Inverness. In addition to the Airdrie-Bathgate-Edinburgh project due to open in 2010, the SNP supports an electrification rolling programme including the Glasgow-Falkirk-Edinburgh route by 2013. In their recent study for the Scottish Government comparing Scottish railways with similar countries and regions, consultants SDG commended integrated plans for rail (and tram) electrification and a rising share of Scottish electricity from renewable sources. Electrification is also seen as boosting rail usage and modal shift helping to stabilize road traffic in, and between, Scottish cities and larger towns. Finally, the DfT report on Towards a Sustainable Transport System, published just before completion of the continental high-speed rail link to London St Pancras in November 2007, has indicated a shift from previous negative views on high-speed rail in Britain to the possibility of a 200mph electrified line from London to the West Midlands and Manchester by 2020. This would bring trip times between London and Edinburgh/Glasgow below three hours and add impetus to air to rail shifts between Scotland and England as well as between England and the closer continent.

PART 3:

Present and Future Options -
Other Than Renewable Energy

High voltage power lines criss-cross the landscape © Colin Galbraith

PART 3:

Present and Future Options - Other Than Renewable Energy

As climate change begins to impact at both the global and local levels it is more important than ever for countries to be able to develop a forward plan, identifying how they will meet their future energy needs. Ideally future energy generation should have minimal environmental impact, in order to help maintain existing ecosystem functioning, and should minimize CO_2 emissions. The conservation of energy will undoubtedly form a key part of future strategies and new advances may increase the cost-effectiveness of existing technologies or indeed aid the development of new ones. In the following part a number of these issues are considered, all of which have the potential to assist in meeting the overall energy requirements of the country, or, in the specific case of carbon capture and storage to help reduce the amount of carbon in the atmosphere.

Firstly the chapter by Kate Mills and Peter Hutchinson outlines some key aspects of building design, each of which could lead to lowering the carbon emissions from this sector in future. They use the construction of Great Glen House in Inverness as a case study, showing how a low-carbon emissions building can be constructed in a way that maximizes the use of recycled materials and still is cost effective compared to conventional construction techniques. The key question now is whether the construction industry more widely will adopt similar techniques and approaches.

The chapters by Kerr Walker and by Sinclair Gair outline the potential uses of liquid biofuels and of hydrogen technology respectively. Both these technologies have considerable potential but have yet to be "mainstreamed" by industry. Recent publicity relating to biofuels has, in particular, highlighted the impact of cultivation in some parts of Asia where large areas of native forest have been cleared to allow biofuel crops to be grown. Clearly in considering the development of such energy systems it will be necessary to take an international perspective and to strive to maintain natural ecosystems. The potential of biofuels in a Scottish context has yet to be fully evaluated but the industry has the potential to become part of the mix of energy sources for the future.

Whilst much attention over recent years has focused on the production of energy, mainly by considering the generation of electricity, current thinking is moving to consider whether it is possible to manage carbon budgets by capturing CO_2 after it has been emitted. The chapter by Bushby *et al.* reviews current thinking around carbon sequestration and suggests that the UK has considerable potential to develop the necessary technologies. They note also that the UK has areas of suitable rock formation beneath the seabed in several locations to make long-term carbon sequestration possible. The key question for the future is whether this technology is indeed feasible at the large scale and whether it will prove cost effective.

The final chapter in this part considers the potential role of the nuclear industry in the 21st century. As mentioned in the introduction to this book, nuclear power offers a relatively carbon free option, however, other environmental issues related to the industry such as the disposal of waste or the risk of leakages, do tend to polarize opinion. In this chapter Tony Cooper considers the way forward.

Canisp, Suilven and Cul Mor from viewpoint near Lochinver, Assynt. North Highland Area. © Lorne Gill/SNH

7 Buildings and Energy: Minimizing the Effects on the Natural Heritage

Kate Mills - *Building Research Establishment, Bucknalls Lane, Watford WD25 9XX.*

Peter Hutchinson - *Scottish Natural Heritage, Battleby, Redgorton, Perth PH1 3EW.*

Summary

1. The construction industry has a key role in helping to meet the UK Government's commitment to a reduction of 60% in UK CO_2 emissions by 2050.
2. The construction industry needs to lead and embrace change, educating and pulling its clients along if required – shifting thinking away from low or lowest capital cost to considering whole life costs, low energy use for the life of the building and more efficient use of building materials.
3. Although not widespread, potential initiatives do exist to help take up this challenge such as Private Finance Partnership and Private Finance Initiative projects that encourage more holistic thinking.
4. This chapter outlines what organizations and individuals can do to drive down energy consumption.
5. The industry needs to capture the knowledge and experience that it already holds. To this end: a checklist has been compiled to help advance sustainability opportunities; and a case study on Great Glen House in Inverness is presented to illustrate how the building attained an Excellent rating (and the highest score ever of 84%) under the Building Research Establishment Environmental Assessment Method for Offices.
6. The momentum and drivers for change in the built environment are growing consistently year-by-year.
7. We need to move to a position where minimizing environmental impacts becomes as second nature and is as mandatory as complying with health and safety regulations.

7.1 Introduction

Climate change is currently the most significant threat to the earth. It is increasingly making the headline news as the rate of change and options for reducing the threat are discussed by politicians, scientists and others. The general consensus is that current climate change is due in large part to our increased CO_2 emissions and other greenhouse gases.

Mills, K. & Hutchinson, P. (2008). Buildings and Energy: Minimizing the Effects on the Natural Heritage. In *Energy and the Natural Heritage*, ed. by C.A. Galbraith and J.M. Baxter. TSO Scotland, Edinburgh. pp. 83-92

Whether or not you believe in human-induced climate change, or think it is too late, many believe that we need to adopt the precautionary principle as the potential consequences of not acting are too great. A reduction in carbon emissions will go some way to reducing the rate of change, and we need to do it now.

In view of this, the UK government has now committed to a reduction of 60% in UK CO_2 emissions by 2050. The construction industry has a key role in meeting this commitment because it is responsible for:

- 40% of the total world flow of raw materials such as sand, gravel, clay and iron ore;
- 40% of world energy use;
- 25% of all virgin wood use; and
- 16% of water withdrawals.

In the UK, commercial and domestic buildings are currently responsible for around 16% and 28% of carbon emissions, respectively. The latter figure will rise considerably because it does not include the 3.8 million households scheduled to be built before 2021 in the UK. This is a significant contribution to CO_2 emissions, but fortunately is one that could be reduced substantially. We already have the solutions but what we need to do is implement them.

This paper will outline the main ways emissions from UK buildings can be reduced and how we, as individuals, can play our part.

7.2 How can we reduce the environmental impacts of buildings?
7.2.1 The construction industry

For the UK to meet its target of a 60% reduction in CO_2 emissions by 2050, the construction industry needs to lead and embrace change, educating and pulling its clients along if required. The industry needs to take up the challenge of refurbishing or constructing more efficient buildings. This will involve a major shift in thinking away from low or lowest capital cost to considering whole life costs, low energy use for the life of the building and more efficient use of building materials. This is a tall order for companies used to working on a low capital cost basis for many years. Indeed, history has shown that the construction industry can be very conservative and slow to take up new challenges.

However, potential initiatives do exist to help take up this challenge. For example, newer forms of procurement such as Private Finance Partnership and Private Finance Initiative projects encourage more holistic thinking because they require the developer to run and maintain the building for a period of 25 years or more. They can overcome the traditional forms of procurement that rely on the client to specify their requirements for energy efficiency/sustainability - where success is dependent on the client having knowledge in these areas or employing effective professional advisers.

Unfortunately, these examples of projects are not widespread and contractors working on speculative developments currently have little incentive to build energy efficient, sustainable buildings. Often in the commercial sector, the need for higher monetary returns results in highly serviced mechanical ventilated office buildings being built because they can command a higher rent over the life of the building therefore give a quicker financial payback.

Plate 7.1 Great Glen House, Inverness © Colin Galbraith

Thus, for a significant reduction in CO_2 emissions, a transformation needs to happen in the construction industry. It needs to:

- attract and recruit professionals with a knowledge of construction but with an appreciation of the environmental impacts of their industry; and
- train up existing staff to take on board the new agenda and see this as an integral part of their professional role to enable integrated working across the disciplines.

In addition, the industry needs to capture the knowledge and experience that it already holds. Unfortunately, many construction teams are only together for one construction project. This means that valuable knowledge gained on leaner more efficient construction and new technologies or materials is often lost without ever being captured and passed on to other teams. Experience has shown that having a person responsible for championing sustainability throughout the design and construction of a building is essential to ensuring any sustainability targets or measures are met. Sustainable construction cuts across all the construction disciplines which means issues may fall between the disciplines. It is vital that one person is able to coordinate responsibilities, stand back to look at the bigger picture and re-direct professionals if the project is not on track.

Environmental policies are also an essential starting point - provided that they are not seen as the end of the story. For example, some construction companies have already established their own environmental policies but very few have established their own certified environmental management systems to ensure that their policy is put into practice. In short, unless you have a system that measures and manages the environmental impacts of the construction company as a whole, as well as individual projects on site, there is no way of reporting that your environmental policy is being put into practice. This means that the policy itself is of little value if it cannot be verified on the ground in a systematic way. Fortunately, there is growing pressure from shareholders and funders for more 'Socially Responsible Investments' which will increase pressure on companies to report their environmental impacts annually. Companies will need to have an environmental policy and management system to provide an accurate annual report. Pressure is growing from potential clients of construction companies, who are asking for evidence of an environmental policy and a certified management system as part of their selection criteria in a tender process.

7.2.2 Summary check list of sustainability opportunities for construction projects

In considering construction projects, the following checklist has been compiled to help advance sustainability opportunities:

- Sustainability can be used as a competitive advantage for bidders.
- Sustainable construction can provide savings if principles are incorporated in the initial stages.
- Whole Life Costing principles are key in Public Private Partnership contracts but need to be incorporated correctly.
- Comparison of tenders need to be made on a like-for-like basis.
- Benchmarks and targets should be set to quantify design performance.
- The output brief document should encourage sustainability in the construction phase and require method statements and policies from the providers.
- In construction and operation phases, the costs of sending waste to landfill can be minimized by reuse or recycling.
- Innovation can be encouraged by allowing flexibility in the brief to enable developers to meet or exceed targets in new and innovative ways.
- Contractor performance can be maximized by offering incentives for good performance. Payment mechanisms for energy efficiency need to acknowledge that providers have limited control over end users, but encourage training, awareness and diligence in monitoring of energy.
- The output specification should include provision for metering, monitoring and reporting structures with positive incentives.
- Reducing energy bills and greenhouse gas emissions can limit liability under the climate change levy.
- Performance can be improved simply by good management.
- By incorporating sustainability, risks of failing to meet new environmental legislation/ requirements can be reduced to minimize future financial impact.
- Transport impacts can be limited through green transport plans and sourcing local products in the construction phase.

7.2.3 Summary check list of potential sustainability pitfalls for construction projects

In addition, the following list of pitfalls in construction projects can be used to guard against threats to sustainability:

- There needs to be vision and commitment from all parties to sustainability. The whole team from client to contractor must 'buy in'.
- Sustainability needs to be considered from inception and integrated into the earliest strategic decisions.
- Clients need good independent advice when setting briefs and commissioning to ensure that the brief achieves their expectations and produces a sustainable outcome. CABE (Commission for Architecture and the Built Environment) are now offering advice on design quality in Public Private Partnership schemes.
- Monitoring of the emerging design should take place to prevent time pressures leading to declining standards. If problems are not picked up early then there may be no opportunity to resolve the issues without compromising the overall programme. In this situation, compromise of standards is very prevalent.
- Poor communication between the team will make sustainability difficult to achieve, it is important to get all disciplines involved.
- If timescales are too tight there is no room for debate or finding the most sustainable solution. Clients must be firm in refusing to accept tariff reductions in exchange for abandoning environmental and energy targets or sustainability indices.
- Sustainable cost data are not, to our knowledge, in the public domain; only when it is, can it be fully analysed and incorporated into accurate costing for real projects.
- Contractors with a limited sustainability knowledge will tend to build large risk factors into their bid to insure against failing to meet sustainability targets or indices.
- Lack of awareness of changing sustainability requirements/ legislation may make the building obsolete before it is operational.
- Fear of the unknown and new technologies can lead to innovative approaches not being taken.

7.2.4 Organizations

Organizations who are owner-occupiers have the greatest scope to influence their energy consumption. They can procure or refurbish their buildings to maximize energy efficiency, manage their energy consumption more effectively in-house and benefit from the savings made.

However, all is not lost for organizations who are tenants because they can select a building on its energy efficiency or aim to influence landlords to increase energy efficiency measures in return for renewing tenancy agreements. There is a wide range of free guidance available on measures for energy efficiency in commercial and other buildings through the Carbon Trust at www.thecarbontrust.co.uk or on 020 7170 7000.

The following publications may be a useful start to try to drive down energy consumption within your organization (all are available free on the Carbon Trust web site).

- Energy savings in buildings – methods for quickly identifying opportunities (GIL050)
- Organizational aspects of energy management (GIR012)
- A strategic approach to energy and environmental management (GPG376)

Basic measures to drive down energy consumption in commercial and public offices include:

Plate 7.2 Infrared thermal heat loss survey of house © BRE

1. Set up an effective energy policy with board commitment.
2. Monitor present consumption.
3. Set short and long term objectives and targets (based on previous monitoring).
4. Develop strategic action plans.
5. Implement action plans.
6. Review progress.
7. Audit performance.
8. Produce a formal report on energy performance.

Some organizations may have the opportunity to procure their own building(s) and therefore directly influence their own energy efficiency and sustainability. However, for many organizations they may only ever procure one building and the learning curve is steep. It is essential if your organization does not have in-house expertise to employ a qualified sustainability/energy efficiency adviser who will be able to assist in setting a solid brief with clear quantifiable targets to be achieved. The brief can take two approaches either providing incentives or penalizing performance against the targets or a mixture of both.

One of the first steps for an organization to take to reduce its own emissions is to set up an environmental policy to set a clear direction. Any new building or refurbishments projects can be evaluated against the policy – assessing whether you are achieving what you have set out in the policy.

If you are in your own building or leasing accommodation, set up your own in-house environmental management system to meet the objectives of your environmental policy. An environmental management system is a formal method of setting, monitoring and managing environmental impacts. It gives a framework and provides a way of reporting back against your policy and can be incorporated into a formal Annual Environmental Report.

7.2.5 Case study: Sustainability and the 'new' Great Glen House at Westercraigs, Inverness

In 2004, Scottish Natural Heritage (SNH) began construction of a new corporate office in Inverness. This case study illustrates how SNH - an Non-Departmental Public Body - purchased a new building based on their brief, with sustainable construction and energy targets at the core of the building requirements. The reward for this was attaining an Excellent rating and the highest score ever of 84% under the Building Research Establishment Environmental Assessment Method for Offices. Between 1998 and 2004 there have been only four other Excellent rated offices in Scotland.

The building attained this rating through the following 'sustainable' measures and issues:

Carbon target - to encourage innovation and efficiency the user requirement for the new SNH office in Inverness set a carbon target of less than 8 kg of carbon per square metre per annum. By setting an overall carbon target this allowed the developer to choose between a wide range of strategies for meeting the target using a holistic approach.

To have any chance of meeting the target, however, energy efficiency played a large part in the new building. In this instance the strategy adopted was based on passive solar design using an atrium and 'natural' ventilation. The building has a Building Energy Management System to monitor the energy consumption against the carbon target set.

The target is similar to the figure being achieved by the BRE Environmental Office Building at BRE's site in Watford (approximately 9 kg/carbon/m^2). This compares to a figure of around 40 kg/carbon/m^2 for a mechanically ventilated prestige office building.

Demolition and construction waste - the main elements of the demolished nurses' home on the site were reused and recycled. A pre-demolition audit was carried out to minimize waste being sent to landfill. For example, the roof slates from the existing nurses' home were reused as cladding on the new external walls, timber was reclaimed and used for timber finishes in the new building, aggregate was crushed and recycled and incorporated into the design. New construction waste was segregated and monitored on site.

Construction phase – the site was registered under the Considerate Constructors Scheme to minimize environmental and social impacts in the construction phase. On the first inspection by an independent assessor for the scheme the site scored an exceptional score of 34 out of a possible 40 points with the comment "a highly efficient approach to all aspects of site management". All transport impacts associated with the delivery of materials and personnel to the site were monitored during the construction phase.

The developer also implemented an environmental management system on site to minimize and monitor the environmental impacts of the construction.

Materials and embodied energy – the building was designed to minimize the environmental impacts from construction materials by:

- using softwood sustainable timber for window frames;
- using untreated larch for external cladding;
- specifying insulation with zero Ozone Depleting Properties and a Global Warming Potential of less than 5;
- specifying solvent free paints, natural oils and waxes;
- adopting a 'natural' finish to internal timber panelling and other woodwork; and
- use of recycled carpet (category A rated in the Green Guide to Specification).

Ventilation – the building is naturally ventilated using the thermal mass from concrete floor slabs to maintain a constant temperature and allow night cooling of the structure.

Lighting – maximum lux levels were set in the output specification and are automatically controlled in response to external daylight conditions by lighting software. Average daylight and uniformity factors were also set in the output specification at best practice figures of 4% and 0.4 to minimize the use of artificial lighting wherever possible.

Landscaping and ecology – the impact on the ecological value of the site was minimized through retention of trees and enhanced through new landscaping comprising locally sourced native species. This aims to create the appearance of the new building in a woodland bowl.

A Traffic Impact Assessment and Green Transport Plan has been produced for the site. This encourages public transport through an increase in the frequency of the bus service and pedestrian and cycle access through the provision of an appropriate infrastructure – both on and off site.

A Sustainable Urban Drainage strategy has been put in place to reduce rainwater run-off from the site. This includes rainwater harvesting, overflow ponds and porous surfaces. The Sustainable Urban Drainage (SUDs) pond has the dual purpose of collecting surface run off and acting as a wildlife pond to enhance biodiversity on site.

Green management – design and provision is a start, but the management of the building backs this up through monitoring of the energy consumption of the building through the Building Energy Management System, recycling of 'office rubbish' and provision of shared printers.

7.2.6 Individuals

As UK homes contribute 28% of UK carbon emissions, homeowners can make a significant contribution to reducing emissions by taking measures to cut energy use in the home. The Energy Saving Trust was set up by the UK Government after the 1992 Earth Summit in Rio de Janeiro to help reduce the UK's CO_2 emissions. Its web site at www.est.org provides useful impartial advice and information to help save energy in the home.

In summary, homeowners should consider the following measures to increase their energy efficiency and therefore reduce their own carbon emissions:

Plate 7.3 Small scale aero electricity generator © Lorne Gill / SNH

- Choose energy efficient "A rated" white goods and boilers.
- Install cavity wall insulation where possible.
- Install loft insulation to a depth of 25cm.
- Install double glazing.
- Ensure hot water tanks are well insulated.
- Use energy efficient light bulbs marked with the energy efficiency logo.
- Install a thermostat to control heating and turn it down by a degree.
- Decrease personal emissions generated by cars and flights.

7.3 The drivers for change

The momentum and drivers for change in the built environment are growing consistently year-by-year. There is, however, no room to be complacent, as there is much yet to be achieved. The strongest drivers currently include:

- Increasingly strict building regulations.
- A legally binding commitment by government to increase energy efficiency in housing in England by 20% by 2010.
- The new Code for Sustainable Homes.
- Energy suppliers being required to sign up to Energy Efficiency Commitment schemes offering customers reductions on energy efficient technologies and insulation products.
- A drive to more Socially Responsible Investment by funders and shareholders.
- A drive towards Building Research Establishment Environmental Assessment Method (BREEAM) Excellent ratings for all public sector buildings.
- An awareness by building insurers of the potential impacts of climate change and the

move away from developing in flood risk areas and the need for buildings to stand up to extreme weather.

- A growing expectation for construction companies to produce an annual environmental report and be accountable for their environmental impacts.
- More educated clients demanding more sustainable and energy efficient buildings.

In conclusion, the positive news is that the solutions are out there. The case study of Great Glen House procured by SNH demonstrates this point perfectly. SNH have shown that by setting a brief with quantifiable sustainability targets, getting the right sustainability advice throughout the process and their own client commitment, an exemplar building can be built under public procurement affordability criteria. This building has generated much interest and has raised the bar for office buildings in Scotland and the UK. It has set an example of achievable practice that many other organizations wish to follow. Many prospective building procurers and members of the construction industry are now visiting the building to see first hand one of the most sustainable office buildings in the UK.

The biggest challenge is a timely culture change in the construction industry, educating clients and procuring buildings based on life cycle and whole life costings. In short, we need to move to a position where minimizing environmental impacts occurs as second nature and is as mandatory as complying with health and safety regulations.

8 Liquid Biofuels: Environmental Implications of their Development

Kerr C Walker – *Scottish Agricultural College Craibstone, Bucksburn Aberdeen AB21 9YA.*

Summary

1. The two major liquid biofuel options open to UK growers are biodiesel and bioethanol.
2. For biodiesel production, oilseed rape is the source feedstock of choice in the UK whilst for bioethanol it is wheat or barley.
3. Both biofuels have reduced exhaust emissions from fuel use and offer overall air quality benefits. However, growing crops specifically for biofuels carries the environmental disbenefits associated with fertilizer, fuel and pesticides use.
4. Waste cooking oils and tallow offer a cheap biodiesel feedstock providing additional benefits from waste disposal avoidance, but are technically more difficult for achieving fuel quality standards.
5. Energy balance (ratio of energy used to energy produced) is positive for all but the worst case scenarios for biodiesel.
6. In contrast, the energy balance for bioethanol is always negative unless by-products are considered.
7. EU directives have set biofuel production targets which the UK cannot reach even using all set-aside for fuel production, indicating the need for some agricultural restructuring.

8.1 Introduction

The energy crisis that resulted after the quadrupling of world oil prices in 1973 renewed interest across the world in the potential for biofuels. The fragility of the world economy and its heavy dependence on inexpensive energy from politically unstable areas of the world suddenly became apparent at that time. In addition, public concern was emerging over the rapid consumption of non-renewable finite fossil-based fuel reserves and the environmental impact of their use, particularly in terms of global warming. These factors all contributed to the interest in developing renewable forms of energy.

Brazil initiated a national fuel ethanol programme (proalcohol) in 1975 (Homewood, 1993) in order to reduce dependency on imported oil and thus alleviate the country's severe trade deficit. In the US, a similar programme was set up in 1979 to increase 'energy security'. Whilst the rationale for these developments on economic grounds has been a

Walker, K.C. (2008). Liquid Biofuels: Environmental Implications of their Development. In *Energy and the Natural Heritage*, ed. by C.A. Galbraith and J.M. Baxter. TSO Scotland, Edinburgh. pp. 93-104 matter of ongoing debate, their justification has increasingly been on the basis of them being an 'environmentally friendly' alternative to fossil fuels.

In Europe, the main impetus for interest in biofuels came from the agricultural sector where surplus food production necessitated common agricultural reforms resulting in land being set-aside from food production. During the last decade when these policies were developed, growing of non-food crops or industrial crops such as biofuels was permitted.

This chapter examines the potential for biofuels in the UK particularly in relation to the environmental implications of their production and use. Solid biofuels for electricity and the non-commercial liquid biofuels - biomethanol and bio-oil will not be included in this chapter. Most attention will be directed to biodiesel and (to a lesser extent), bioethanol, reflecting their relative importance within Europe as renewable transport fuels.

8.2 Source crops for liquid biofuel production

The two most widely produced biofuels world-wide are biodiesel and bioethanol (Entwistle *et al.*, 2002). The biofuel of choice usually depends on the relative availability of the feedstock with some countries (e.g. USA, France) producing both.

8.2.1 Source crops for biodiesel production

Most vegetable oils can be used as fuels in the diesel engine (Diesel, 1895). At the World Exhibition in Paris in 1900 the engine that Rudolf Diesel demonstrated was run on peanut oil. At that time, vegetable oils were cheaper than mineral oils but this soon changed and the technical development of the diesel engine has been based on mineral fuels. Vegetable oils used for biodiesel production include corn oil, sunflower oil, soyabean oil, cotton oil and palm oil. Some oils e.g. castor oil, are less suitable because of their extreme viscosity and others such as linseed oil because of their rapid oxidation and polymerization. Ideally the vegetable oil should have low saturation and low polyunsaturation, i.e. it should be high in mono-unsaturated fatty acids. Rapeseed has been targeted for fuel use in Europe because it produces an oil with a set of fuel characteristics close to optimum, and because it grows well in northern Europe.

Biodiesel can also be produced from used frying oils or from used hydraulic oils derived from vegetable oils. This is much more technically demanding as there may be a wide range and variation in fatty acid analysis of the oils collected yet quality of the biodiesel produced must be constant. Environmentally, biodiesel produced in this way is very attractive in that it utilizes a waste product, prevents environmental damage from waste oils being discharged into sewerage systems and obviates the need for crop production with its associated environmental implications. In addition, this opens up a new market for collected vegetable oils which might have been destined for land-fill following legislation preventing the feeding of livestock with such wastes. However, logistics suggest that production in this way can only supply a tiny proportion of demand. In addition, where hydraulic oils are used, distillation costs for removal of additives may adversely affect production economics.

Tallow may also be used for the production of biodiesel. Technical difficulties primarily relate to the high degree of saturation resulting in a high freezing point of the feedstock (it is solid at room temperature) and the variability of that feedstock depending on the proportion of beef : sheep : pig tallow. However, environmentally, use of tallow is attractive in that a feedstock likely destined for land-fill is used to produce environmentally friendly fuel.

Biodiesel can be used in diesel engines in four ways:

* as pure vegetable oil;
* as mixture of the vegetable oil with diesel;
* as the vegetable oil (or tallow) methyl ester (e.g. rape methyl ester - RME);
* in mixtures of the ester with diesel.

Modern engines are less suited to the use of pure vegetable oils and its mixtures with diesel, so most users of biodiesel either utilize the pure ester or mixtures of that ester with diesel. Advantages of the mixture are that it is much easier to achieve the desired fuel quality as the mineral diesel acts as a buffer: for example, some "biodiesels" marketed consist of 95% mineral diesel : 5% biodiesel. Where tallow or recycled vegetable oils are the feedstock, such mixes greatly ease processing. However, use of the biodiesel produced cannot then be targeted to the location or operation type where environmental benefits from the biofuel use would be greatest.

8.2.2 Source crops for bioethanol production

Bioethanol is ethanol (an alcohol with the formula C_2H_5OH) that has been manufactured from carbohydrates by the biological process of fermentation. The synthetic alternative is produced by catalytic hydration of ethylene derived from petroleum or natural gas - synthetic ethanol. Ethanol produced by either method can be used as a fuel. Both bio- and synthetic ethanol are currently manufactured for a range of markets, so production technology is established and production capacity already exists.

The use of ethanol as a transport fuel dates back to the early days of the motor car. It was used as a motor fuel for the first time in 1890 (Lewis, 1983), and in the 1920s, Henry Ford's Model T was designed to run on alcohol, petrol or any mixture of the two (Ward, 1989).

Feedstocks for bioethanol production fall into three main categories: sugar based, starch based and cellulosic. These feedstocks are all carbohydrates of varying size and complexity. Most bioethanol is produced using strains of yeast (*Saccharomyces* spp.) which use simple sugars as a feedstock producing alcohol and CO_2. Starch and cellulose are larger more complex molecules based on multiple sugar units and which cannot be used directly by the yeast. Some form of pre-treatment is necessary prior to the fermentation process.

Sugar from sugar-cane is the basis of the world's largest bioethanol programme in Brazil (Batchelor *et al.*, 1994). In the EU, however, sugar beet is more suited to northern latitudes and is the main sugar crop. France is the most notable producer of ethanol in this way.

Starch feedstocks include most of the cereal grains, particularly maize, wheat and barley. In the US, maize is the most widely grown cereal and is the preferred feedstock while in Europe wheat is generally preferred to barley as yields per unit area are higher. Where wheat does not grow well, barley is used (e.g. Finland). It is notable that all three cereals are used in Scotland for the production of blended whisky, although it is barley alone that is used for malt whisky.

It has been argued that if bioethanol is to become a major alternative fuel at an attractive cost, production must be based on lignocellulosic feedstocks as opposed to sugar or starch (Anon., 1990). The term lignocellulosic refers to the complex of lignin and cellulose found

Plate 8.1 Oilseed rape field in full flower near Luncarty, Perthshire © Lorne Gill / SNH

in woody plant cell walls; cellulose is composed of long straight chains of glucose units and much research in enzyme technology is looking at ways of breaking up these complex carbohydrates into forms that can be fermented by yeast. Source crops could, for example, be willow coppice, wood residues, or straw, but at present such technology is some way from commercial realization.

8.3 Production of source crops

If crop production for biofuels is developed, then this suggests that additional land will be cropped or else existing markets will find new competition. In the UK, there were 680,000 hectares of set-aside land in 2003, and in Scotland the equivalent 2004 figure was 75,000 hectares. Thus a sizeable area would potentially be available for biofuel production. For the marketing year 2004/05 over 3 million tonnes of wheat were available for export from the UK-equivalent to over 1 million tonnes of bioethanol (Booth *et al.*, 2005). However, production at this level would not come close to that required to meet the indicative guideline of 5.75% of all transport fuel set for 2010 under EU Directive 2003/30/C (see Section 8.8).

8.3.1 Production of crops for biodiesel production

In the UK as in the rest of Europe, oilseed rape is the crop of choice. Whilst biodiesel can be produced from other European crops e.g. sunflower and soya, there are difficulties in achieving the EU quality specification with these crops (see Table 8.1) particularly in terms of the iodine value. Scotland not only produces some of the highest oilseed rape yields in Europe, but the northerly latitude is associated with high oil contents thereby contributing to very high oil yields. Another positive aspect of oilseed rape is that the varieties ideal for

Table 8.1 EU Biodiesel specification (EN 14214) (see Glossary for explanation of Units)

Property	Unit	Limits minimum	maximum	Test method
Ester content	% (m/m)	96.5		prEN 14103
Density at 15% C	kg/m^3	860	900	EN ISO 3676
				EN ISO 12185
Viscosity at 40°C	mm^2/s	3.5	5,0	EN ISO 3104
Flash point	° C	above 101	-	SO/CD 3679
Sulphur content	mg/kg	-	10	
Carbon residue				
(on 10% distillation residue)	% (m/m)	-	0.3	EN ISO 10370
Cetane number		51.0		EN ISO 5165
Sulfated ash content	% (m/m)	-	0.02	ISO 3987
Water content	mg/kg	-	500	EN ISO 12937
Total contamination	mg/kg	-	24	EN 12662
Copper strip corrosion				
(3 h at 50° C)	rating	class 1		EN ISO 2160
Thermal stability				
Oxidation stability, 110° C	hours	6	-	prEN 14112
Acid value	mg			
KOH/g		0.5		prEN 14104
Iodine value			120	prEN 14111
Linolenic acid methyl ester	% (m/m)		12	prEN 14103
Polyunsaturated (>=4 double				
bonds) methyl esters	% (m/m)		1	
Methanol content	% (m/m)		0.2	prEN 14110
Monoglyceride content	% (m/m)		0.8	prEN 14105
Diglyceride content	% (m/m)		0.2	prEN 14105
Triglyceride content	% (m/m)		0.2	prEN 14105
Free glycerol	% (m/m)		0.02	prEN 14105
				prEN 14106
Total glycerol	% (m/m)		0.25	prEN 14105
Alkaline metal (Na+K)n	mg/kg		5	prEN 14108
				prEN 14109
Phosphorus content	mg/kg		10	prEN 14107

human consumption are also best suited for biodiesel consumption. In terms of oil quality, attempts are being made by breeders to raise oleic acid levels at the expense of poly and saturated fatty acids, thereby further improving the health credentials of the oil. For biodiesel production, high oleic oils are seen as ideal.

On the negative side, oilseed rape is very responsive to high agronomic inputs particularly nitrogen, and this has implications in terms of the energy balance and the environment (see Section 8.5.1).

8.3.2 Production of crops for bioethanol production

Unlike biodiesel production, bioethanol quality is not affected by variety type. The agricultural objective is simply to produce as much sugar or starch per unit area as cheaply as possible. Whilst sugar beet can produce very high yields of sugar, the seasonality of production and the difficulty of storing the beet throughout the year to maintain year long bioethanol production detracts from this as a source crop. Cereals, however, can be stored and transported with ease and are the feedstock of choice. In the USA, maize is the usual bioethanol substrate, but in Europe it tends to be wheat (France) or barley (Scandinavia). At present, no bioethanol is produced in the UK but the high yields of wheat would suggest that this would be the crop chosen, particularly in England. In contrast, despite high yields from wheat in Scotland, climatic limitations restrict the area grown and there is already a wheat deficit in Scotland. Consequently, barley would more likely be selected for any Scottish bioethanol plant although this would compete with and perhaps undermine the use of barley for whisky production.

Plate 8.2 Cereal production, a potential source of bioethanol © Lorne Gill

8.4 Production of liquid biofuels

As a generality, there are distinct economies of scale associated with the production of biofuels. Whilst there are strong sociological arguments for the siting of small local biofuel plants producing fuels for the community from crops grown within that community using local labour, most studies indicate that the capital cost of such small plants (when expressed in terms of per litre produced) makes the biofuel uncompetitive without excessive intervention and support.

8.4.1 Production of biodiesel

There are three major steps in the production of biodiesel. Firstly the oilseed is crushed to extract the oil; the oil is then refined and finally, for use in modern diesel engines, the oil is esterified. There are a variety of crushing and refining technologies available and the choice of technology is dependent on the end use and scale of operation (Table 8.2).

Table 8.2 Biodiesel production (2001) except Italy (2000) and estimated production capacity (2003)

	Production (2001)	Capacity (2003)
Austria	28,000	140,000
Czech Republic	50,000	70,000
Denmark	100,000	100,000
France	275,000	410,000
Germany	450,000	1,100,000
Italy	70,000 (2000)	600,000
Slovakia	50,000	125,000
Spain	-	6,000
Sweden	7,000	8,000
Switzerland	2,000	2,000

Source: Walker (2004)

Oil extraction on a small scale involves high powered pressing of the seed taking the oil content down from approximately 42% in the seed to 8% in the remaining cake. These processes are electrically driven and are high energy consumers. High volume crushers use this physical process to extract only half the oil, and rely on solvent extraction to remove the remainder. Whilst involving less energy on a unit basis, the solvents used (e.g. hexane) are recognized as environmentally damaging.

After oil extraction, the oil is refined in three stages involving degumming, neutralization and bleaching. The fourth stage (used for oil for human consumption) is de-odorisation but this is not necessary for oil biodiesel. The refined oil is then esterified using a batch (small scale) or continuous (large scale) process and involves adding an alcohol to the oil in the presence of a catalyst (usually KOH), thereby producing an ester on cleaving the fatty acid from the glycerol. Choice of the combination of technologies very much depends on the scale of operation: large scale plants tend to be much more efficient and will contribute to an enhanced energy balance (see Section 8.5.1).

8.4.2 Production of bioethanol

Where cereals are used for ethanol production, the starch in the grains must be broken down into sugars prior to fermentation. Starch is generally converted to glucose by enzymatic hydrolysis which is a two-step process. The first step is liquefaction and involves mixing the prepared feedstock with water to form a slurry and adding the liquefying enzyme alpha amylase. The enzyme breaks down the starch molecules into dextrins (non-fermentable sugars). The second step, saccharification, breaks down the dextrins to fermentable sugars and requires adjustment of pH and temperature and the addition of a second enzyme (Houghton-Alico, 1982).

The final stage for ethanol production involves the use of yeasts to produce the alcohol. The by-product from this process is Distillers Dried Grains with Solubles (DDGS) usually sold as a high protein animal feed. A process of distillation then raises the concentration of the alcohol produced.

8.5 Energy balance

The energy balance or energy ratio of a biofuel can be defined as the ratio of the non-renewable energy used in its production to the energy value of the fuel and any utilized by-products, i.e. energy input : energy output. For a biofuel to be justifiably described as renewable, the energy balance must be positive; the energy produced must be greater than the energy used in its production and should take into consideration all aspects of crop growing, crop drying, handling and transport, biofuel processing and distribution.

8.5.1 Energy balance of biodiesel

Batchelor *et al.* (1995) examined a range of scenarios in terms of growing conditions, yields and assumptions in energy utilization. They described their scenarios as best case, worst case, and good or poor intermediate scenarios (See Table 8.3). In addition the outputs they considered included the biodiesel alone (1), the biodiesel together with rape meal (2), the biodiesel together with rape meal, and glycerol (3), and finally the biodiesel together with the rape meal glycerol, and straw (4).

The results indicated that biodiesel production under UK conditions was sustainable under all but the worst conditions. Utilization of rape meal greatly improved the energy ratio but there remained a net loss in energy under the worst-case scenario. Glycerol utilization had relatively little effect on the energy ratio whilst the use of straw resulted in a net energy gain from the production of biodiesel under all scenarios. However, in practical terms use of the straw is relatively uncommon and so the fourth scenario should be regarded with caution.

Table 8.3 Energy ratios for rape methyl ester (RME) production from winter rape

Outputs included	Energy Ratio			
	Best-case scenario	Good intermediate scenario	Poor intermediate scenario	Worst-case scenario
1	1:2.23	1:1.158	1:1.12	1:0.675
2	1:3.83	1:2.22	1:1.60	1:0.88
3	1:3.95	1:2.30	1:1.65	1:0.91
4	1:9.18	1:5.46	1:3.95	1:2.22

1 = RME only; 2 = RME + rape meal; 3 - RME + rape meal + glycerol;
4 = RME + rape meal + glycerol + straw
Batchelor *et al.* (1995)

8.5.2 Energy analysis of bioethanol

Similar calculations to those made for biodiesel were made by the same authors for bioethanol produced from UK wheat using similar techniques (Batchelor *et al.*, 1994). Energy ratios for bioethanol produced from wheat under a range of scenarios accounting for variation in climate, fertilizer application, yield and pesticide applications in the UK are given in Table 8.4.

Table 8.4 Energy ratios for bioethanol produced from wheat in the UK

Output	Best-case scenario	Good intermediate scenario	Poor intermediate scenario	worst-case scenario
Ethanol	1:0.78	1:0.69	1:0.62	1:0.47
Ethanol + DDGS	1:1.21	1:1.06	1:0.95	1:0.72
Ethanol + DDGS + straw	1:1.79	1:1.70	1:1.54	1:1.3

Source: Batchelor *et al.* (1994)

The ratios show that where only ethanol is considered, there is a net loss in energy under all conditions. If use of the by-product DDGS is accounted for, the energy ratio improves, but a net energy gain is only achieved under good conditions. Only when the use of straw is accounted for is there a net gain in energy under all conditions. Major energy inputs were in the processing of the bioethanol - particularly the distillation part of the process. Improvement of the energy balance can be achieved through economies of scale (the Batchelor *et al.* (1994) study was based on Swedish technology producing 30 million litres/year bioethanol) and through associating the production process with another industrial process e.g. fructose production or starch production. Opportunities for improving the energy balance from on farm managerial changes were limited.

8.6 Exhaust emissions from fuel use

Many studies have been conducted which compare the exhaust emission of mineral based fuels with biofuels. It is important to note that the comparative exhaust emissions from an engine will vary with the engine design, the engine running cycle, the age of the engine and whether the engine has been adjusted for biofuel use. Even individual engines of the same make and model and age will vary in their comparative emissions. Where emissions from biofuel use and mineral fuels are compared, conclusions should only be drawn where large data sets are compared rather than single vehicle comparisons.

8.6.1 Exhaust emissions from biodiesel use

Table 8.5 presents data from Austrian bus trials and indicates the level of reduction in a range of emissions which might be expected from biodiesel use. Not surprisingly, as rapeseed oil contains no sulphur, emissions of SOx are virtually eliminated; the sulphur present in the emissions coming from combustion of traces of the engine sump oil. Generally speaking, results tend to indicate that most emissions are down except perhaps for NOx, which can be up by 3-5% (Mittelbach and Tritthard, 1988). As NOx is a greenhouse gas that is particularly damaging, more detailed studies have been conducted to show how engine timing adjustments specifically for biodiesel use can improve the NOx figure (Table 8.5).

Table 8.5 Emissions from Austrian bus trials, biodiesel relative to low-sulfur fossil diesel

Emission	SOx	CO	NOx	NOx*	PM	VOC	BS
% change with biodiesel	-99	-20	+1	-23	-39	-32	-50

-99 indicates a reduction by 99% (almost complete elimination), +1 indicates an increase of 1%
NOx* result for an engine adjusted for biodiesel use.
Source: Sams (1996)

Legend

SOx = oxides of sulphur
CO = carbon monoxide
NOx = oxides of nitrogen
PM = particulate matter
VOC = volatile organic compounds
BS = smoke

Carbon emissions overall are contained within a closed loop as the carbon released from the 'burning' of the crop is recaptured during photosynthesis by the next crop. However, some emissions during processing (e.g. hexane) are not included in this assessment.

8.6.2 Emissions from bioethanol use

To gain maximum efficiency from fuel ethanol, it should be used in engines with a high compression ratio. Use of pure ethanol increases the specific power output of a vehicle by 5-10% compared with a petrol fuelled car. In theory, a vehicle's efficiency can be increased by 30% if run on ethanol and optimized for that fuel (Holman *et al.*, 1991), and any comparisons between bioethanol and petrol should take this into account. Most bioethanol programmes, however, use the product as a fuel additive to petrol as a means of enhancing combustion.

Pro-rata, SO_2 emissions have been reported to be up to 30% lower and NOx emissions up to 15% lower than those from petrol run engines. The position regarding CO_2 is less clear. Taking into account production and use of ethanol, particularly the CO_2 produced during the fermentation process, CO_2 production may actually be higher (Holman *et al.*, 1991). These studies may simply be a reflection of the relatively poor energy balance of bioethanol production at the time the studies were conducted.

One potential disadvantage of using ethanol as a fuel is that formaldehyde and acetaldehyde emissions are dramatically increased. These aldehydes are sometimes categorized as unburned fuel emissions and may be carcinogenic (Homewood, 1993) and may decrease ozone levels (Brower, 1992).

8.7 Other environmental factors

Other characteristics of biofuels may have environmental implications. Both bioethanol and biodiesel are natural food-stuffs and are therefore naturally biodegraded much more quickly than mineral oils. Biodiesel for example shows 95% biodegradability in 21 days compared with 72% for mineral diesel. Degradation of the remaining 28% in the mineral fuel may take a considerable time as this portion principally contains the heavier oils.

Similarly, spillages on water indicate rapid biodegradability of biodiesel and low toxicity against fish, water plants, algae and bacteria (Rodinger, 1994). However, the rapid degradation of biodiesel may be a major disadvantage in certain situations e.g. spillage into restricted volumes of water, as the oxygen in the water is rapidly used up with consequent detrimental effects to wildlife.

8.8 Current production of biofuels

EU Directive 2003/30/EC (May 2003) provides indicative guidelines for liquid biofuel production for transport. The target for 2005 is 2% of all transport fuel to be biofuel, rising to 5.75% by 2010. For the UK, 2% is equivalent to 800,000 tonnes biodiesel: UK production in 2004 was only 25,000 tonnes though planned building of biodiesel plants may raise the UK's capacity up to a maximum of 300,000 tonnes by the end of 2005. No bioethanol is produced for fuel in the UK; in comparison with the rest of Europe the UK lags behind.

However, Clause 128 of the UK 2004 Energy Act empowers the Government to require oil companies to provide biofuels as a given percentage of their annual sales. This power, should it be used, could allow the Government to help meet the EU directive and also various international environmental agreements (e.g. Kyoto). Such a move could have a dramatic effect on biofuel production in the UK but could also help create a new market that would encourage imports.

Current UK set-aside of around 700,000 hectares, even if all used for biofuel production, would still be unlikely to reach the 2005 EU target for the UK. A major change in the structure of UK agriculture with consequent major impacts on the environment will be required to meet the 2010 target.

References

Anon. (1990). Substitute Fuels for Road Transport. A technological assessment. OECD/IEA Paris, 1990.

Batchelor, S.E., Booth, E.J., Walker, K.C. and Cook, P. (1994). 'The potential for Bioethanol Production from Wheat in the UK'. Home Grown Cereals Authority Research Review No. 29. HGCA London, 1994.

Batchelor, S.E., Booth, E.J. and Walker, K.C. (1995). Energy Analysis of Rape Methyl Ester (RME) Production from Winter Oilseed Rape. *Industrial Crops and Products.* **4**: 193-202.

Booth, E., Booth, J. and Walker, K.C. (2005). Economic Evaluation of Bioethanol Production in Scotland. SAC report prepared for ITI Life Sciences. 40pp.

Brower, M. (1992). *Renewable solutions to the enviromental problems.* MIT Press. 220pp.

Diesel, R. (1895). German Patent No. 82168.

Entwistle, G., Walker, K.C. and Booth, E.J. (2002). Non-food Markets: Outlook and Policy Issues - an overview. Pub OECD Paris 2002.

Holman, C., Fergusson, M. and Mitchel, C. (1991). 'Road Transport and Air Pollution'. Rees Jeffreys Road Fund; 'Transport and Society' Discussion Paper 25.

Homewood, B. (1993). 'Will Brazil's cars go on the wagon?'. *New Scientist,* 9 January 1993.

Houghton-Alico, D. (1982). *Alcohol Fuels. Policies, Production and Potential.* Westview Press, Boulder, Colorado.

Lewis, C. (1983). *'Biological Fuels'.* Studies in Biology No. 153. Edward Arnold, London, 1983.

Mittelbach, M. and Tritthard, P. (1988). Diesel Fuel derived from Vegetable Oils. III Emission tests using methyl esters of used frying oil. *Journal of the American Oil Chemistry Society.* **65**: 7.

Rodinger, W. (1994). New data on Environmental Parameters of RME in comparison to Diesel Fuel, Bundesanstalt für Wassergate, Schiffmuhlenstr 120 A-1223 Vienna, Austria.

Sams, S. (1996). Use of Biofuels under Real World Engine Operation. *2nd European Biofuels Forum.* 225-233.

Walker, K.C. (2004). *Non Food Uses in 'Rapeseed and Canola Oil, Production, Processing, Properties and Uses'.* Ed. F.D. Gunstone. Blackwells Publishing, Oxford, UK.

Ward, O.P. (1989). *Fermentation Biotechnology. Principles, Processes and Products.* OUP, Milton Keynes.

9 Hydrogen Technology – What Impacts?

Sinclair Gair – *Institute for Energy and Environment, University of Strathclyde, 204 George Street, Glasgow G1 1XW.*

Summary

1. The EU is aiming for a reduction in the use of oil and an increase in the use of hydrogen from natural gas and possibly coal in the medium term, and from renewable energy in the long term.

2. Commercial interest in hydrogen and fuel cells is now growing rapidly as more businesses, investors and countries recognize the potential opportunities and benefits this technology could bring. This in turn is accelerating the rate at which the fuel cell/hydrogen industry will commercialize globally, although commercialization is still some way off.

3. The global fuel cell and hydrogen industry proponents claim to be able to deliver major improvements in efficiency, greenhouse gas emissions, and quality of life.

4. However, as indigenous energy supplies dwindle, the UK will shift from being a net energy exporter to being a net importer. This makes the UK potentially more vulnerable to interruptions in supply (due to regulatory failure, political instability and conflict) and price fluctuations.

5. With its strong link to renewables, hydrogen technology, if successful, has the potential to be a zero emission technology, and thus to significantly reduce the impacts of energy consumption on the natural environment.

9.1 Introduction

Hydrogen and fuel cell technology has become one of the most innovative areas of engineering science. It is anticipated that fuel cells will become one of the key energy technologies of the coming century: they can create emission-free electrical power, and are optimally suited for use with a wide number of different fuels including hydrogen, natural gas, methanol and liquid hydrocarbons.

From the Scottish perspective, two specific drivers for the use of hydrogen and fuel cells appear to dominate. One of these is clearly the benefit to Scotland in becoming less reliant on conventional carbon-based fossil fuels as older, mature industries decline. The second is the potential for fuel cells to help meet greenhouse gas emissions reduction agreements, especially in the transport sector. Given our renewable energy potential, it is likely that the UK could be made into an attractive hydrogen market.

Gair, S. (2008). Hydrogen Technology – What Impacts? In *Energy and the Natural Heritage*, ed. by C.A. Galbraith and J.M. Baxter. TSO Scotland, Edinburgh. pp. 105-116

A large number of sizeable and significant potential markets have been identified, such as premium power static applications, portable use in lap-top computers and hand-held mobile phones, large static grid independent units, and transport. However, estimating the overall size of the market for fuel cells is difficult due to uncertainty over production and development costs. Furthermore, there is no hydrogen infrastructure in place to support widespread adoption of fuel cells, and until such infrastructure exists, demand will be limited, so delaying its development. It is anticipated that the market will develop in small pockets through demonstration schemes, but transition to a fuel cell/hydrogen economy is still uncertain.

9.2 Unique advantages of fuel cells

Fuel cells have a potentially unique combination of advantages over degradation and energy security (Audus *et al.*, 1997; Nurdin, 2001; Stephenson, 2001; Baldur and Bossel, 2002).

Fuel cells' key characteristics:

- produce zero pollutant emissions when fuelled with hydrogen; fuelled with hydrocarbons, toxic emissions are greatly reduced;
- offer increased energy efficiency and reduced CO_2 emissions, even with a hydrocarbon or fossil fuel as the source for hydrogen. If fuelled with regenerative hydrogen, they produce zero CO_2 emissions;
- promote energy security, as hydrogen (the most abundant element in the universe) can be derived from a variety of sources, including renewables;
- promote efficiency; unlike conventional generating equipment, fuel cell efficiency is not compromised by small unit sizes, and they can also operate efficiently at part load;
- being clean and quiet, can be sited where electricity is needed, and flexibility in siting allows by-product heat to be used, doubling energy efficiency;
- could be made to be more reliable than internal combustion engines in stationary and vehicular applications as they have fewer moving parts;
- are ultimately expected to result in lower running costs due to the combination of superior efficiency and lower maintenance.

A potential major application for fuel cells is in powering road vehicles, the main determinant of suitability being the operating temperature and the consequent start up time. The classification of fuel cells is shown in Table 9.1, but two types are generally considered to have potential for powering road transportation:

1. Proton Exchange Membrane fuel cells (PEMs); and in the future
2. Direct Methanol PEM fuel cells (DMPEMs).

Alkaline fuel cells have been used in the US space programme for decades and are proven in concept. However, due to the need to circulate the potassium hydroxide electrolyte, these units are considered less suitable for transport applications. Overall, it is generally considered that no sizeable market for fuel cell vehicles will emerge until around 2015–2020, but when it does, it is expected to produce worthwhile reductions in CO_2 emissions.

Table 9.1 Current fuel cell types and classification.

Type	Temperature (°C)	Efficiency (%)	Specification of Fuel
AFC (Alkaline)	70 – 90	Hydrogen 50%	S < 1 ppm CO < 10-100ppm
PEM Proton Exchange Membrane	50 – 90	Natural Gas 40% Hydrogen 50-60%	S < 1 ppm CO < 10-100ppm
PAFC (Phosphoric Acid)	160 – 220	Natural Gas 40%	S < 1 ppm CO < 1% N2 < 4% Cl < 1 ppm
MCFC Molten Carbonate	600 – 700	Natural Gas 50%	S < 1 ppm Cl < 1 ppm
SOFC (Solid Oxide)	850 – 1000	Natural Gas 50-55%	S < 1 ppm Cl < 1 ppm

9.3 Overview of hydrogen as a fuel

Hydrogen (H_2) is the most abundant element in the universe: it is commonly stored within chemical compounds rather than as pure H_2, and therefore requires to be 'extracted' in some fashion before it can be used as a fuel. Hydrogen can be produced from water by electrolysis, from hydrocarbon fuels by reforming or thermal cracking, or from other hydrogen carriers by adapted chemical processes. If clean hydrogen is to be produced, i.e. without greenhouse gas emissions in the production chain, then clean energies such as electricity from solar, wind, wave, and hydro must be applied. Hydrogen may actually be the only meaningful link between renewable energy and chemical energy carriers. Hydrogen is currently extensively used in the chemical process, food and fuels industries and, for example, within many large scale electricity generators as a gaseous coolant.

The 'Hydrogen Economy' involves not only production and use of hydrogen but also packaging, storage, delivery, transfer and all the other ingredients of an energy market. Such a market can flourish only if the energy consumed within the market itself is small compared to the energy delivered to the customer. This is generally the case in today's energy markets. The energy lost in power transmission, oil refining, sea and land transport of fuels usually amounts to less than 10% of the energy traded. Hence, the energy required to operate a 'Hydrogen Economy' must be fully analysed and included in the economic appraisal. While it has never been more urgent to find energy resources that do not produce emissions of greenhouse gases, it is recognized that another possible path is to continue using fossil fuels for producing hydrogen, but to capture and sequester the greenhouse gases, i.e. CO_2, before they are emitted into the atmosphere.

It should also be recognized that technical solutions can be developed for a hydrogen economy: on a daily basis, enormous amounts of hydrogen are generated, handled, transported and used in the chemical industries. The importance of this is that hydrogen is a chemical substance – not an energy commodity. The costs of production, storage and transportation of hydrogen when used as a chemical substance are finally absorbed in the price of the synthesized chemicals, i.e. the cost of hydrogen remains irrelevant as long as the products find markets. Hence, today's cost of hydrogen is set by economic manufacturing considerations – not by energy considerations.

9.3.1 Properties of hydrogen

Hydrogen is the smallest of all atoms, and consequently hydrogen is the lightest gas, about 8 times lighter than methane (natural gas). The volumetric heating values (Higher and Lower Heating Value) compared to methane (at 1 bar, 25° C) are:

HHV H_2:	11.7 kJ/litre
LHV H_2:	9.9 kJ/litre
HHV CH_4:	36.5 kJ/litre
LHV CH_4:	32.9 kJ/litre

The volumetric (as opposed to gravimetric) comparison is made on the basis that volume considerations are of major importance in transport applications. Hydrogen has to be compacted by compression or liquefaction for storage, transport or transfer. In today's energy economy the handling of natural gas and liquid fuels does not pose any major problems. However, Figure 9.1 presents the volumetric HHV energy densities of different energy carrier options, from which it can be seen that even when compressed to 200 bar,

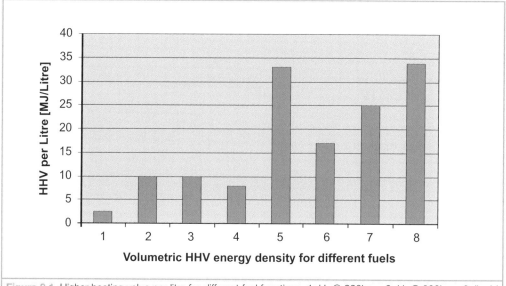

Figure 9.1 Higher heating value per litre for different fuel functions. 1: H_2 @ 200bar; 2: H_2 @ 800bar; 3: liquid H_2; 4: methane @ 200bar; 5: methane @800bar; 6: liquid methanol; 7: liquid propane; 8: liquid octane.

hydrogen clearly carries less energy per volume than methane (representing natural gas), methanol, propane or octane (representing gasoline). At 800 bar gaseous hydrogen reaches the volumetric energy density of liquid hydrogen, but the volumetric energy density of methane at 800 bar is about 3.3 times higher. However, methanol, propane and octane surpass liquid hydrogen by factors of 1.7 to 3.4 respectively. Furthermore, at such densities hydrogen must be contained in an 800 bar pressure tank or in a cryogenic container, while the other more common fuels are kept under atmospheric conditions.

The following sections present an overview of hydrogen, including common methods for producing, storing and transporting hydrogen as a fuel, and an overview of its properties.

9.3.2 Hydrogen safety – hydrogen as a vehicle fuel

Hydrogen is an odourless and colourless gas, with a boiling point of -252.77° C. It has a density of 0.0899 grams/litre, which is lighter than the surrounding air, and hydrogen will always dissipate rapidly if released into the atmosphere or is 'spilled' from a tank. Table 9.2 provides details of various comparative properties of hydrogen with natural gas (methane), and petrol (gasoline – four star equivalent).

Table 9.2 Fuel Comparison

Comparison of Different Fuels			
Property	Gasoline	Methane	Hydrogen
Energy Density by Weight (kWh/kg)	12.7	13.9	33.3
Energy Density by Weight (MJ/kg)	45.72	50.04	119.88
Energy Density by volume (kWh/l)	8.76 (liquid)	5.8 (liquid)	2.36 (liquid)
Density (Kg/m³)	690 (liquid)	0.72 (gas)	0.0899 (gas)
Diffusion Coefficient In Air (cm²/Sec)	0.05	0.16	0.610
Specific Heat at Constant Pressure (J/Gk)	1.20	2.22	14.89
Ignition Limits In Air (vol %)	1.0 - 7.6	5.3 - 15.0	4.0 - 75.0
Ignition Energy In Air (MJ)	0.24	0.29	0.02
Ignition Temperature (°C)	228-471	540	585
Flame Temperature In Air (°C)	2197	1875	2045
Explosion Energy (G TNT/kJ)	0.25	0.19	0.17
Flame Emissivity (%)	34-43	25-33	17-25

Comparing the energy density by weight of a number of fuels, it is clear that hydrogen has the highest energy to weight ratio of any fuel but suffers from one of the lowest energy densities by volume. As a consequence, a hydrogen tank will typically occupy a far greater volume than an equivalent petrol tank on a vehicle, and hydrogen storage technologies are currently an area of intense research world-wide. As a result, this defines the limit of the potential driving range for hydrogen-powered cars/vehicles.

The explosive limit for hydrogen gas, when spontaneous combustion may happen, lies in the region of 4 - 75% concentration by volume in air. Although a 4% mixture of hydrogen in air may appear a low level concentration, the comparable lower explosive limit for petrol is 1%, implying that hydrogen offers a significantly lower risk of explosion. In addition, low density and an ability to disperse rapidly allow hydrogen to escape to the atmosphere if a leak should occur. Propane and petrol, with their respective high densities and therefore slow dispersal from a spillage, allow the fuels to accumulate near or on the ground, both increasing the risk of explosion and sustaining that risk as both fuels will 'linger' until treated safely.

9.3.3 The 'public image' of hydrogen

Hydrogen is commonly associated with two things: the Hindenburg disaster and the hydrogen bomb. In 1937, the Hindenburg airship was destroyed attempting to land in an electrical storm on the outskirts of Lakehurst, New Jersey, USA. Witnesses reported observing a blue glow on the top of the ill-fated airship, often indicative of extremely high electrical activity, i.e. corona discharge, and it is now believed that the static electricity around the skin of the ship probably ignited the skin. The skin of the airship, designed to support the hydrogen 'pockets' as buoyancy, was composed of either cellulose nitrate or cellulose acetate in combination with aluminium flakes to reflect sunlight in order to keep the airship cool. This combination of cellulose nitrate and aluminium is commonly known today as the recipe for rocket fuel, which is highly explosive. Hence, although the hydrogen contained in the airship did burn, current evidence points to the skin of the airship igniting first and not the hydrogen, i.e. it was not a disaster caused by hydrogen.

9.3.4 Hydrogen production options

There are several different common methods of extracting/deriving hydrogen, as follows:

Electro-chemical processing: Electrolysis is the process whereby electricity is used to 'break down' water into its constituent gases, namely hydrogen and oxygen, in the ratio of one mole of water producing two moles of hydrogen and one mole of oxygen. Overall energy efficiencies for electrolysers are typically 80-85%. The basic electrolysis process is:

$$2H_2O + \text{'electrical energy'} \Rightarrow 2H_2 + O_2$$

Both PEM and alkaline electrolyser technologies exist commercially from, for example Proton Energy Systems, Stuart Energy Systems and Norsk Hydro respectively.

Chemical processing: Every elemental metal that is less noble than hydrogen will displace hydrogen from water, for example for the proposed 'Powerball' device utilizing sodium (Fuel Cell Today, 2006):

$$2Na + 2 H_2O \Rightarrow H_2 + 2NaOH + HEAT$$

The "producer" reaction has been practised since its discovery in about 1800 for producing hydrogen from a carbon donor and water, giving 'town gas':

$$HEAT + C + H_2O \Rightarrow H_2 + CO$$

Further, following the discovery of higher hydrocarbons such as oil and natural gas, hydrogen has been produced in large quantities by reacting steam with petroleum hydrocarbons:

$$HEAT + CxHy + xH_2O \Rightarrow (x + 0.5y)\ H_2 + xCO$$

This last reaction is currently the typical means of producing our existing large-scale supply of hydrogen gas.

Photoconversion: Numerous bacteria and all green plants dissociate water into hydrogen and oxygen as the first step of photosynthesis. Hydrogen is retained to build plant tissues (carbohydrates) by reactions that combine carbon from atmospheric carbon dioxide with hydrogen. Oxygen is released to the atmosphere in the process.

$$LIGHT + 2H_2O \Rightarrow 2H_2 + O_2$$
$$LIGHT + H_2 + CO_2 \Rightarrow Plant\ Tissues\ (i.e.\ carbohydrates)$$

9.4 Hydrogen storage options

It is possible to store and subsequently use hydrogen in a number of forms, as follows:

9.4.1 Compressed gas

Compressed gas storage and transportation has been widely used for more than 100 years. Common materials for storage canisters are mild steel, aluminium, and composites, and storage pressures of 3,000 to 10,000 psi (200-700 bar) are common. However, compression of gases depends on a thermodynamic compression process for which energy is needed, and the ideal isothermal compression cannot be realized for high compression ratios.

The energy invested [MJ/kg] in the adiabatic compression of the monatomic noble gas helium, the diatomic hydrogen, and the five-atomic methane from atmospheric conditions (1bar = 98,100 Pa) to pressures of 200 bar and 800 bar are presented in Table 9.3:

Table 9.3 Energy invested [MJ/kg] to compress hydrogen, helium and methane.

Fuel	Pressure (200 bar)	Pressure (800 bar)
H_2	14.0	23.0
He	10.0	18.0
CH_4	1.8	2.7

Clearly, much more energy is required to compress hydrogen than methane. The energy invested in compression is related to the higher heating value (HHV) of the compressed hydrogen and methane. The theoretical relative energy input remains reasonable for methane, but for hydrogen it amounts to 10% and 16% for 200 and 800 bar respectively. In reality, the energy losses may be closer to 15 and 25% if the efficiencies of compressor, electric motor and power transmission are also considered.

9.4.2 Liquid

Cooling hydrogen to below the boiling point of -252.7°C allows storage as a cryogenic liquid without the need for pressurization; this allows regular shipment by truck and rail. Many commercial processes require regular deliveries of liquid hydrogen, with the US space programme currently the world's largest user. BMW currently opt for a liquid hydrogen storage system on their hydrogen powered combustion engine cars.

However, even more energy is needed to compact hydrogen by liquefaction. Theoretically, fewer than 5 kJ/kg have to be removed to cool hydrogen down and condense the gas to its boiling temperature of -252.7°C at atmospheric pressure, but the cooling process is extremely energy intensive. A theoretical analysis of the complicated liquefaction process is difficult, but estimates of the energy requirements of existing hydrogen liquefaction plants are available.

9.4.3 Metal hydrides

Metal hydride systems store hydrogen in the inter-atomic spaces of a granular metal. Various metals can be used, and the hydrogen is released by heating. These systems are reliable and compact but can be heavy and expensive.

In the chemical case, a substantial amount of energy is needed to combine hydrogen with alkali metals. This energy is released when the hydrogen is liberated from the compound. The generated heat has to be removed by cooling and is normally lost. For physical hydride storage, the hydrogen gas must be pressurized. Hydride storage of hydrogen is by no means a low-energy process, but is comparable to the compression of hydrogen.

9.5 Hydrogen transportation options

9.5.1 Pipeline

Hydrogen can be transported via pipelines in a similar fashion to existing natural gas and oil pipelines. Hydrogen 'corrosion' of the pipeline materials (or hydrogen embrittlement) is a concern and affects the type and quality of pipeline material employed.

Hydrogen pipelines exist, but they are used to transport a chemical commodity from one to another production site. The energy required to move the gas is irrelevant in this context, because energy costs are part of the production costs. This is not so for energy transport through pipelines. For example, in a natural gas pipeline, pumps are required at regular intervals to keep the gas moving: these pumps are energized by energy taken from the delivery stream: typically, about 0.3 % of the natural gas is used every 150 km to energize a compressor to keep the gas moving.

The energy consumed to move hydrogen through pipelines may be roughly compared to a natural gas pipeline. This comparison assumes equal energy flows, i.e. the same amount of energy is delivered to the consumer through the same pipeline either in the form of natural gas or hydrogen. However, it should be noted that existing pipelines cannot be used for hydrogen transmission because of diffusion losses, brittleness of materials and seals, incompatibility of pump lubrication with hydrogen and other technical issues. The comparison should also take account of the different viscosities of hydrogen and methane. Furthermore, because of the low volumetric energy density of hydrogen, the flow velocity must be increased by over three times to deliver the same amount of energy. Consequently, the flow resistance is also increased, but the viscosity difference partially compensates this effect. Consideration of these factors shows that about 4.6 times more power is required to move hydrogen through the pipeline than is required for natural gas.

Table 9.4 shows some indicative values of gas consumed to move the gas through a pipeline in terms of the distance along the pipeline from the source. These values indicate that while the energy consumption for methane (representing natural gas) appears reasonable, the energy needed to move hydrogen through pipelines makes this type of hydrogen distribution difficult. Not 0.3 % but almost 1.4 % of the hydrogen flow is consumed every 150 km to energize the compressors, with the result that only 60 to 70% of the hydrogen fed into a hypothetical pipeline in Africa would actually arrive in Europe.

Table 9.4 Gas consumed to move gas through pipeline.

% of initial gas consumed		Distance from pipeline source (km)
H_2	CH_4	
9	2	1000
18	4	2000
24	7	3000
31	8.5	4000
37.5	10	5000

9.5.2 Energy needed to deliver hydrogen by road transport

A hydrogen economy would certainly involve hydrogen transport by road, whether to serve remote communities or to provide back-up fuel to filling stations at times of peak demand. A comparative analysis has been carried out using the following assumptions: hydrogen (200bar), methane (200bar), methanol, propane and octane (representing gasoline) are trucked from the refinery or hydrogen plant to the consumer. In all cases, trucks with a gross weight of 40 tons are fitted with tanks or pressure vessels (the delivery of liquid hydrogen is not considered in this context). At full load the trucks consume 40 kg of diesel per 100 km, equivalent to 1 kg per ton per 100 km. The fuel consumption is reduced accordingly for the return journey with empty tanks, and the same engine efficiency is used throughout.

The hydrogen and methane pressure tanks can be emptied only from 200 bar to about 42 bar to accommodate for the 40 bar pressure systems of the receiver. Such pressure cascades are standard practice today, otherwise compressors must be used to completely empty the content of the delivery tank into a storage vessel at higher pressure. This would not only make the gas transfer more difficult, but also result in a renewed consumption of compression energy. Therefore, pressurized gas carriers deliver only 80% of their freight, while 20% of the load remains in the tanks and is returned to the gas plant.

The assumption made is that each 40 ton truck is designed to carry the maximum load of fuel. For methanol and octane the tare load is about 25 tons, and for propane about 20 tons because of some degree of pressurization. At 200 bar pressure about 3.2 tons of methane, but only 0.32 tons of hydrogen can be delivered by a 40 ton truck as a direct consequence of the low density of hydrogen and the weight of the pressure vessels and other safety equipment. Of this load, only 80% or 400 kg can actually be delivered to the customer: even allowing for advances in technology, 39.6 tons of dead weight have to be moved on the road to deliver 400 kg of hydrogen. More energy is required to transport methane, but the relative energy consumption becomes unacceptable for hydrogen at almost any distance.

9.6 Summary

The key points are:

- Fuel cells appear to have significant commercial potential worldwide, but considerable challenges are faced in terms of cost and technological competitiveness.
- The Government must play a key role in stimulating the market to provide the necessary pull through. This in turn will help provide the incentives necessary to improve the technology and realize infrastructure investments to achieve market success.
- The UK has the potential to benefit directly by stimulating its own markets in applications of high value intellectual property and supply chain activities.
- To meet agreements on CO_2 reduction, fuel cell vehicles may be the only future way forward.
- The difficulties associated with the production, storage and transportation of hydrogen are key issues still to be solved, but solutions would provide one way of achieving a zero-carbon energy source.
- The environmental spin-off opportunities appear to be immense – it is clear that our clean air future in towns and cities depends on the commercialization of zero emission technologies.
- Advanced stationary and vehicular (cars and buses) application of fuel cell technologies can be instrumental in not only reducing ozone precursor emissions, but also providing improvements in efficiency and low CO_2 emissions. The advantages of fuel cell technology, either apparent or alleged, are now beginning to be demonstrated, but a full-grown market has not yet evolved, and further development efforts are necessary both in the technologies available and in the market sector. On the other hand, confidence in the technology is growing fast, as illustrated by the increasing numbers of developers and manufacturers, field trials and demonstrations, and number of applications addressed, as well as the growing interest of customers and venture capital suppliers.
- As experience with hydrogen/new fuel cell technologies grows, so will the application to other sectors of industry and to other locations throughout the UK and world-wide, i.e. there are significant opportunities for replication. Our vision of the future should be one of providing zero emission technologies based on (i) renewables, (ii) hydrogen, and (iii) fuel cells.

References

Audus, H., Kaarstad, O. and Kowal, M. (1997). Decarbonisation of fossil fuels: hydrogen as an energy carrier. CO_2 Conference., Boston/Cambridge 1997. *In Energy Conversion Management*. **38**: Suppl. 431-436.

Baldur, E. and Bossel, U. (2002). The future of the hydrogen economy: bright or bleak. *Proceedings: The Fuel Cell World*, 1 – 5 July, 2002, Lucerne, Switzerland.

Fuel Cell Today. 2006: Powerball: http://www.fuelcelltoday.com/FuelCellToday/IndustryDirectory/ IndustryDirectoryExternal/IndustryDirectoryDisplayCompany/0,1664,363,00.html : accessed 16 June 2006.

Norsk Hydro: http://www.norskhydro.se/ Web page accessed 16 June 2006.

Nurdin, M. (2001). Fuel cells in stationary and portable applications. *International Conference: The Fuel Cell Home*, Lucerne, Switzerland, 2 – 6 July, 2001.

Proton Energy Systems: http://www.protonenergy.com/ : accessed 16 June 2006.

Stephenson, S. (2001). *Building a hydrogen infrastructure*. Shell Fuels Business Group seminar presentation, Scottish Executive, Victoria Quay, Leith. 10th October 2001.

Stuart Energy Systems /Hydrogenics: http://www.hydrogenics.com/ir_newsdetail.asp?RELEASEID=147848 Web page accessed 16 June 2006.

A boggy flush with sedges and sphagnum moss © Lorne Gill/SNH

10 Carbon Capture and Storage in the UK

Yasmin E. Bushby – *Scottish Centre for Carbon Storage, School of GeoSciences, University of Edinburgh, Edinburgh EH9 3JW.*

Stuart M.V. Gilfillan – *Scottish Centre for Carbon Storage, School of GeoSciences, University of Edinburgh, Edinburgh EH9 3JW.*

R. Stuart Haszeldine – *Scottish Centre for Carbon Storage, School of GeoSciences, University of Edinburgh, Edinburgh EH9 3JW.*

Summary

1. About three quarters of electricity in the UK is produced using fossil fuels which in turn produces approximately one third of total UK CO_2 emissions. Carbon Capture and Storage (CCS) can reduce UK emissions rapidly, whilst renewable energy and low-carbon generation technologies are developed and built.
2. Capture of CO_2 is most beneficial at large point sources such as power stations and industrial facilities. Existing power stations can be retrofitted with carbon capture equipment and new power stations can be built to be ready for capture.
3. Capture of CO_2 is already a common industrial process, although the amount of carbon captured will need to be much greater for use on power station emissions. Transport of CO_2 is already used on a similar scale onshore in the oil industry.
4. Storage of CO_2 is feasible by injection through boreholes into deep geological formations. Many of these formations have stored oil and gas for millions of years and their natural trapping mechanisms can be utilized. Possible storage sites are old oil and gas reservoirs, unmineable coal seams and saline aquifers.
5. With well designed, selected, and managed storage sites, scientists estimate that 99% of CO_2 can be retained over a period of several thousand years. This would store the carbon well beyond the era of fossil fuel use.
6. The UK is well suited to CCS technology. A quarter of existing power plants must be replaced by 2025 and this poses a perfect opportunity for CCS to be implemented. There are a large number of suitable storage sites present in the North Sea. These could economically and safely store hundreds of years' worth of CO_2 from UK electricity generation and are located close to many potential carbon capture sites.

Bushby, Y.E., Gilfillan, S.M.V. & Haszeldine R.S. (2008). Carbon Capture and Storage in the UK. In *Energy and the Natural Heritage*, ed. by C.A. Galbraith and J.M. Baxter. TSO Scotland, Edinburgh. pp. 117-134

10.1 Introduction

Climate change is a global problem which requires global solutions. One significant cause of recent and projected climate change is an increase in greenhouse gas concentrations in the Earth's atmosphere. These increased proportions of greenhouse gases have enhanced the Earth's natural greenhouse effect. The greenhouse gas making the largest contribution is CO_2 and it is now clear that most of the increase in atmospheric CO_2 levels are the direct result of combustion of fossil fuels and biomass since the industrial revolution of the 1850s (IPCC, 2007) (Figure 10.1). Global greenhouse gas emissions have increased by 70% between 1970 and 2004.

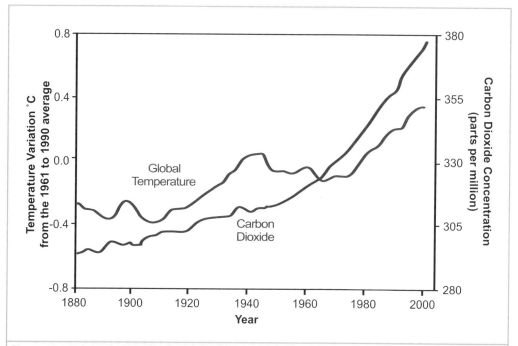

Figure 10.1 This graph shows the increase of CO_2 concentration in the atmosphere and the corresponding rise in global temperature since the industrial revolution. It can be seen that the biggest increase in CO_2 levels and global temperature has been since the 1970s. (Atmospheric CO_2 concentrations from IPCC Report, Climate Change 2001: The Scientific Basis, and temperature data from National Oceanic and Atmospheric Administration, Feb 2006).

10.1.1 Threat of climate change on global ecosystems

Many ecosystems around the world are, and will be, threatened by climate change and its associated disturbances (e.g. sea-level rise, ocean acidification and an increase in severe weather events such as drought, wildfire and flooding). Complex life on the surface of planet earth participates in a carbon cycle, where carbon is exchanged through natural processes between the biosphere, geosphere, hydrosphere and atmosphere. It is currently believed that net carbon uptake by terrestrial forest ecosystems is likely to reach a peak within the next 50 years and then weaken or even reverse (IPCC, 2007). This is predicted to have the effect of accelerating climate change and thereby placing more species, and human civilizations, in danger.

The most recent Intergovernmental Panel on Climate Change (IPCC) report in 2007 identified that approximately 20-30% of plant and animal species studied are likely to be at an increased risk of extinction if global average temperatures rise by just 1.5 - 2.5°C (IPCC, 2007). These increased temperatures would cause major changes in ecosystem structure and function, species, ecological interactions and species' geographic ranges (IPCC, 2007). It would drastically reduce biodiversity and cause severe disruption to both the natural world and to people, due to reducing water and food supplies. Additionally, increasing atmospheric CO_2 is already leading to the progressive acidification of oceans which is expected to cause major impacts on the metabolism of invertebrates, the ecology of the shallow seabed, and marine shell forming organisms (The Royal Society, 2005; IPCC, 2007).

10.1.2 Global CO_2 emissions and fossil fuel use

Global emissions of greenhouse gases from human activity are estimated to range between 22.8 and 25.3 billion tonnes of CO_2 equivalent per year (Marland *et al.*, 2003) (CO_2 equivalent includes the contribution to global warming made by other greenhouse gases such as methane and nitrous oxide). The vast majority of these greenhouse gases are the direct result of the burning of fossil fuels for transport, heating and electricity generation (Figure 10.2).

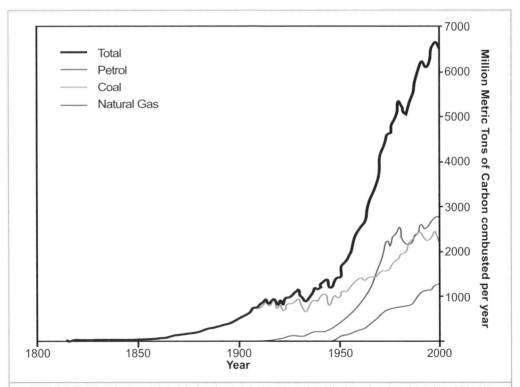

Figure 10.2 This graph shows the global carbon emissions from fossil fuel combustion since the 1850s. It can be seen that the biggest increase in carbon levels has been since the 1950s. To convert combusted carbon to CO_2, multiply by 3.67. (Redrawn from www.globalwarmingart.com. Original data from Marland *et al.*, (2003)).

Modern industrialized society is dependent upon fossil fuels to meet its energy requirements and will be for the foreseeable future (Figure 10.3). At the present time an estimated 75% of the world's energy is produced from fossil fuels (BP, 2006; REN21, 2006) accounting for the release of more than 7 billion tonnes of carbon in 2006. In order to effectively tackle climate change and ocean acidification, the world must drastically reduce its CO_2 emissions.

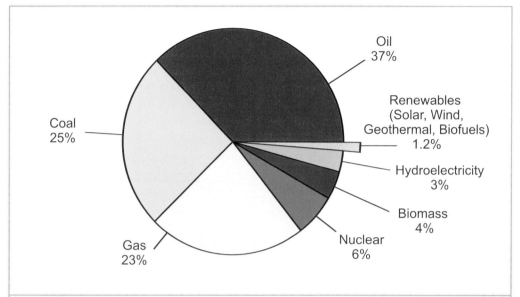

Figure 10.3 Sources of energy worldwide. It can be seen that most of the energy is produced from fossil-fuel based sources, all of which release CO_2 during combustion (Figure 10.2). (Data from the BP statistical review and REN21 global status report on renewable energy).

Even with strong development in the renewables sector, the International Energy Agency projections show that it is very probable that more than half of the industrial world's energy will still be generated by burning fossil fuels in 2050 (IEA, 2004). This is primarily because energy produced from fossil fuels is considerably cheaper, and easier to transport or transmit, than that produced by renewable sources. Many developing countries are unable to sustain both renewable energy development and improvements in healthcare, water and food supplies. Further pressure is created by increasing energy demands in China and India where there are no CO_2 reduction aims. The world also has the added pressure of an increasing population. China and India are predicted to become major emitters of CO_2, and in 2007 China surpassed the USA as the largest CO_2 emitter (NEAA, 2007) – some seven years ahead of previous predictions by the International Energy Agency (IEA, 2006).

10.1.3 The UK perspective

The UK contributes about 2% of global man-made greenhouse gas emissions (IPCC, 2007), with 556 million tonnes of CO_2 equivalent in 2005.

Nearly 75% of electricity in the UK is generated from fossil fuels (Figure 10.4) and has contributed the majority of the 208 million tonnes of CO_2 equivalent produced by the energy industries. An additional 99 million tonnes of CO_2 equivalent was produced by other industries (Figure 10.5).

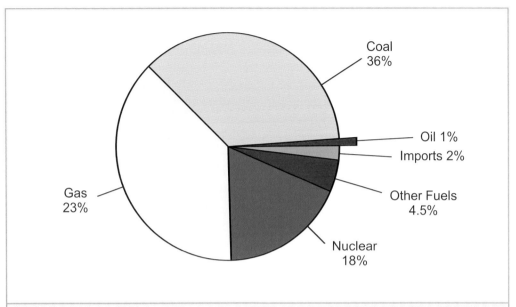

Figure 10.4 Sources of UK electricity generation in 2006. Note that fossil fuel combustion generates nearly 75% of total electricity. Other energy sources comprise hydro, solar, wind, biofuels and waste gas combustion. (Data from DBERR).

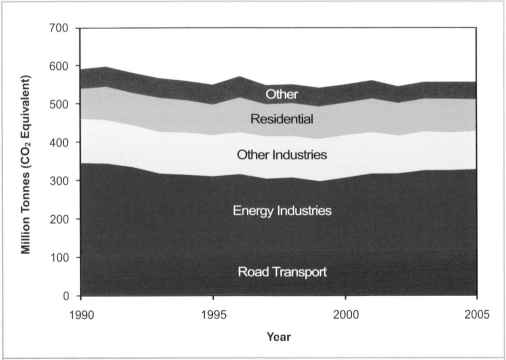

Figure 10.5 UK CO_2 emissions by source between 1990 – 2005. Overall CO_2 emissions have reduced from 1990. However, since 2003 an increase in the number, and especially the use, of fossil fuel power stations (coal and gas fired) is increasing emissions from the energy industries. The red "other" portion comprises commercial and public sector emissions (data from AEA Energy and Environment from Defra, 2007).

Whilst the UK is slowly reducing its greenhouse gas emissions, the government has realized the threat of climate change to both the UK economy (Stern, 2007; WWF, 2007) and the global population. For this reason the UK Government has committed to drastically reduce UK CO_2 emissions by 2050, by 60% of 1990 emission levels. The UK Parliament Climate Bill of 2007-08, will commit the UK to the world's first legally binding reduction of CO_2, with specified intermediate targets. In order for these targets to be met the UK must engage in multiple options to decarbonise energy, especially electricity. There are numerous policy and technology options, amongst these different options are:

1) **Reduce UK energy use by reducing demand.**
   This can be expressed by using less energy, and by using energy more efficiently to continue producing wealth. This is typically a cost effective method but difficult for the government to implement and to produce rapid changes.

2) **Develop low carbon and renewable energy technology, e.g. hydro, wind, tidal, solar.**
   Renewable energy is typically highly favoured by the public. However, there are significant problems in overcoming the time and high initial capital costs needed to develop reliable and cost-effective electricity.

3) **Consider the re-introduction of nuclear electricity generation**
   This can be costed as being financially attractive, however, there is no appealing solution to waste storage and it is subject to the long term availability of fuel-grade uranium resources (Sustainable Development Commission, 2006).

4) **Discover and deploy methods of low carbon transport, for individual and mass transit, air and sea travel and freight.**
   Transport fuels are the most difficult to decarbonise. Biofuels are impossible to grow nationally, in the quantities needed by the UK, and imports compete with food or forest land use. Greatly improved use of public transport is possible, but requires behavioural change by many individuals. Hybrid vehicles are a near-term improvement, although zero-carbon electric, or hydrogen, vehicles will need decarbonized supplies (possibly from CCS).

5) **Capturing and storing large amounts of CO_2 from fossil fuel power stations.**
   This is the subject of active and achievable development and rapid deployment. However, the CCS process means that fuel needs to be imported, more fuel is used to generate the same net electricity, and there will be waste streams of CO_2 solvents.

Capturing and storing the CO_2 from fossil fuel power stations has the potential to be an effective tool for climate change mitigation. The majority of electricity in the UK is supplied by fossil fuels which generate approximately 37% of UK CO_2 emissions. If releasing this to the atmosphere were to be avoided through the implementation of CCS technologies, the UK would reduce its CO_2 emissions by up to 30%. The added benefit is that CCS will permit the UK continued use of fossil fuels for electricity and heat generation during the timespan that is required to develop renewables, and possibly nuclear energy, into more reliably engineered and cost-effective methods of electricity production.

10.2 Introducing Carbon Capture and Storage

Power stations and most industrial plants emit CO_2 in large volumes at individual sites. These are known as point sources and it is now possible for this CO_2 to be captured from these point sources instead of emitting it into the atmosphere. This CO_2 can then be transported and stored safely underground. This process is simply called Carbon Capture and Storage (CCS for short).

Carbon Capture and Storage therefore holds a great promise to dramatically reduce global CO_2 emissions from the burning of fossil fuels. This chapter will now provide an overview of the processes involved in CCS, and thereafter address some of the questions commonly posed regarding the benefits, costs and risks of the technology. A short discussion about what policies are needed to implement CCS concludes the chapter.

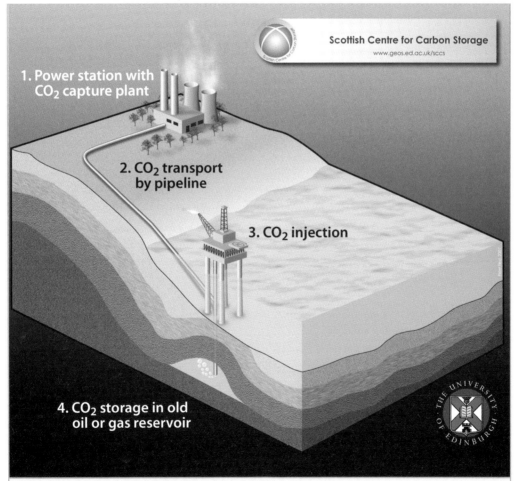

Figure 10.6 Schematic diagram illustrating the main stages of the Carbon Capture and Storage process. For the UK this will consist of a capture plant at the fossil fuel power station, transport of the captured CO_2 by pipeline followed by injection into an old oil or gas field, or aquifer offshore.

10.2.1 How does Carbon Capture and Storage work?

Carbon Capture and Storage technology has three individual steps (Figure 10.6):

1) Capture or removal of CO_2 from fossil fuel combustion or biofuel combustion at industrial processes, most importantly electrical power stations.
2) Transportation of the CO_2 from the point of capture to a storage site.
3) Injection of the CO_2 underground into deep geological formations for long term storage (more than 10,000 years).

10.2.1.1 Capture of CO_2

Capture of CO_2 is a common industrial process. Nevertheless, to apply this existing technology to power plants would require an increase of size scale by a factor of 3 to 10. Capture has been used for several decades to provide CO_2 for industries, such as those making carbonated (fizzy) soft drinks, de-caffeinating coffee, or dry cleaning of clothes. The oil industry has also used CO_2 separation to purify natural methane gas, and in refineries where hydrogen gas is made from natural hydrocarbons. At present there are three different ways that can be used to capture CO_2 from a point source (IPCC, 2005) and these are:

1) Post-combustion capture
2) Pre-combustion capture
3) Oxyfuel combustion

1) **Post-combustion capture**

    Post-combustion capture describes the capture of CO_2, which forms 3-15% of the flue gas **after** it is produced from burning a fossil fuel. Capture of the CO_2 usually occurs by passing the flue gas through an amine solvent, allowing the CO_2 to dissolve. Once dissolved the amine solvent can be pumped to a different part of the power station where it is heated to release the pure CO_2. A distinct advantage of this technology is that it could be fitted to existing power plants, such as those that burn coal, the fossil fuel that produces the most CO_2 per unit of electricity generated. This practice is called retrofitting and several sites around the UK are being considered for this.

2) **Pre-combustion capture**

    Pre-combustion capture involves the capture of CO_2 **before** the fuel is burned. To do this the fossil fuel is gasified or 'partially' burned in a combustion chamber at a higher pressure than normal and with a controlled amount of oxygen. This produces hydrogen and a relatively pure stream of CO_2 (15-60%) that can be easily separated and captured. The hydrogen can then be burned to produce heat for electricity generation without producing any further CO_2 (water vapour is the main by-product). This capture technology is well understood and is already used in industrial applications such as the production of CO_2 during production of hydrogen from splitting hydrocarbon in oil refineries. This technology has not yet been applied to a process as large as power generation.

3) Oxyfuel combustion

Oxyfuel combustion involves burning hydrocarbon fuel in a chamber which is rich in oxygen (more than 95%), rather than air (which contains 16% oxygen). This produces water and more than 80% CO_2 as by-products. Cooling of this mixture of gases allows the water to be condensed. This leaves an almost pure stream of CO_2 which is then ready for transport to a storage site. At the time of writing (2007) this is the least developed of the three capture technologies.

10.2.1.2 Costs of capture

The capture step of CCS is the most expensive, and is the step that has been least well developed technologically. The biggest problem is that all of the capture processes require energy to separate the CO_2 from the other gases. This is known as the energy penalty and is the main expense of the process, typically comprising 75% of the costs (IPCC, 2005). As a result of the energy required for the process, CO_2 capture makes a power station less efficient, meaning more fossil fuels need to be burnt for the same amount of electricity produced. However, the technology is currently being researched extensively and at the time of writing it is believed that a power station using CCS, by any of the three capture methods listed above, will emit 85-95% less CO_2 than one which has no CO_2 capture. Additional problems are the production of wastes: ash from coal (as at present), and new streams of degraded solvents – especially from post-combustion capture.

10.2.1.3 Transportation of CO_2

Once the CO_2 has been captured, it is pressurized to greater than 70 atmospheres, when it forms a liquid. The liquid is denser than gas, and consequently allows the CO_2 to be transported, as it can easily be pumped.

Special CO_2 pipelines can be used to transport it in a similar way to natural gas which is transported to homes around the world. Transport of CO_2 is carried out extensively in the United States to be used for Enhanced Oil Recovery (see below). Small amounts of CO_2 can also be transported in tanker ships similar to those that transport oil. Ship transport has been used for many years to supply CO_2 for the brewing and soft drink industries. However, as the tankers can only transport a limited amount at a time, pipeline transport is more efficient for distances up to 500 kilometres.

Liquefied CO_2 has already been utilized around the world for Enhanced Oil Recovery projects (EOR). This technology involves injecting CO_2 into old oil reservoirs in order to increase oil production. When the CO_2 is injected into oil reservoirs, it makes the oil less sticky, freeing it from the small pore spaces where it is trapped. The addition of CO_2 also increases the pressure acting on the oil in the reservoir and effectively pushes oil out from the pore spaces in the rock where it is trapped.

The costs and the energy required for CO_2 transport must be considered. The conversion of the CO_2 gas to a liquid requires energy, in addition to the energy required for pumping. Increased revenue from using captured CO_2 for enhanced oil recovery can be used to offset some costs. To minimize any environmental and economic costs, storage sites would ideally be located as close as possible to the power plant.

10.2.1.4 Storage of CO_2

Once the CO_2 has been captured and transported to the storage site it can then be injected. In the early stages of CCS research two distinct settings for storage were considered. They were:

1) Ocean Storage
2) Deep geological formations

1) Ocean Storage - Can CO_2 be stored in oceans?

Storage of CO_2 at the bottom of deep oceans was investigated as a possible method in the early stages of CCS research. The process would involve injecting a stream of CO_2 into the ocean from a fixed pipeline or below a moving ship.

The environmental impacts of this technique were found to be generally negative and the UK Government does not support this type of storage. Additionally, this method is currently outlawed by international marine treaties and injection of large amounts of CO_2 into the marine environment may acidify large amounts of sea water. Marine life is highly sensitive to such changes and therefore injecting CO_2 is certain to adversely affect marine life.

A final negative reason is that ocean storage is not a permanent method of CO_2 storage. There is a high risk that CO_2 will, over time, return to the atmosphere, as there is not a distinct physical barrier to prevent it from doing so. For these reasons this method of storage has been deemed unsuitable and no further research into it is being undertaken.

2) Deep geological formations – can we store CO_2 underground?

Many deep geological formations have acted as natural storage facilities for oil and gas for millions of years. It is therefore easy to appreciate why those natural trapping structures could be utilized to store CO_2 underground for many thousands of years. There are several different types of underground sites which could be used to store it:

– Exhausted oil and gas fields

Oil and gas fields consist of a layer of porous rock with a non-porous cap rock above. The oil and gas is held in the small pore spaces within the porous rock structure in a similar fashion to how the spaces in a sponge hold water. Oil and gas are trapped in these reservoirs by the cap rock, which has a dense non–porous structure with few spaces, preventing gas or oil movement through it. This acts as a lid on the reservoir, sealing the oil and gas underneath.

Once the fossil fuels have been removed, CO_2 can be injected through a well into the layer of porous, sponge-like rock. The sediment grains and clay particles which form the cap rock are too densely packed for the CO_2 to move through it, meaning that it is permanently trapped in the field.

Exhausted oil and gas fields are ideal for CO_2 storage. A great deal is known about these sites and the knowledge gained from Enhanced Oil Recovery (see section 10.2.1.3) means that CO_2 injection has already been conducted on a range of sites and associated injection technology has been developed. However, a programme of monitoring must be undertaken after CO_2 injection, to ensure that pre-existing boreholes, which have punctured the natural cap rock seal, do not act as leakage pathways for CO_2. It is thought that oil and gas fields could hold about 30 years of emissions from UK power plants.

– Unmineable coal seams

Unmineable coal seams offer another method of CO_2 storage. Whilst underground, coal has a layer of natural gas (usually methane - CH_4) chemically attached to it. Once CO_2 is injected, CO_2 will push the methane off the coal and adsorb onto the coal in place of the methane. An additional benefit is that during CO_2 injection, the methane could be recovered and used to produce energy. This could be used to cover some of the cost of the CO_2 storage.

However, there are two problems with this technique. Firstly burning of the methane will produce more CO_2 and secondly, in order for the CO_2 to be permanently stored the coal can never be mined. The coal is 'sterilized' as a fuel resource even if the coal becomes economically worthwhile to mine it in the future. There are no coals in the UK (in 2007) where this technique has been applied.

– Saline aquifers

Saline aquifers are deep underground stores of salt water. They are an attractive option as they are commonly found offshore, could hold a very large amount of CO_2 and are of no real use to humans due to the un-drinkable water. The UK North Sea contains several large saline aquifers and their use would keep transport costs to a minimum. The current estimates indicate that several centuries' worth of total UK CO_2 emissions could be held in these aquifers.

The main problem with this type of storage is that a relatively small amount of information is available when compared to old oil and gas reservoirs. Further research needs to be completed to determine if the potential storage capacity is as large as preliminary research suggests.

10.3 How would the CO_2 be stored in the rock?

CO_2 can be trapped in four distinct ways (Figure 10.7) which are explained in the following section.

10.3.1 Structural Storage

CO_2 is more buoyant than water meaning that when injected into a reservoir it will rise up through the pore spaces in the reservoir rock until it reaches the impermeable cap rock. Good cap rocks such as shales and mudstones are impenetrable to the CO_2 and will prevent it from leaking back to the atmosphere. As already mentioned, many natural gas fields around the world have stored both CO_2 and natural gas for millions of years in this way.

10.3.2 Residual Storage

The porous rocks in oil and gas reservoirs behave like a tight, rigid sponge. A sponge traps air residually and, for this reason, to soak a sponge in water it must be squeezed several times to replace the trapped air with water. In a similar fashion when liquid CO_2 is injected into a rock formation, much of it is trapped as isolated microscopic bubbles within the pore spaces of the rock and this is known as residual trapping.

10.3.3 Dissolution Storage

In the same way that sugar dissolves in hot tea, CO_2 quickly dissolves in water. This water containing CO_2 is denser than the freshwater surrounding it and will therefore sink to the bottom of the reservoir, so trapping the CO_2.

10.3.4 Mineral Storage

When CO_2 is dissolved in water it forms a weak acid (carbonic acid) which can dissolve and react with the minerals in the reservoir rock. If the conditions in the reservoir are favourable new minerals can be formed. They would coat the interior of pores within the

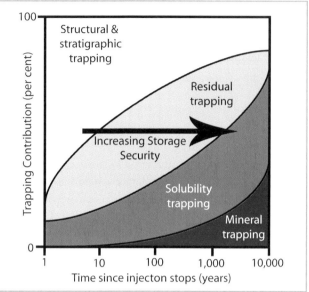

Figure 10.7 CO_2 trapping methods and time since injection stops (redrawn from IPCC Special report on Carbon Capture and Storage, 2005).

reservoir rock and lock away the CO_2 within the rock. However, under most conditions this process is extremely slow and this is therefore the least useful storage mechanism.

10.4 Monitoring and Verification of CO_2

Verifiably measuring the quantities of stored CO_2 is essential, especially if this technology is to be used to meet national or international commitments on reducing emissions or is to be used as a basis for emissions trading. Operators of CO_2 storage sites will also need to monitor site performance to verify that there is no leakage from the storage reservoir.

CO_2 can be measured at any stage of the CCS chain, and techniques for this are already available. During the CO_2 capture process, flows of gas would be measured as a normal part of the operation. During transport, CO_2 pipelines in the USA constantly monitor large quantities of pumped CO_2. At the injection site, metering on oil rigs is established to measure oil and gas production for tax purposes, similar methods could be used to measure the amount of CO_2 injected into geological storage sites.

Oil and gas companies now have the technology to trace gas flows in underground reservoirs using a number of methods which are directly applicable to monitoring stored CO_2. Whilst all of these methods are currently in use in the hydrocarbon industry, monitoring CO_2 storage will need to be carried out accurately and cheaply over a much longer time period than current monitoring technologies will allow and hence further research is this area is required (DTI, 2005).

10.5 Commonly Asked questions

The following section briefly answers some of the most commonly asked questions asked in relation to CCS technologies.

10.5.1 Will the CO_2 escape?

As outlined in the previous section of this chapter there are several ways in which CO_2 is held within the rock structure. The initial means is structural storage, where the CO_2 is trapped beneath a non-permeable (no flow) cap rock. This is the same mechanism by which most of the oil and gas fields around the world trap oil and gas. Many of these fields have stored oil and gas for hundreds of thousands to many millions of years and provided that the man-made CO_2 is placed in a similar geological site which has been adequately characterized and well chosen, long term storage can be achieved.

As well as oil and gas, around the world there are many sites that have naturally contained CO_2 from natural sources for millions of years. Hence, with thorough planning, research and testing of storage sites, CO_2 can be reliably trapped underground for thousands and possibly millions of years. One of the conclusions of the latest IPCC (the UN Inter-governmental Panel on Climate Change) report states that more than 99% of the CO_2 could be retained over 1000 years with well designed, selected and managed sites (IPCC, 2005). This would store the CO_2 well beyond the era of extravagant fossil fuel use by humans.

10.5.2 Has Carbon Capture and Storage been used before?

As of 2007, only a handful of industrial scale projects are in operation world wide. Sleipner in the North Sea has been operating since 1996 and is the world's oldest CO_2 storage project injecting over 1 million tonnes of CO_2 per year into a saline aquifer. In Salah in Algeria has been operating since 2004 and injects about 1 million tonnes of CO_2 per year into the saline aquifer beneath a gas field. Weyburn in Saskatchewan is a commercial Enhanced Oil Recovery operation where CO_2 has been stored and monitored. Smaller injection sites are in the Lacq region in France, and a range of Enhanced Oil Recovery and CCS test sites in the US and Canada. Large commercial injection sites are planned to be operational during 2007 at Snøhvit in Norway, and 2008 in Western Australia (Figure 10.8).

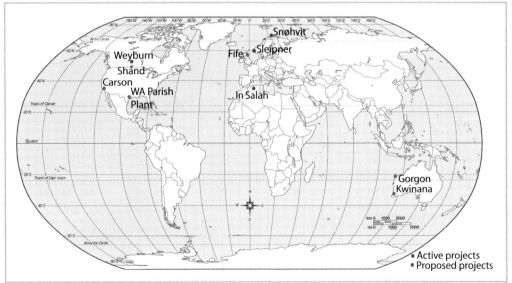

Figure 10.8 World map illustrating the location of commercially active and proposed storage sites which inject or intend to inject over 700,000 tonnes of CO_2 per year.

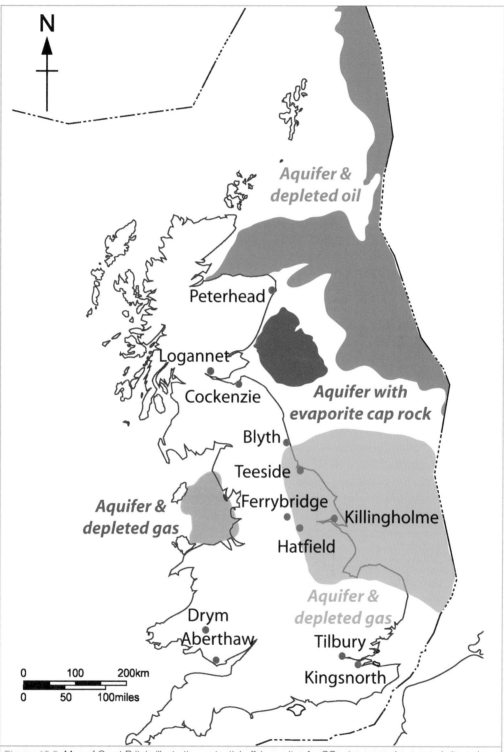

N

Aquifer &
depleted oil

Peterhead

Logannet

Aquifer with
evaporite cap rock

Cockenzie

Blyth

Teeside

Aquifer &
depleted gas

Ferrybridge

Killingholme

Hatfield

Aquifer &
depleted gas

Drym

Aberthaw

Tilbury

Kingsnorth

0   100   200km
0   50   100miles

Figure 10.9 Map of Great Britain illustrating potential offshore sites for CO_2 storage and proposed sites where CO_2 capture is being planned.

The UK is a good location for CCS. The UK has a large number of exhausted oil and gas fields and a large number of saline aquifers offshore (Figure 10.9). Coal and gas fired power plant are within tens to hundreds of kilometres of a wide range of geological storage sites (Figure 10.9). There is extensive expertise within the country in pipeline engineering and offshore oil and gas production. This expertise could be readily applied to CCS.

10.5.3 Will Carbon Capture and Storage be expensive?

The costs of CCS technologies depend on a number of factors including the type of power station, the type of capture technology used, transport distances, whether Enhanced Oil Recovery could be used to offset initial costs and future oil prices. The main cost factor is that CO_2 capture plants require more energy to operate. This reduces net plant efficiency and more fuel is required to create the same amount of energy. Electricity prices will therefore increase. This is widely estimated to increase by 1.0 p/kWhr, from 3.0 to 4.0p/kWhr wholesale price. If this is passed on to UK domestic consumers without additional profit, this is only about £30-£50 extra per average household per year.

Oil production in the UK North Sea is nearing the end of its life and Enhanced Oil Recovery could postpone abandonment of the old oil fields. However, Enhanced Oil Recovery has never yet been used for oil fields under the sea. Several evaluations have been made of Forties and of Miller in the UK North Sea, Gullfaks, Draugen and Heidrun in the Norwegian North Sea, but all have been rejected on economic reasons.

The high initial costs of new plant for CCS technologies, and extra operating cost, do mean that governments will have to provide financial incentives and support to help implement the capture and storage technologies for the first plant(s). In 2007 the UK government announced a competition to build the first joined up CCS system in the UK from power plant to storage (DBERR, 2007). This is intended to be operational at a 300 MW scale by 2014. The EU plans to encourage the build of 12 CCS plants to be operational by 2015. These will lead to improved plant built before 2020. After 2020, the EU ambition is for all new fossil fuel plants to be using CCS.

As with all new developments, building commercial scale plants will help to bring costs down. Therefore companies must be encouraged by government to incorporate CCS technologies into their new build and existing power stations. Governments must make clear statements on the importance of CCS on the future economy, clear subsidies must be given to develop cheaper capture technologies. CO_2 storage in Norway's Sleipner field was encouraged by the Norwegian CO_2 emissions tax and many US Enhanced Oil Recovery projects are financially viable due to tax incentives.

The UK requires 80 Giga Watts of electricity generation at peak load. Before 2020, 25 GigaWatts of this generation capacity (including nuclear) needs to be replaced because it is out of date or polluting. This rebuild of a number of plants is the perfect opportunity for CCS to be implemented. Planning consent granted for new power plants during 2007 started to reflect this, to require that CCS equipment can be retrofitted later.

10.5.4 Shouldn't the UK be investing more money into renewables rather than Carbon Capture and Storage?

Even with above average estimates (IEA, 2006 Alternative scenario) on the deployment of renewable energy, fossil fuels will still be the main source of electricity for the UK for at least another 40 years. No single renewable technology is currently deployable in that timescale to meet the UK electricity needs, and fossil fuels will need to fill the energy gap. Carbon Capture and Storage offers the UK the window to store carbon whilst renewables or other low carbon technologies are being developed and deployed.

10.5.5 Is the UK ready to demonstrate this technology?

The UK has the technical and business ability to start CCS immediately. The different technologies that make up CCS are now mature enough for full-scale demonstration. Delays mean that CO_2 in the atmosphere and ocean continues to increase and the effects of climate change and ocean acidification will increase. Many of these changes, and poorly known feedbacks, are irreversible on human timescales. The industrial world will simply run out of time. Carbon Capture and Storage has the potential of significantly reducing UK emissions very soon. As early as 2020, CCS offers emission cuts of 5-10Mt CO_2 per year on each coal or gas plant with commercially functioning sites. An aggressive programme could decarbonise all the UK fossil power plant fleet by 2025, by a combination of retro-fits onto existing power plants, and as part of new-built plants. This would reduce UK CO_2 emissions by over 150Mt/yr. This is a small part of worldwide CO_2 emissions, but the key point here is that, once a technology has been proven to work – then the technical and commercial risk greatly decreases and other industries and nations can confidently replicate that system. Before the first aeroplane, flight could be a theory. The first flight proved that machines heavier than air could fly. The first CCS challenge is to build a handful of power plants. The second challenge is to spread that learning globally. Five years saved from UK emissions by rapid CCS development, could mean five years saved from Chinese emissions soon after.

Acknowledgements

The authors are financially supported by the Scottish Funding Council, The UK Energy Research Centre, and NERC

References

BP. (June 2006). BP Statistical review of world energy June 2006 (XLS). Retrieved on 2007-04-03.

Department for Business Enterprise & Regulatory Reform. (July 2007). UK Energy in Brief. http://www.berr.gov.uk/files/file39881.pdf Retrieved on 19th Nov 2007.

BERR. (2007). CCS competition http://www.berr.gov.uk/energy/sources/sustainable/carbon-abatement-tech/ccs-demo/page40961.html

Defra. (2007). e-Digest Statistics about Climate Change: AEA Energy and Environment. source http://www.defra.gov.uk/environment/statistics/globatmos/gagccukem.htm Retrieved on 19th Nov 2007.

Department of Trade and Industry. (2005). 05/583 Developing Monitoring, Reporting And Verification Guidelines For carbon dioxide Capture And Storage Under The EU ETS http://www.berr.gov.uk/files/file19224.pdf Retrieved on 19th Nov 2007.

International Energy Agency. (2004). World Energy Outlook http://www.iea.org//textbase/nppdf/free/2004/weo2004.pdf

International Energy Agency. (2006). Summary and Conclusions of World Energy Outlook http://www.iea.org/Textbase/npsum/WEO2006SUM.pdf Retrieved on 19th Nov 2007.

IPCC. (2005). Special Report on Carbon Capture and Storage http://www.ipcc.ch/pdf/special-reports/srccs/srccs_wholereport.pdf Retrieved on 19th Nov 2007.

IPCC. (2007). Summary for Policymakers. In: Climate Change 2007: Mitigation. Contribution of Working Group III to the Fourth Assessment Report of the Intergovernmental Panel on Climate Change [B. Metz, O.R. Davidson, P.R. Bosch, R. Dave, L.A. Meyer (eds)], Cambridge University Press, Cambridge, United Kingdom and New York, NY, USA   www.ipcc.ch

Marland, G., Boden, T. A. and Andres, R. J. (2003). "Global, Regional, and National CO_2 Emissions" in *Trends: A Compendium of Data on Global Change*. Oak Ridge, Tenn., U.S.A.: Carbon Dioxide Information Analysis Center, Oak Ridge National Laboratory, U.S. Department of Energy. www.ornl.gov/sci/fossil/

Netherlands Environment Assessment Agency. (2007). http://www.mnp.nl/en/dossiers/Climatechange/moreinfo/Chinanowno1inCO2emissionsUSAinsecondposition.html Retrieved on 19th Nov 2007.

REN21. (2006). Renewable Global Status Report 2006 Update. Paris: REN21 Secretariat and Washington, DC: Worldwatch Institute.

Stern, N. (2007). *The Economics of Climate Change - The Stern Review*. CUP, UK.

Sustainable Development Commission. (2006). The role of nuclear power in a low carbon economy www.sd-commission.org.uk

The Royal Society. (2005). Ocean acidification due to increasing atmospheric carbon dioxide. *Royal Society of London* Policy document 12/05.

WWF. (2007). Speech on Climate Change at WWF London by PM Gordon Brown 19th November 2007 http://www.number10.gov.uk/output/Page13791.asp

Satellite image of parts of Western Europe from space at night © NASA

11 21st Century Nuclear Generation – How Clean and Green could it be?

Tony Cooper* – *Chairman Nuclear Industry Association*
First Floor, Whitehall House, 41 Whitehall, London SW1A 2BY.

Current address: Carlton House, 22a St James's Square, London SW1Y 4JH.

Summary

1. This chapter outlines the options in relation to future energy supply in the UK.
2. It sets the nuclear industry in context alongside other possible energy sources and suggests that future energy supply should be market driven rather than politically determined.
3. It highlights that, compared to older technologies, current nuclear technologies are more flexible, cheaper to build, produce a fraction of the waste of older designs, have safety systems that are based on more passive processes and are readily engineered to withstand any feasible attack.
4. It suggests that nuclear power has a key role to play in meeting future energy demand.

11.1 Introduction: the global warming dilemma

This chapter briefly addresses the potential role of nuclear power in addressing the looming energy crisis, and the extent to which it can do so by providing clean, green energy. The views presented are mine alone, and do not necessarily represent those of any organization with which I am associated.

The much vaunted Kyoto agreement will delay global warming by a mere four years, even if implemented in full, as the biggest and or fastest growing CO_2 polluters are not even signatories, and most countries will not meet their targets.

So far as the UK is concerned, it would have more symbolic significance if we ourselves were to meet our target by design rather than accident. In fact we will meet those targets because, for commercial reasons only, we switched over 33% of our electricity generation from coal to gas over a period of nine years following privatization, before Kyoto was even contemplated. Germany will meet its target also by accident, following the closure of large, inefficient and highly polluting manufacturing industries and generation plants in East Germany. Otherwise only Finland and Luxembourg will meet their targets within Europe. Finland, of course, is to build a new nuclear power station. The European Union may also meet its overall targets by accident entirely on the back of the German and British accidents.

---

* Tony Cooper has since resigned from the NIA to join the Board of the Nuclear Decommissioning Authority.

Cooper, T. (2007). 21st Century Nuclear Generation – How Clean and Green could it be? In *Energy and the Natural Heritage*, ed. by C.A. Galbraith and J.M. Baxter. TSO Scotland, Edinburgh. pp. 135-142

Over the next 15 years, it appears that:

- even if all renewable targets are met, electricity generation from gas will rise from the current 34% to 80% in the UK, replacing not only the remaining coal stations but also most of the nuclear stations;
- a modest demand growth of 2% per annum for electricity would add around an extra 40% total demand in that time;
- CO_2 emissions will therefore rise significantly (as they are already beginning to do);
- gas will no longer be cheap reliable North Sea gas, but gas from the Caspian and North Africa regions with an oil price linked to Ukraine.

Worrying as these statistics are, they are trivial in relation to predictions about global climate change. If we are serious about making a significant impact, we would need to cut greenhouse gases emissions by at least 60% over the next 50 years just to stabilize the current position and that would do nothing to reverse the damage done to date.

The next 50 years will coincide with a period of world population growth of as much as 50%: we will have half as many people again to feed, clothe and keep warm. This will be compounded by rapidly accelerating GDP growth in the developing world, particularly in Asia, with a consequent acceleration in demand for power, in particular electricity for water desalination, space cooling and the production of hydrogen from water as a transport fuel.

In short the problem we face is staggering and we are at the moment merely playing round the edges. There has been lots of debate in isolation about renewables, or efficiency or even the nuclear option, but on their own such debates have little value unless they also focus on the interactions and trade-offs we will have to make. Without such a debate the environmental lobby (of which I count myself a part) will be in danger of overselling its potential contribution, creating unsustainable expectations and an inevitable backlash.

11.2 Renewables

So what contribution could renewables and improved efficiency really make? Renewables are a hugely important clutch of technologies, but it is pointless to exaggerate their potential and minimize their limitations. Virtually every available renewable technology suffers from all, or a combination of, a number of intrinsic problems that include low energy density, unpredictable intermittency, high capital cost and its own environmental drawbacks. For instance:

- Low energy density: it takes 20 to 25 times more land area to fuel a car on biofuels as it does to feed a person. We will have 50% more mouths to feed and cannot rely in the longer term on land "set-aside" by the absurdities of the CAP. Clearly there is a huge potential for waste products and forest by-products, but we should not exaggerate that potential. (Incidentally the ultimate biofuel is paper which could be far more efficiently used for this purpose than for recycling.)
- Unpredictable intermittency: wind is clearly a crucial natural energy source, but it too has its limitations. It is estimated that the 2003 heat wave killed nearly 30,000 people across Europe. During that heat wave, with the demand for air conditioning at maximum, central European wind farms were able to generate only 1.3% of the time because the wind did not blow.

- We also have periods of UK-wide anticyclones (including the offshore domain) in mid winter. Anticyclones are associated with still air, clear skies, minimum temperatures and maximum power demand, and often alternate with depressions bringing gale force winds from the west with wind speeds above the operating limits of wind farms across the whole crucial western sea board.

All this means is that, as the proportion of such sources approaches 15-20% in the generation mix, it becomes essential to provide 100% back-up generating capacity from conventional power stations to ensure there are no power cuts when windfarms cannot generate. That back-up capacity has to be kept fully resourced and functional at all times at huge cost. An average availability of 30% would be excellent for any wind turbine implying an extra 70% to cover average unavailability in 'normal' circumstances. The cost of all this has to be added to the cost of extra transmission capacity because the key sources of wind generation are a long way from the market.

For precisely these kinds of reasons, Ireland is now limiting wind farm development and countries like Denmark with a high installed capacity can only cope by relying on imported electricity, most of it ultimately from French nuclear power stations. To bring the scale of this dilemma a little closer to home, an installed wind capacity of 1135.02 MW could produce around 20% of Scottish demand, assuming a 30% availability and demand growth over the next 15 years of around the current trends. That would require, however, the installation of a 600 KW turbine every week throughout a 15 year period, plus the installation of new conventional back-up capacity to cover the whole of that demand in case of widespread unavailability, and major transmission and distribution upgrade. This new conventional capacity would be essential because the existing conventional capacity in Scotland will have been closed because of its age by the end of that 15 year period.

Hydroelectricity schemes are clearly significant in Scotland and tidal barriers could make a substantial contribution, but both have environmental costs, and their practical scope is limited; detailed discussion of these aspects is outwith the scope of this chapter.

11.3 Energy efficiency

The improvement of energy efficiency is in principle the most promising avenue, but in practice, it too, has significant draw backs. We are actually achieving a great deal already. Energy density, the amount of energy used to produce 1 unit of GDP, has been falling for many years but demand is still rising and we have made no dent in either of these trends despite much political attention. Efficiency has not been and will not be a key priority for people or organizations while energy is relatively so cheap. However, expensive energy is not compatible with other political objectives of affordable energy.

The real and continuing problem is our own behaviour: 40 years ago a family car had a 1000cc engine, but although engines are now far more efficient, we have traded up to 2000cc and are trading up fast into larger four-wheel drive and multi-purpose vehicles. Forty years ago only the rich had central heating now virtually everybody has central heating and we are on the verge of an explosion in demand for air conditioning. Unfortunately personal behaviour is notoriously difficult to change, especially by governments as evidenced by the fuel protests against the perfectly reasonable fuel tax escalator or the difficulty in persuading people to stop smoking despite manifest personal harm.

The fact is that if we are serious about tackling global warming, the implementation of all these technologies and all that we can do to improve energy efficiency will have an important and valued place, but they will remain marginal unless we are prepared to significantly change:

- our way of life;
- our rural landscape and economy, and thereby, inevitably, the current ecosystems; and, or
- come to terms with currently pariah technologies.

Or we could just blame the Government, participate in numerous think tanks and reviews and continue to generate a great deal of heat but very little light. In this context it would be wrong not to consider the potential role of the nuclear industry in helping to find a solution.

11.4 Potential nuclear contribution

Before looking to the future it is worth considering the past and current positions, not as a zealot or apologist, but simply to create a context and perspective, hopefully free of the many anti-pathetic mythologies.

11.4.1 Emissions

A few simple background facts help set nuclear power in context:

- Natural background radiation exposure amounts to about 85% of our total exposure, while medical procedures add a further 14.5% on average: that leaves a balance of 0.5% of which nuclear tests and high altitude flights make up by far the greatest proportion.
- As we are all radioactive naturally, we all experience a higher exposure level by sleeping with a partner than sleeping alone on the perimeter of a nuclear power station.
- The natural background radiation in places like Cornwall or Aberdeen is about five times the permitted level for a radiation worker. There is no evidence of excessive illness or birth defects in those places, other than problems associated with radon gas.
- A coal fired power station would fail the emissions standard required on a licensed nuclear power station site .

11.4.2 Discharges

There has been an unfortunate legacy of discharges particularly to the sea, in particular from Sellafield and Dounreay. However, it is a legacy issue with no implications for future power stations; discharges have fallen dramatically until alpha and beta discharges are virtually undetectable, and they will eventually fall to zero. To place the figures given in McSorley (this volume) in context, the consumption of seven North Sea lobsters at a sitting would impart the same radiation dose as a single naturally grown brazil nut from Brazil.

Plate 11.1 Torness nuclear power station, East Lothian © John Baxter

11.4.3 Accidents

Chernobyl was without doubt the worst nuclear accident ever, but let us place it in perspective:

- By 2004, 47 people are known to have died as a direct result of that accident.
- Around 1,750 excess cases of thyroid cancer attributable to the Chernobyl accident can be identified; thyroid cancer is eminently treatable and preventable by early distribution of iodine capsules.
- There is no evidence of increases in other cancers, including leukaemia.
- There is no evidence of increases in birth defects, though around 50,000 local women, terrified by the hysteria and panic surrounding the accident had unnecessary abortions.
- Radiation levels locally around Chernobyl have fallen now to well below the natural background levels in places like Cornwall.
- This, the worst accident ever to happen, occurred with an unsafe design, unskilled operators and inadequate regulation, none of which apply in the west. Compare this over a 50 to 60 year period with the chemical, coal or oil industries: e.g. in West Cumberland hundreds died in accidents in the pits and thousands had their health broken; when these men began to move from the pits to Sellafield they couldn't believe how clean and safe it was, or the extent to which the management and systems prevailing regarded their health as important.

11.4.4 Waste

There is indeed a huge legacy problem with waste management, including clean-up and disposal. Putting this into context:

- About 80% of the waste is at Sellafield and Dounreay. Most of that is wholly legacy waste and includes that of early defence activity and early start up or experimental procedures which would not be tolerated today.

- A nuclear new build programme to replace every single one of the existing nuclear power stations using current technology rather than the 30 to 50 year old technology in use today would add just 10% to our current stock of intermediate and high level wastes. With process and procedures and facilities in place (as they have to be) to deal with the legacy, new waste would simply be a marginal extra burden.
- Contrary to the popular impression, nuclear waste is not uniquely long lived: by definition it decays. Some of the other by-products of our civilization such as heavy metals do not decay at all.
- The really significant measure of how long it takes waste to decay is not the time to zero radioactive activity which is frequently quoted, because virtually nothing on earth displays zero radioactivity; the appropriate measure is the time taken to return back to the natural uranium level from which the material came in the first place. In the majority of circumstances that is below 1,000 years. That is a very long time and requires careful management, but it is not the hundreds of thousands of years often quoted and which in reality applies to a tiny percent of the waste.

Dealing with this waste is inevitably going to be expensive: the current estimate is of about £80 billion for decommissioning, plus disposal and long term management. That is a large figure by any standard, but it is in fact trivial compared to the cost to be imposed on us by the consequences of fossil fuel burning. That in turn reflects the fact that it is small in volume (the total amount of high level waste produced by all the UK power stations in a year is about the size of a standard taxi) and though difficult to handle it is not as difficult as the massive quantity of CO_2 emissions. Yet, it is worth remembering that without that fossil fuel burning we would all still be living in a basically medieval world. The financial, if not the environmental costs of both nuclear and fossil fuel burning clean-up, is a minute fraction of the total wealth which those technologies have enabled us to create.

Finally, somewhat controversially, the real costs of decommissioning have only been disclosed in the run up to a competitive clean-up market regime.

All these points are made not to diminish the problems or from any sense of complacency: nuclear power is potentially both dangerous and environmentally destructive, but it is essential to put that into context. In summary:

- in terms of actual environmental impact, nuclear power is significantly greener than the CO_2 producing technology we currently have;
- backend legacy costs look superficially large but they are legacy and are very small compared to the cost of fossil fuel burning technology to date never mind the future.

11.4.5 Nuclear generating costs

One further issue to be considered before looking to the future. Nuclear power in Britain really has had a chequered history when it comes to cost, and there are a number of reasons for this. We were the first country to move into civil nuclear power generation. In any new technology, it is simply not true that there are substantial first mover advantages. In the great majority of cases, the first mover makes the initial expensive mistakes and second mover makes the cash!

Because civil nuclear power originally grew out of a defence programme, it carried with it a culture of secrecy which not only had a negative impact on the public perception of nuclear power, but a culture of secrecy is a culture in which costly decisions are least likely to be challenged. The UK persisted with designs which, however technologically advanced at the time, proved commercially problematic and which no one else wanted to buy or construct and which were frequently amended so that even we did not obtain any advantage from repeat construction. Costs were hidden and therefore not addressed, not because of any malicious intent, but because public sector utilities like the Central Electricity Generating Board (CEGB) did not accurately attribute costs, and in any case were able to charge prices to cover all their overall costs whatever they were.

During this period government energy policy effectively subsidized coal production for social reasons while building nuclear power stations to ensure that coal did not have a total monopoly. This was called a 'balanced energy policy'. Whatever the merits of the underlying aim, the consequences were a complete misallocation of resources and fundamental lack of transparency. All of this only became clear when the industry was being prepared for privatization and competition and real costs were exposed and properly attributed. An exact analogy, in other words, to the process which has more recently revealed the true level of legacy costs.

In short both the legacy waste and running cost problems of the nuclear industry are not essentially an industry problem but a public utility problem common to all the old public utilities. I emphasize this point simply to explain that:

- The nuclear industry recognizes the benefit of competition even though it has been a painful experience, and is committed to a market-based future.
- In such a future, costs simply cannot be distorted or hidden.
- It also follows that investment proposals in the future will be judged, not on the basis of esoteric economic analysis presented to government by specialists embedded in the industry, but on the basis of open, public assessment of the assumptions and the judgements made by individual private investors.
- Most significantly of all, any comparisons of costs based on technology which is now 30 to 50 years old and on operating systems and structures unique to the public utilities, are meaningless.

11.5 The future

The future of the nuclear industry must be market driven rather than politically determined. It is, however, quite clear that the only large scale technology available to us which is capable at one and the same time of maintaining our security of energy supply and addressing the huge and growing impact of CO_2 emissions is the nuclear industry. It is important therefore to consider current and future nuclear technologies and the development of the electricity and energy markets.

11.5.1 Available technologies

Compared to old technologies, currently available nuclear power technologies:

- are more flexible;
- are cheaper to build;
- produce a fraction of the waste of the older designs;

- have safety systems which are based on more passive processes (e.g. cooling based on gravity and convection rather than pumps) that are simpler to build and demand less operator intervention; and
- are readily engineered to withstand any feasible attack.

11.5.2 Future technologies

The next generation of nuclear power stations will add to the current technological improvements.

- Intrinsic safety systems (based more on the physics of the reactor than designed control systems).
- Designs that produce no waste which could be useful in nuclear weapon proliferation.
- Designs that are able to operate at significantly higher temperatures to produce electricity whilst at the same time splitting water to make hydrogen available for transport purposes.

In the still longer term we are likely to see designs based on thorium rather than uranium (there is virtually an unlimited supply of thorium and no plutonium by-product); reactor designs that are capable of transmutation of long-lived waste to short-lived waste with the production of energy at the same time, and of course there is fusion which has been with us for a long time experimentally, but which looks likely to emerge from the experimental stage in the foreseeable future.

11.5.3 Electricity market

It is now quite clear that the most efficient mechanism to produce and distribute energy at low financial and environmental cost is a well designed and properly regulated market, not a system of technology and investment choice by government or agents of government. While the current electricity market has conferred many benefits compared to the old system, it is still far from adequate and suffers specifically from the following problems. The market does not:

- specifically reward energy production which does not produce CO_2 or which captures the CO_2 it does produce;
- reward specific contributions to energy security;
- stimulate or encourage long term investment, being both volatile and long-term unpredictable, in particular because of the likely development of external political intervention as the UK becomes more and more dependent on imported gas, particularly from Russia.

It is eminently possible for government to design a market which will meet these requirements (after all the electricity markets were in fact designed by government in the first place) and in such a market the nuclear industry would be happy to compete on equal terms with all other fossil fuel and non-fossil fuel energy technologies. I am personally convinced that the nuclear industry would then compete extremely effectively, but I am content to let a properly designed market decide.

PART 4:

Present and Future Options -
Renewable Energy

Wind turbines, Dun Law Windfarm © George Logan

Present and Future Options - Renewable Energy

Developing an energy source that is renewable, that has minimal carbon emissions and that impacts as little as possible on the environment, whilst being cost effective is perhaps the holy grail of energy production. Recent strides in technology have brought the production of energy in this way a lot nearer, yet significant challenges remain. The following part considers several of the leading technologies in this area and considers the environmental issues associated with each.

Firstly Ian Todd and Bill Band provide an overview of the scene, outlining recent trends and challenges. They consider the role of Government in encouraging energy generation from renewable sources, and review the various national and international targets set in this regard. They review the role of the various technologies in the present national energy mix and consider how this might alter in future.

Hydropower remains an important part of the "renewable mix" in energy generation within Scotland at the present time. Terry Langford's chapter in Part 2 of this book looked at the inheritance from this industry through to the present day. The chapter from Colin Bean and Frances Thin in this part presents a review of the potential environmental impacts of hydroschemes, particularly small-scale developments, and considers to what degree negative impacts can be reduced or offset by natural heritage gains.

The development of biomass for energy production is an expanding area. The chapter by Tomas Käberger indicates just how significant this form of production has become in countries around Europe. He cites Sweden as a key example where bioenergy has grown to become the second largest source of energy, and is contributing to reducing emissions of CO_2 and to the security of energy supply. Clearly, in a Scottish and UK context, the full potential of biomass has still to be realized.

The next two chapters deal with issues relating to onshore wind power and the possible impacts it may have on the environment. Laura Campbell reviews the impacts on landscapes; a subject that has generated considerable debate in recent years, as the number of windfarms has increased significantly in the Scottish countryside. She considers how to minimize these impacts by selecting appropriate sites and developing sympathetic design. This is a complex area and the issue of cumulative change to the Scottish landscape remains to be considered in the future.

The chapter by Philip Whitfield and Andrew Coupar reviews the effects of terrestrial windfarms on birds and upland habitats. These two issues have been at the forefront of the debate on where to locate windfarms over recent years. The potential negative effects of windfarms are reviewed and the current state of knowledge in this area is assessed. Whilst some studies have been undertaken, it is apparent that there are many aspects of the interactions between windfarms and birds that have to be fully evaluated. It is in the interests of the industry and of the conservation community to see that clear and unambiguous results, collected through rigorous and objective means underpin future discussions in this area.

The following two chapters deal with the development of renewable technologies in the marine environment. Whilst not yet as fully developed as renewable energy production on land, this area offers considerable potential for the future. Ian Bryden outlines the main developments in this area and notes that Scotland and the UK are well placed to exploit this source of energy. Recent advances in wave power and in tidal stream generation both offer considerable promise for the future. No technology comes without some cost to the environment, and as on land, the aim has to be to minimize any impact whilst developing low cost, low carbon technologies. The chapter by Alexander Downie *et al.* reviews the potential impacts of marine renewable energy technologies on the natural heritage. They highlight the relative lack of information relating to the marine environment, making it difficult to give comprehensive comment on any proposal. Importantly, the authors suggest a provisional ranking of the major technologies, from those likely to have the least impact on the natural heritage through to the those likely to have the greatest impact. They stress that the location of any development is likely to have the biggest influence on this ranking.

12 Renewable Energy – Overview, Trends and Challenges

Iain Todd – Sunnyside, Ruthven, Huntly, Aberdeenshire
AB54 4TA.

Bill Band – Scottish Natural Heritage, Battleby, Redgorton,
Perth PH1 3EW.

Summary

1. The Government has set ambitious targets for the growth of renewable energy as part of UK energy production – 10% of electricity by 2010, aspiring to reach 20% by 2020. It has set in place powerful legal duties on electricity suppliers to bring this about, and these are supported by a number of financial support programmes for the various renewable technologies. The Government is also enthusiastic about the employment potential that this sector could provide for the UK. These moves form part of a wider move into renewable energy across Europe, and beyond.

2. These mechanisms are proving effective. Energy companies are bringing forward significant renewables projects to meet their obligations. The UK is developing as a world leader in technologies such as offshore wind, and marine renewables (wave/tidal).

3. Policy change of this magnitude affects a number of broader stakeholders, whose support is important for the delivery of Government objectives. Important issues arise for organizations dealing with environmental issues, aviation issues (both civil and military), and electricity grid/transmission. The views of local communities are also important – communications issues are becoming an increasingly important aspect of this policy area.

4. SNH has stated its support for the development of renewable energy, in the interest of addressing climate change. However, renewable energy projects impact upon the natural heritage, and these impacts vary considerably according to the technology and the attributes of the site. Onshore windfarms affect landscapes and present a risk to birds, while hydroschemes can affect freshwater habitats. There is a need to ensure that a correct balance is struck between all interests in assessing renewable energy projects.

12.1 Introduction

There is now very wide scientific agreement that climate change is real, and that it poses an immense threat to our environment. It will worsen global problems such as drought,

Todd, I. & Band, B. (2008). Renewable Energy – Overview, Trends and Challenges. In *Energy and the Natural Heritage*, ed. by C.A. Galbraith and J.M. Baxter. TSO Scotland, Edinburgh. pp. 147-154

Figure 12.1 Windfarm at Langholm, Dumfriesshire © Colin Galbraith

famine and disease. Extreme events will become more common and more frequent. Such changes have the potential to affect many aspects of Scotland's environment – from machair to snow buntings. Action is needed now.

The UK Government has responded to this challenge in an ambitious manner. In its 2003 Energy White Paper (Department of Trade and Industry, 2003) it set a goal of reducing carbon emissions in the UK by 60% by 2050. It estimated that the costs of doing so would be equivalent to a loss of 6 months growth over 50 years, against a backdrop of tripling national income. It believes this to be a justifiable price to pay – the price of failing to act would be much higher.

The White Paper sets in place a number of ambitious national policies to assist the delivery of the 2050 goal. One of these is a dramatic increase to the UK energy mix of the contribution provided by renewable energy. This mirrors developments in many other countries, not least in some of our major European partners.

A major switch to renewable energy in the UK will deliver not only environmental benefits. It will enhance the UK's security of energy supply, through using a wider range of technologies at our own disposal (against a backdrop of increasing reliance on oil and gas imports). It will also provide employment opportunities in areas where the UK has valuable skills – notably on offshore wind, and in wave/tidal technologies.

12.2 UK policy on renewable energy

The UK Government has announced that by 2010, 10% of the UK's electricity should come from renewable sources. It has also announced that it wishes to double that proportion again by 2020. It is a challenging target, given that less that 3% of UK electricity came from renewables in 2003.

In Scotland the equivalent figures for 2010 and 2020 are 18% (reflecting the existing 8% hydro capacity) and a challenging aspiration of 40% renewables by 2020 (Scottish Executive, 2003).

The main mechanism for delivering these targets is the Renewables Obligation, introduced in April 2002. It requires all electricity suppliers to provide a specified and growing proportion of their electricity sales from eligible renewable sources. The specified proportion was 3% in 2002, and it increases each year to 10.4% in 2010. The Government has also announced that it plans to legislate for 15.4% in 2015.

One Renewables Obligation Certificate (ROC) is issued for each megawatt-hour of electricity generated renewably. Suppliers can meet their obligation either by presenting ROCs or by paying a 'buy-out price' set by Government for that part of their obligation not met by ROCs. The buy-out fund is then paid out in full to those suppliers who have presented ROCs, so boosting the incentive for suppliers to obtain them. To provide a stable and long-term market for renewable energy, the obligation is set in legislation to 2027.

The Renewables Obligation supports all eligible renewable energy technologies equally. For certain technologies – onshore wind and land-fill gas – the Government considers this form of support to be sufficient to stimulate the market. For others, further support is needed and the Government does this in one of two ways. For technologies which are close to market, the Government provides capital grants to assist with project construction. Furthermore, this varies as a proportion of the project cost – 10% for offshore wind, 40% for biomass, and 50% for photovoltaic projects and for these technologies which are further from market, the Government makes research and development finance available through competitive rounds, under which applications are assessed by independent examiners. Technologies such as wave/tidal and fuel cells have made significant steps forward in recent years under this scheme.

12.3 The Renewables Obligation in practice

The first two years of operation of the Renewables Obligation are widely viewed as being successful in bringing forward very significant investment by industry on renewables projects. All major energy companies in the UK have announced their investment plans for the rest of the decade, running into billions of pounds. For *Centrica* alone, the figure is £1billion. While most of this investment is off balance-sheet, in the case of *npower* this includes an injection of £400 million from city investors. The move to external finance is expected to grow in future years.

The legislation has been monitored in its early years of operation – as planned – and a number of minor modifications have been introduced. In April 2004, the duration of the biomass co-firing policy (in which ROCs are awarded for biomass combusted at coal-fired stations) was extended by five years. In April 2005, the Government plans to introduce the 2015 obligation level, extend ROCs to Northen Ireland, and introduce measures to reduce risks to the ROC market associated with electricity suppliers going into administration.

The Government will also be reviewing the obligation more formally during 2005, to consider if its effectiveness can be improved further. But stability of the ROC market will be a key consideration, and Ministers are likely to keep changes to a minimum.

12.4 The role of different technologies

During 2003, the DTI conducted a review of the role that different technologies are expected to play in the expansion of renewable energy in the UK. The results are shown in Figure 12.1. This clearly shows that wind technology will play the dominant role in delivering renewable output up to 2010 – up to 8% of the 10% target (4% onshore wind and 4% offshore wind). While wind turbine construction capacity in the UK totalled only 100MW in 2003, the figure for 2004 is expected to be close to 300MW, while for 2005 it will be in excess of 500MW.

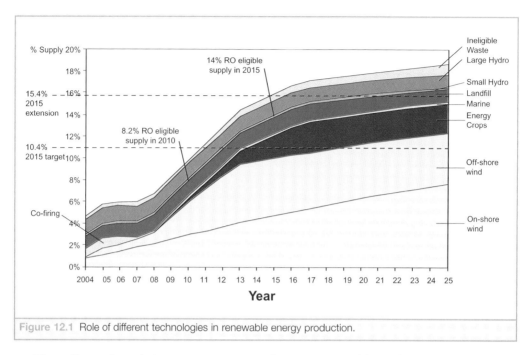

Figure 12.1 Role of different technologies in renewable energy production.

These figures have led some to comment that UK renewables policy is over-reliant on wind technology. The report of the Scottish Parliamentary Committee on renewable energy (Scottish Parliament Enterprise and Culture Committee, 2004) states:

> "The Renewables Obligation (Scotland) scheme has been successful, but in a single direction – that of promoting onshore wind power. It has led to the invigoration of the market for wind power by energy companies, but without developing other sectors. Whilst this may be welcome in terms of meeting targets, it has raised concerns over the merits of wind power and has not stimulated other renewable generating technologies to a significant degree. By focussing power companies' attention on wind, it may even have hindered the commercialisation of other renewable technologies."

This reflects evidence submitted to it by SNH (SNH, 2004a) and others.

It is clear that wind is the dominant technology under development at present as shown in Figures 12.2 and 12.3 – which show the proportions of each renewable technology at present, and the map of proposed windfarm sites in Scotland.

Marine energy in particular could be highly significant for Scotland, which has world-class resources in this area. The DTI has supported the development of a number of wave and tidal devices through its grants programmes, and some are now at the point of commercial development. The European Marine Energy Centre (EMEC) has been created on Orkney. In the summer of 2004, the DTI announced a further £50million available to this sector.

12.5 Natural heritage issues

Most types of renewable energy developments make extensive use of land, sea or fresh water and an important factor governing their acceptability is the effect they have on landscapes,

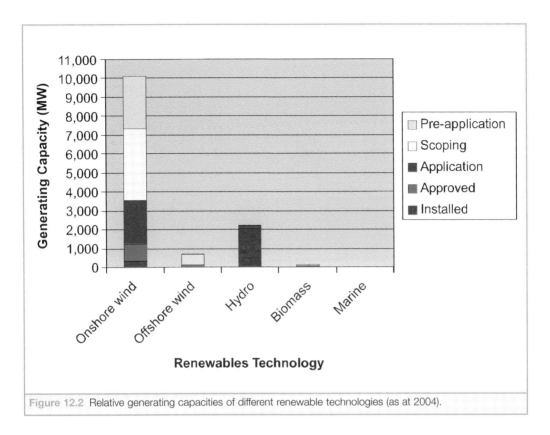

Figure 12.2 Relative generating capacities of different renewable technologies (as at 2004).

habitats and wildlife. Nonetheless, SNH considers climate change to be the most critical issue which will affect Scotland's natural heritage this century and issued a policy statement in 2001 indicating its support for the development of renewable energy as an integral part of Government's climate change programme (SNH, 2001). This statement stresses the need for development to be planned strategically, using the technologies and sites where there will be least impact on landscapes and habitats, and ensuring that sites of national or international importance for their natural heritage are safeguarded.

Scotland is renowned both for the quality of its scenery, and for its areas of 'wild land' where there is little obvious evidence of human impact. As a result, windfarm developments offer a particular challenge to Scotland's landscapes, on account of their size and the substantial arrays of access tracks they require. They may also affect bird populations, either by deterring birds from using a site, or by the moving rotors presenting a collision risk. For onshore windfarms, SNH has published guidance at a strategic level, indicating the broad natural heritage sensitivity of different parts of Scotland to this type of development (SNH, 2002).

Large-scale hydroschemes lead to major changes in the freshwater hydrology of a river, and the impoundment, dams and turbine buildings required also impact on the landscape. Many of the remaining new opportunities for large-scale hydro are to be found in areas valued for their wild land character. There are more opportunities for smaller-scale run-of-river schemes, though in terms of total generating capacity these can only make a small overall contribution to targets.

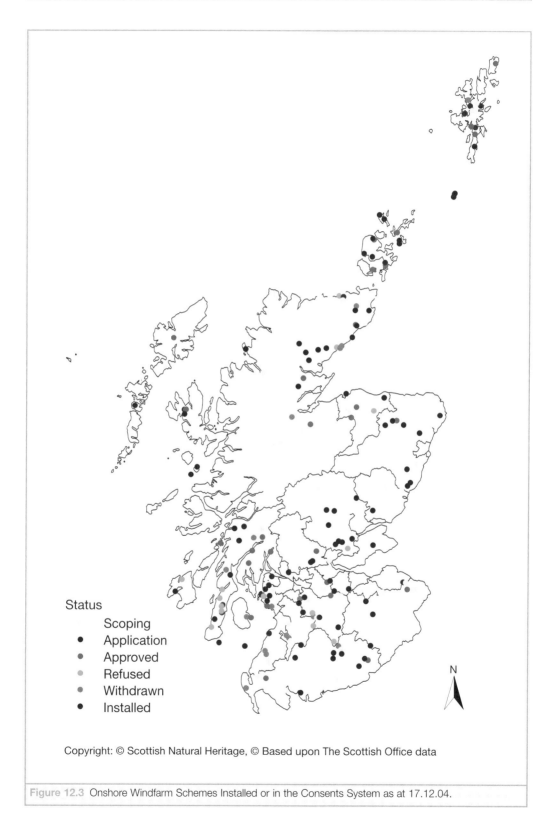

Status
- Scoping
- Application
- Approved
- Refused
- Withdrawn
- Installed

N

Copyright: © Scottish Natural Heritage, © Based upon The Scottish Office data

Figure 12.3 Onshore Windfarm Schemes Installed or in the Consents System as at 17.12.04.

SNH has reviewed the likely impacts of marine developments (SNH, 2004b), and in general anticipates that wave and tidal generation, and to a lesser extent offshore windfarms, will have a lesser adverse impact on the natural heritage than equivalent generation onshore. Tidal barrage schemes, though, would involve major change to estuarine habitats.

Finally, the use of forest crops or residues for biomass generation seems unlikely to affect the natural heritage in any major way, unless it were to involve planting up of long-term agricultural set-aside, or the afforestation of areas of semi-natural habitat.

The potential natural heritage impacts therefore differ quite substantially according to the technology type, and according to the sensitivity and particular attributes of the site. SNH therefore has an important statutory role in the consents process, in advising the Scottish Government and planning authorities on the likely effects of a development on the natural heritage, and on the significance of such effects. SNH has opposed development in a small number of cases, but in a majority of cases SNH is able to help the applicant in designing an appropriate and satisfactory scheme.

12.6 Current issues

There is a range of other issues – political, planning, technical and about communication – which will either help or hinder the industry to develop over the next decade.

Political – given the long-term investment required in renewable projects, the incentive regime has to be a stable one if investors are to find it attractive. Politicians need to take a long term view if the aspiration of a 60% carbon emissions reduction by 2050 is to be met.

Planning – there is a need to ensure that the planning system operates in a fair, thorough and timely manner to ensure a balanced assessment of the impacts and benefits of renewable energy projects. Good science and sound but pragmatic local judgement will both be needed. Issues of cumulative impact will become of increasing importance.

Technical – while technologies like onshore wind are well established, others like wave and tidal are in their infancy and present demanding engineering challenges. Special support will be needed during the early years to support research, development and trial of demonstrator devices.

Communication – the views of local communities will be increasingly important as renewable projects become more widespread. Effort will be needed, both nationally and in the development of projects, to ensure that the public and decision-makers are fully aware of both the costs and the benefits of renewable energy projects.

References

Department of Trade and Industry. (2003). Our energy future – creating a low carbon economy. Energy White Paper.

Scottish Executive. (2003). Securing a Renewable Future: Scotland's Renewable Energy.

SNH. (2001). SNH's Policy on Renewable Energy. Policy Statement 01/02.

SNH. (2002). Strategic Locational Guidance for Onshore Windfarms in respect of the Natural Heritage. Policy Statement 02/02.

SNH. (2004a). Evidence to Scottish Parliament Enterprise and Culture Committee. SNH Website.

SNH. (2004b). Marine Renewable Energy and the Natural Heritage: an Overview and Policy Statement. Policy Statement 04/01.

Scottish Parliament Enterprise and Culture Committee. (June 2004). Report on Inquiry on Renewable Energy in Scotland. Scottish Parliament Website.

13 Hydroelectricity – Impacts and Opportunities for the Natural Heritage

Colin Bean – *Scottish Natural Heritage, Freshwater and Wetlands Group, Caspian House, Clydebank Business Park, Clydebank G81 2NR.*

Frances Thin – *Scottish Natural Heritage, Landscape Group, Great Glen House, Leachkin Road, Inverness IV3 8NW.*

Summary

1. Hydroelectric schemes have been present in Scotland since at least 1896, when the first significant development was constructed at Foyers on Loch Ness. The construction of further large-scale (25-100 MW) developments followed during the first half of the 20th century, although the largest phase of hydroelectric scheme development took place between 1945 and 1965. These developments pre-dated the requirement for Environmental Impact Assessments and, as a result, little is known about the real environmental impacts of large-scale hydroelectric schemes within Scotland.

2. The majority of new hydroelectric schemes are generally described as small-scale (<5 MW) and development consents are now tightly controlled by domestic planning regulations. It has long been assumed that, despite the obvious benefits of 'clean' energy, both large and small-scale hydroelectric schemes have had a negative impact on the aquatic environments and landscape of Scotland.

3. This chapter presents a review of the potential environmental impacts of hydroelectric schemes, particularly small-scale developments, and considers to what degree negative impacts can be reduced and/or offset by natural heritage gains.

13.1 Introduction

Hydroelectric power within the UK is limited by the fact that many of its rivers are relatively small, have modest flows and low gradients (Johnson, 1994). Scotland's topography, geology and climate mean that it has the most favourable conditions for hydropower development within the UK.

The generation of energy from moving water within Scotland is not new and the first significant hydroelectric scheme was commissioned at Foyers in 1896. This facility was followed by the development a number of larger (>10 MW) schemes during the first half of the 20th century, most notably the Kinlochleven, Grampian (Tummel) and Galloway

Bean, C. & Thin, F. (2008). Hydroelectricity – Impacts and Opportunities for the Natural Heritage. In *Energy and the Natural Heritage*, ed. by C.A. Galbraith and J.M. Baxter. TSO Scotland, Edinburgh. pp. 155-184

(Kirkcudbrightshire Dee) schemes. The publication of *Hydro-Electric Development in Scotland* by the Cooper Committee (1942) was the first serious attempt to quantify the potential for hydropower generation within the Highlands of Scotland, suggesting that hydropower development could amount to 4000 GWh yr[-1]. The North of Scotland Hydro-Electric Board's *Development Scheme*, published in 1944 revisited this issue and identified 102 sites where hydro-generation may be economically feasible, suggesting that the estimated generating capacity for Highland water resources may be as high as 6274 GWh yr[-1].

The 20 year period between 1945-1965 saw the biggest expansion in hydroelectric scheme development, with the construction of 28 hydroschemes >10 MW, 11 of which had an installed capacity that exceeded 20 MW. Twenty smaller schemes within the 1-10 MW range were also constructed. The development of the large (>20 MW) schemes alone, involved the construction of 66 dams, 275 km of tulles and 166 km of aqueduct, as well as 51 power stations (Payne, 1988; Johnson, 1994).

The Mackenzie Committee (1962) reviewed electricity generating capacity throughout Scotland, in the light of technological advances in thermal power generation and the prevailing economy at that time. The Committee's report *Electricity in Scotland*, suggested that the potential for hydropower within Scotland as a whole may be as much as 7250 GWh yr[-1], although it also recommended that future investment in electricity production should focus on the development of thermal, rather than hydro, installations.

More recently, in light of government commitments to tackle climate change, the UK Government outlined in its 2003 Energy White Paper a commitment to reduce carbon emissions by 60% by 2050. To contribute to this, the Scottish Executive set a target of raising the proportion of electricity generated from renewable sources to 18% by 2010 and 40% by 2020 (Scottish Executive, 2003). This is to be achieved through a mix of technologies, including onshore and offshore wind, wave, tidal stream, hydro and biomass. To ensure these targets are met, a statutory obligation has been placed on electricity suppliers to supply at least 10% of electricity from new renewable sources by 2010. The Scottish Executive has recently extended this obligation to 15% by 2015. This has led to an increase in the number of new hydroschemes within the planning system.

The best available data provided by the British Hydropower Association (BHA) (*pers. comm.*), Dti (www.dtistats.net/energystats) and the Scottish Executive (SNH, 2004) suggest that the installed capacity of hydropower schemes within Scotland is currently 2193.77 MW (Table 13.1); although the total installed capacity is likely to be around 2900 MW.

Table 13.1 Installed capacity and number of hydroelectric schemes within Scotland. Data provided by the British Hydropower Association, Dti and the Scottish Executive.

Scheme Size	Installed capacity	Number of Installations
>20 MW (Conventional)	1082.20	27
> 20MW (Pumped Storage)	699.00	2
1-20 MW	389.95	63
<1 MW	22.62	51
Total	2193.77	143

Despite their relatively small contribution to the overall Scottish installed capacity, small scale (<1 MW) hydroschemes, according to BHA, Dti and Scottish Executive figures, comprise 35.7 % of the 143 installed facilities within Scotland. Schemes within the 1-20 MW range account for 44.1% of the total number, but larger developments account for only 18.9 %.

The potential for new hydropower developments within Scotland is hard to quantify. The 'Salford Study' *"Small Scale Hydroelectric Generation Potential in the UK"* (Salford Civil Engineering Limited, 1989) provides the only contemporary examination of hydropower potential within Scotland. This study identified 823 economically viable sites within the 25 kW to 5 MW range within Scotland, with a total potential generating capacity of 236.6 MW. This accounts for 88.7% of the UK total identified. The installed capacity of these potential sites ranged from 15 kW to 3.97 MW. Given that the Salford Study dates back to 1989, it is clear that some of the sites identified in this report have since been developed and new, previously marginal, sites may now have become more viable due to improvements in turbine design and generating technology. Data held by SNH up to 2005 suggest that there are 173 hydroelectric schemes which are either installed or within the planning system in Scotland with a number of others under active consideration. The BHA suggest that there could be some 300-350 MW of technically feasible potential for hydropower development in Scotland in addition to 236.6 MW identified within the Salford Study (1989).

13.2 General legislative framework
13.2.1 Electricity Acts
Hydroelectric development appears to have been poorly regulated in the early years of the 20th century. Despite this, it was recognized as early as the late 1930s and 1940s that hydropower scheme developments within Scotland adversely affected both the ecology of freshwater habitats and the surrounding landscape (Johnson, 1994). In an attempt to address this issue, statutory Fisheries and Amenity Committees were set up to advise both the North of Scotland Hydro Electricity Board and the Secretary of State for Scotland on environmental matters. Up until its dissolution in 1982, the 'Amenity Committee' succeeded in developing a range of guidelines for hydroscheme developers and worked with them to develop schemes which incorporated modifications which would satisfy the need to optimize electricity production and alleviate environmental concerns. A full description of these guidelines is provided by Johnson (*op. cit.*). The 'Fisheries Committee' was also first established as an advisory Non-Departmental Public Body (NDPB) in 1943 and reflects both the historical and current importance of freshwater, particularly migratory salmonid, fisheries within Scotland. The Fisheries Committee continues to advise the Scottish Government on fisheries matters in relation to new hydro proposals, it does not, however, provide comment on the impacts of hydroelectric developments on anything other than fish.

Within the Electricity (Scotland) Act 1989, Section 36 covers the construction of any hydroscheme above 1MW, and the application must be submitted to the Scottish Government's Energy Division for determination. Schedule 9 of the Electricity (Scotland) Act 1989 [as modified by The Electricity Act 1989 (Requirement of Consent for hydroelectric Generating Stations) (Scotland) Order 1990] requires that any person wishing to construct, extend or operate a hydroelectric generating station with a capacity of more than 1 MW before, or on, making such an application the applicant must consult the 'Fisheries Committee' prior to submitting the application to Scottish Ministers and that they (the Scottish Ministers) may refuse consent under section 36 if an applicant does not undertake to implement a recommendation made by the Fisheries Committee.

13.2.2 Planning and Environmental Impact Assessment

The development of renewables schemes in Scotland is also covered by development consent in the planning system, under the Town & Country Planning (Scotland) Act 1997, for any proposals under a certain threshold. Any small-scale schemes below 1 MW will be subject to planning consent procedures, with the application determined by the Planning Authority. Above that size the consenting authority is the Scottish Government. The developer is required to prepare and submit an Environmental Statement under Schedule II of the Environmental Assessment (Scotland) Regulations 1999 if the proposal is likely to have significant effects on the environment. Circular 15/1999 indicates that EIA is more likely to be required for any new hydroelectric scheme which has more than 5 MW of generating capacity. The Environmental Assessment (Scotland) Regulations 2000 identify SNH and the Scottish Environment Protection Agency (SEPA) as statutory consultees to assess the potential for wider environmental impacts.

The criteria on which significance of environmental effects are judged are whether:

- a project is of more than local importance in terms of scale;
- a project is intended for a particularly sensitive location such as a Site of Special Scientific Interest (SSSI), Natura site (SAC or SPA) or National Scenic Area (NSA); or
- a project is thought to give rise to particularly complex or adverse effects.

Within this planning framework, applicants are obliged to consider the impact of their planned development on features of natural heritage importance. National Planning Policy Guidelines (i.e. NPPG 6: Renewable Energy Developments, and NPPG 14: Planning for Natural Heritage) as well as Planning Advice Notes (i.e. PAN 45 Renewable Energy Technologies, PAN 58: Environmental Impact Assessment, and PAN 60 Planning for Natural Heritage) have been developed to provide guidance both to planning authorities and potential hydropower developers.

13.2.3 Natural heritage legislation
Domestic legislation

Until recently, the Wildlife & Countryside Act 1981 (as amended), was the primary legislative tool for protecting the natural heritage. This legislation provided the basis for the protection of a number of named plant and animal species as well as the establishment of SSSIs. More recently, The Nature Conservation (Scotland) Act 2004 has strengthened these provisions and, more importantly, placed a statutory duty on all public bodies to further the conservation of biodiversity. This means that public bodies must examine not only how they run their businesses and incorporate actions to conserve biodiversity into these but also how their functions can help to deliver biodiversity conservation objectives. The duty puts the onus on public bodies to take biodiversity into account in all decision making. This has clear implications for the both Local Authorities and other public bodies which may have a role in the planning process.

Within Scotland, a total of 441 running and standing water bodies are included within the SSSI series. Many water bodies have been designated as a SSSI in their own right whilst others contribute to larger designated areas, which encompass a wide range of natural heritage features. Table 13.2 shows the range of interests contained within the SSSI series which have freshwater affinities.

Table 13.2 Features with freshwater affinities within the Scottish SSSI series. (*) denotes interest features for which it is difficult to identify those species which utilize only freshwater habitats.

SSSI Interest Feature	No. SSSIs which contain this interest feature.
Non-vascular plants (bryophytes and lichens)	16
Vascular plants (macrophytes)	26
Freshwater molluscs (including freshwater pearl mussel)	6
Freshwater invertebrates (species and assemblages)	12
Dragonflies	27
Amphibians	8
Fish (including: Atlantic salmon, brook, river and sea lamprey, Arctic charr, powan, sparling and important fish assemblages)	18
Aggregations of breeding birds*	424
Aggregations on non-breeding birds*	404
Bird assemblages*	160
Otters	8
Rivers and streams	10
Standing open waters	146

International obligations

In addition to domestic legislation, a number of international nature conservation and water resource management agreements and directives are directly relevant to the development of hydropower schemes in Scotland. Examples of international agreements include:

- Convention on Wetlands of International Importance especially as Waterfowl Habitat (The 'Ramsar Convention') 1971
- Convention on the Conservation of European Wildlife and Natural Habitats (The 'Bern Convention') 1979
- The Convention on the Conservation of Migratory Species of Wild Animals (The 'Bonn Convention') 1979

The Rio Earth Summit in 1992 called for global action to create and enforce national strategies and action plans to conserve, protect and enhance biological diversity. Following this summit, the UN Convention on Biological Diversity (CBD) led the UK to develop the UK Biodiversity Action Plan (UKBAP). The UKBAP identified a number of species and habitats of conservation concern and these are listed in UK Steering Group Report (UK Steering Group, 1995). As well as having national priorities and targets for a variety of aquatic species and habitats, action was also taken at a local level and this led to the development of Local Biodiversity Action Plans (LBAPs). Scotland is covered by 25 LBAPs and, whilst these plans contain action plans for species which are considered to be national priorities, they also contain measures to protect species which are considered to be threatened at a local level. The Scottish LBAP network is further strengthened by the work of the Scottish Biodiversity Forum, a collective of individuals, Government Agencies and industry, who together, produced the Scottish Biodiversity Strategy. A review of biodiversity and conservation in Scotland can be found in *A Strategy for the Conservation and Enhancement of Biodiversity in Scotland*' (Scottish Executive, 2004). The provisions of The Nature Conservation (Scotland) Act 2004 and Local Agenda 21 strategies play an increasingly important role in ensuring the Planning Authorities consider the impact that new hydro developments will have on the biodiversity of Scotland (Lenthall, 2004).

In addition to these wider international agreements, European Directives are now considered to be the primary driver for improved nature conservation measures within Scotland and the UK. Prominent amongst these are:

- Directive 92/43/EEC on the conservation of natural habitats and of wild fauna and flora. (The 'Habitats' Directive)
- Directive 79/409/EEC on the conservation of wild birds. (The 'Birds' Directive)
- Directive 2000/60/EC establishing a framework for Community action in the field of water policy. (The Water Framework Directive)

Other directives, such as Directive 78/659/EEC (The Freshwater Fish Directive) and the Directive 91/676/EC (The Nitrates Directive) currently play a role in the protection of aquatic habitats, through the maintenance or improvement of surface water quality. These will be overtaken by the provisions of The Water Framework Directive.

The Habitats Directive is transposed into Scottish law by means of The Conservation (Natural Habitats) Regulations 1994 and The Conservation (Natural Habitats) Amendment (Scotland) Regulations 2004 (together referred to as the 'Habitats Regulations'). Taken together with the 1979 Birds Directive, it provides a framework of sites, collectively known as 'Natura 2000', to protect the most seriously threatened habitats and species. A list of water dependent species and habitats contained in Annexes I and II of the Habitats Directive, and the number of sites designated for each feature in Scotland, is provided in Table 13.3.

In addition to sites and species within the Natura 2000 series, both the Habitats and Birds Directives require member states to protect a smaller number of species regardless of their location. A list of 'European Protected Species' (EPS) of plants and animals is provided in Annex IV of the Habitats Directive. A list of specially protected bird species is provided

Plate 13.1 (left) Dipper (*Cinclus cinclus*) typical of fast flowing mountain streams © Lorne Gill and (right) Eurasian otter (*Lutra lutra*) found along many river margins and on the coast © Lorne Gill

Table 13.3 Species and habitats listed under Annexes I and II of the Habitats Directive in Scotland.

Species		No. Scottish Sites
Freshwater pearl mussel	*Margaritifera margaritifera*	19
Sea lamprey	*Petromyzon marinus*	4
Brook lamprey	*Lampetra planeri*	4
River lamprey	*Lampetra fluviatilis*	5
Atlantic salmon	*Salmo salar*	17
Great crested newt	*Triturus cristatus*	2
Slender green feather-moss	*Drepanocladus vernicosus*	2
Slender naiad	*Najas flexilis*	5
Eurasian otter	*Lutra lutra*	43

Habitats	No. Scottish Sites
Oligotrophic waters containing very few minerals of sandy plains (*Littorelletalia uniflorae*)	1
Oligotrophic to mesotrophic standing waters with vegetation of the *Littorelletea uniflorae* and/or of the *Isoëto-Nanojuncetea* type	32
Hard oligo-mesotrophic waters with benthic vegetation of *Chara* spp.	4
Natural eutrophic lakes with *Magnopotamion* or *Hydrocharition*-type vegetation	8
Natural dystrophic lakes and ponds	16
Water courses of plain to montane levels with the *Ranunculion fluitantis* and *Callitricho-Batrachion* vegetation	1

in Annex I of the Birds Directive. This makes it an offence to deliberately or recklessly capture, kill or disturb any EPS of plant or animal. Table 13.4 provides a list of EPS which are known to occur within Scotland and may be impacted by hydropower developments.

Table 13.4 European Protected Species [EPS] which occur in Scotland and may be impacted by hydroelectric developments.

Species	Scientific Name
Bats, typical (all species)	Vespertilionidae
Wild cat	*Felis silvestris*
Eurasian otter	*Lutra lutra*
Natterjack toad	*Bufo calamita*
Great crested newt	*Triturus cristatus*
Killarney fern	*Trichomanes speciosum*
Slender naiad	*Najas flexilis*
Yellow marsh saxifrage	*Saxifraga hirculus*

Scottish Office Circular 6/1995 (SEERAD, 2000) states that the planning decisions reached by local authorities in Scotland must at all times be consistent with the obligations placed on the UK by the Habitats and Bird Directives. This is a duty incumbent on local authorities as a matter of Community law.

Where a proposed hydroelectric scheme is within or likely to have an effect on a Natura site the competent authority has a duty under Regulation 48 of the Habitats Regulations to:

- determine whether the proposal is directly connected with or necessary to site management for conservation; and, if not,
- determine whether the proposal is likely to have a significant effect on the site either individually or in combination with other plans or projects; and, if so, then;
- make an appropriate assessment of the implications (of the proposal) for the site in view of that site's conservation objectives.

It is unlikely that any hydroscheme will be necessary for the conservation management of the site and therefore determination of significance will usually be required. It is important to note that the determination of significance is more of a coarse sieve to decide whether a more detailed appropriate assessment is required. If there is insufficient information to answer this question it must be assumed that there will be a significant effect and an appropriate assessment will therefore be needed.

Nature conservation designations, whether for species, habitats or landscape do not preclude the development of hydroelectric installations if it can be demonstrated that potential impacts can be either eliminated or minimized. Figure 13.1 shows the number of hydroelectric schemes which are currently located within Scottish designated sites.

The Water Framework Directive (2000/60/EC) establishes a new framework for the management and protection of Scotland's natural water environment, including the rivers and lochs which provide the resource on which hydroelectric schemes are based. It was introduced in 2000 and although it aims to coordinate water environment policy across Europe, it will achieve this by: preventing deterioration and improving aquatic ecosystems – including those dependent on groundwater; promoting sustainable water use; reducing pollution; and reducing the effect of floods and droughts.

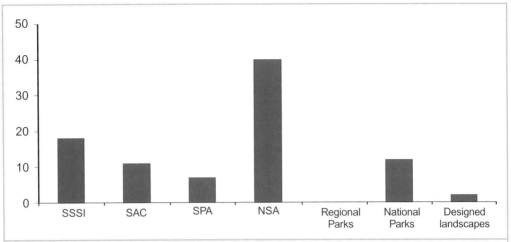

Figure 13.1 Number of hydroelectric schemes located in sites of natural heritage interest. Based on data provided by BHA, Dti and the Scottish Executive.

The Water Framework Directive incorporates the provisions of existing conservation legislation and in Scotland this includes the Wildlife & Countryside Act 1981, the Nature Conservation (Scotland) Act 2004 and the Habitats and Birds Directives. It was transposed into Scottish law as the Water Environment & Water Services Act 2003 (WEWS). The new regulatory regimes required by the WFD and transposed in further detail in Section 20 of the WEWS Act have been introduced by secondary legislation - the Water Environment (Controlled Activities) (Scotland) Regulations 2005 (CAR). CAR establishes measures to regulate activities for the purposes of protection of the water environment, as required by the WFD and will facilitate the achievement of environmental objectives set out in river basin management plans. CAR also introduces controls over abstraction, impoundment and building, engineering and other works that impact on the physical quality of aquatic habitats. The CAR regulations also replace the point source discharge system set up under the Control of Pollution Act 1974 and groundwater controls contained in the Groundwater Regulations 1998. Neither the Section 36 renewables consenting process or the CAR regulations can subsume in their entirety the requirements of the other, although some elements of the Section 26 consenting process will now be considered by SEPA under the CAR Regulations (Scottish Executive Environment Group, 2006). It is therefore likely that, whilst the Section 36 consenting process will be retained, it will be modified to prevent duplication or possible inconsistency between regulating regimes. This will be achieved by way of an Memorandum of Understanding between SEPA and Scottish Energy Ministers.

Schedule 9 of the Electricity (Scotland) Act 1989 will also be amended to ensure that the Fisheries Committee's advice to Scottish Ministers will contribute to the CAR process. As a 'Responsible Authority' under Section 2 of the WEWS Act 2003, the Fisheries Committee is required to exercise its normal statutory functions in a way that secures compliance with WFD objectives. This includes the provision of support to SEPA in its delivery of River Basin Management Plans (SEPA, 2002, 2004, 2005; SEEG, 2006).

In addition to the WFD, the Strategic Environmental Assessment Directive (EC Directive 2001/42/EC), is designed make the planning process more transparent by

Plate 13.2 Loch Sloy hydroelectric pumped storage scheme © Lorne Gill / SNH

involving the public and, by integrating environmental considerations, help overcome criticism about the way the current planning system addresses issues such as the cumulative impact of hydroschemes which are located in the same or neighbouring catchments. The Directive became operational from July 2004 and is enacted in Scotland through The Environmental Assessment of Plans and Programmes (Scotland) Regulations 2004.

Reviews of the legislative framework and approval procedures for hydropower development within Scotland are provided by Reid *et al.* (2004, 2005) and Copestake (2006).

13.3 The potential impact of hydroelectric schemes

13.3.1 Types of hydroelectric scheme

There are four main types of hydroelectric scheme within Scotland: run-of-river, low-head storage, high-head storage and pump-storage (Struthers, 1996). Technological advances in turbine design have, in recent years, led to an increase in the number of small-scale hydro developments in Scotland. Although there appears to be no universally accepted terminology for these schemes, developments which have an installed capacity within the 100 kW to 1 MW range are often referred to as mini-hydro developments. Smaller schemes, which are 5 to 100 kW are often referred to as 'micro' hydro developments, and very small systems, which generate 5kW or less, are known as 'pico' hydroschemes. A guide to mini hydroschemes is provided by BHA (2005).

Generally speaking, hydropower developments within Scotland generally fall into two categories – storage or run-of-river, although the two existing pump-storage schemes provide a disproportionate percentage of the Scottish installed hydropower capacity. A storage scheme, whether high or low head, usually involves the construction of a dam to create a reservoir of water from which flow is controlled to provide energy for turbines. Run-of-river schemes, by contrast, simply divert water flow, generally at the head of a small river to power a turbine and then return the water directly to the river. Some run-of-river schemes may also impound water, but these are generally small when compared to storage schemes. Available data suggests that a total of 102 (67 %) hydro developments within Scotland are storage schemes and these have a potential installed capacity of 2148.42 MW. Fewer run-of-river schemes exist and these account for the remaining 49 (32 %) of the Scottish total. The installed capacity of run-of-river schemes in Scotland is approximately 62.35 MW.

13.3.2 Environmental impacts

The impact of hydropower installations on freshwater fish populations and the landscape in which they are located was recognized as early as the 1940s. These issues received specific mention within the Hydro-Electric Development (Scotland) Act 1943 which stated that: *"In the exercise of its functions, the Board shall have regard to the desirability of preserving the beauty of the scenery and any object of architectural or historical interest and of avoiding as far as possible injury to fisheries or the stock of fish in any waters."* No mention was made of fauna, other than fish, which may be affected by hydropower developments. However, it is clear that impacts on both aquatic ecology and landscape were clearly recognized at a relatively early stage in the development of the hydroelectric industry in Scotland.

Despite their number, scale and local or national importance, relatively few reviews of the potential environmental impacts of hydroschemes have been published over the last 50 years.

Berry (1955) provided the first real assessment of the potential ecological impact of hydropower development on the natural heritage of Scotland. However, despite being written at a time when large-scale hydroelectric developments were under construction within Scotland, landscape issues were not fully covered as part of this review. Many of the issues raised by Berry (*op.cit.*), such as the impact of changes in water level and water flow, loss in biological diversity within impoundments, changes to water chemistry and restricted access for migratory fish, reflect the importance of fish and fisheries within Scotland. This review did not confine itself to aquatic impacts, and the loss of winter grazing opportunities for sheep and cattle, the loss of rare aquatic and wetland plants and insects from littoral habitats and the impact of transmission lines on birds and deer were also considered. Though not specifically a review of hydroelectric development, Murray (1962) sought to identify and describe regions of supreme landscape value. This report spoke out very strongly against the 'disfigurement' caused by hydroelectric works, and, as a result, several areas (such as Loch Quoich, Glen Garry and Glen Cannich) were excluded from the final list.

A later review by Elder (1965) considered the impact of hydropower impoundments on freshwater and associated terrestrial habitats and species. However, the primary focus of this review was the impact of hydro on fisheries, and in particular anadromous salmonids. Given the sporting and economic importance of Atlantic salmon (*Salmo salar*), to the rural economy of Scotland, it is perhaps unsurprising that much of the published work relates to this species. Reid *et al.* (2005), in a recent review of hydro legislation, concluded that the need to respect fishing interests has been a fundamental feature in the development of the hydro industry and that this relationship is enshrined in a number of domestic legislative tools. Perhaps the best example of this was the establishment of the Fisheries Committee under The Hydro-Electric Development (Scotland) Act 1943. Whilst much of the work of the Fisheries Committee has, historically, focussed on migratory salmonids, the Committee has, more recently, adopted a more holistic approach and considered the impact of hydroschemes on a range of other species, for example Arctic charr (*Salvelinus alpinus*) and lamprey spp.

Scottish Hydro-Electric (1992) and Struthers (1996) attempted to describe the impact of hydro on aquatic fauna in Scotland but focused almost exclusively on Atlantic salmon and ignored impacts on other species or habitats. More recent reviews (i.e. SNIFFER, 2004; Copestake, 2006) have been much more holistic in their ecological scope, but continue to ignore the impact of hydropower developments on landscape.

Clearly, the impacts that hydropower developments may have on the natural heritage of Scotland are not restricted to anadromous populations of Atlantic salmon or sea trout (*Salmo trutta trutta*). Considerable evidence exist that the construction and footprint of hydroschemes, regardless of size, can impact a wide variety of aquatic and terrestrial species and habitats. Hydroelectric developments can also have a number of landscape and visual impacts and may also have an effect on the amenity value of the chosen site.

13.3.3 Ecological impacts

Hydropower schemes, regardless as to whether they are run-of-river or storage schemes comprise many of the same structural elements (Figure 13.2). For example, almost all hydroschemes will include an intake, penstock, turbine house and a tailrace. Access must also be available for building works and maintenance and this will necessitate the construction of

Plate 13.3 Faskally hydroelectric dam on the River Tummel © Lorne Gill / SNH

tracks or roads. The electricity which is generated from the scheme must also be transferred to end-users either directly or by connection to the National Grid and this may be achieved through the installation of overhead power lines or underground connections. The impoundment of water is not always essential for small-scale hydroelectric developments and although this type of development is usually associated with storage schemes, it may also occur, at a smaller scale, in some run-of-river schemes, through the creation of weirs.

Table 13.5 provides a broad overview of the type of impacts that each of these structures may have on aquatic species and habitats, although the severity of any impact depends on a number of factors. These include the site location, topography and hydrology, the type of

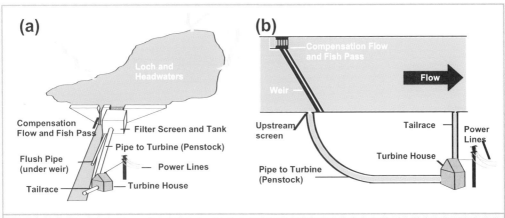

Figure 13.2 Simplified schematic of the structural components of (a) storage and (b) run-of-river hydroelectric generating schemes.

Table 13.5 Summary table of ecological issues to be considered for new hydropower scheme developments.

Structure	Potential Impact
Weir/Dam/Intake	• Changes to flow regime and reduction of discharge • Obstruction to migratory fish, (including lamprey spp. and eels) • Disturbance (species and habitats) • Impact on water quality and/or sediment transport
Impoundment	• Inundation and loss of terrestrial habitat • Impact of drawdown on habitats and species, especially fish spawning areas, littoral invertebrate communities and birds • Impacts on water quality / water temperature / sediment transport
Penstock/Tunnel/Pipeline/Aqueduct	• Reduction in natural river flow regime to regulated compensation flow between intake and powerhouse • Impact on aquatic flora / fauna • Impact on water quality / water temperature / sediment transport • Impact on terrestrial habitats / species • Impact on terrestrial habitat hydrology; e.g. peatlands
Turbine Buildings	• Direct habitat loss • Disturbance; e.g. through noise, lighting and servicing • Possible impact on water quality through industrial / domestic discharge associated with ancillary servicing • Opportunities for habitat creation through design of building(s) / structure(s); e.g. bats
Tail Race	• Flow / discharge velocity and impact on river bank erosion • Effect of creation of spray on flora • Disturbance; e.g. through noise • Possible impact on fish behaviour: attraction to high flows / obstruction to upstream movement • Possible effects of variable flow on other species; e.g. otter, freshwater pearl mussel
Access Tracks	• Impact of river crossings on river flows, water quality and fish access • Impact on water quality through increased sediment run-off / surface water drainage • Disturbance; e.g. through noise / vibration • Loss / damage to terrestrial habitats / species • Introduction of imported materials
Transmission Lines/Grid Connection	• Impact of river crossings on river flows, water quality and fish access • Disturbance • Loss / damage to terrestrial habitats / species

scheme, and the design of its various elements and how these are constructed and operated. Copestake (2006) and Reid *et al.* (2005) provide a number of site-specific examples of the environmental impacts of hydropower schemes in Scotland.

Fish

Physical barriers such as dams and weirs can have a direct impact by impeding the movement of fish in rivers and impounded catchments (Mathers *et al.*, 2002). This, in turn, can reduce overall productivity of a catchment by preventing fish from gaining access to potential spawning or nursery sites. Access to such areas can be particularly crucial for the continued viability of small populations of migrating salmonids. In some cases, this has led to the establishment of fish stocking regimes which, in themselves, can result in damage to native biodiversity through the loss of genetically-adapted behavioural traits and overall fitness (i.e. Hansen, 2002; McGinnity *et al.*, 2004).

Much is known about the biological requirements of Atlantic salmon and trout (e.g. Armstrong *et al.*, 2003; Hendry and Cragg-Hine, 2003) and, in Scotland, it is now a legal requirement to install provision for the passage of migratory salmonids, but not other fish species, under the provisions of The Salmon (Fish Passes and Screens) (Scotland) Regulations 1994. Armstrong *et al.*(2004) provide a review of fish pass legislation in other areas of the UK. Whilst a wide range of fish pass designs exist (Clay, 1995; Jungwirth *et al.*, 1998), Scottish fish passes are designed almost exclusively for migratory salmonids. Little is known about the effectiveness of existing fish passes for the passage of other fish species (Beech, 1984). Evidence from a number of sites suggest that lamprey spp. and European eels may be able to pass some existing structures, but given the existing conservation status of lamprey (Maitland, 2003) and the emerging requirement to protect European eels populations (ICES/EIFAC, 2004), modifications may be required in future years.

Whereas much is known about the upstream requirements for some, principally salmonid, species, downstream fish pass technology is much less advanced (Larinier *et al.*, 2002). Little provision is made for ensuring the successful downstream passage of fish through fish passes, although Coutant and Whitney (2000) suggest that the presence of hydroelectric dams or barrages may increase the pressures on out-migrating smolts. Carr (2000) suggests that fish which undergo stressful downstream migrations may be damaged or disoriented, leaving them more susceptible to delayed mortality or predation.

Entrainment of fish into off-takes or hydropower scheme intakes may occur in both run-of-river and storage schemes if appropriate screening arrangements are not in place. Once drawn into the system, fish may be exposed to rapid pressure changes, hydraulic shear, turbulence and cavitation as well as collision with the turbines themselves (Coutant and Whitney, 2000; Cada, 2001). Increased river flows are a major environmental cue for Atlantic salmon and their passage upstream is closely correlated with increases in river discharge (Alabaster, 1990; Webb, 1990; Smith *et al.*, 1996; Gowans, 1999; Solomon *et al.*, 1999). Amplified flows within tailraces can act as an attractant to migrating fish, drawing them away from fish passes or other areas where fish passage is relatively unimpeded. Chanseau and Larinier (1999) demonstrated that adult Atlantic salmon were attracted to increased flows at the tailrace of some hydro installations and found that this led to significant delays in fish passage rates. Because the maximum swimming speed of fish is inversely proportional to water temperature, significant delays below obstructions or around discharges could also lead to the creation of a physiological barrier for some species (Beech, 1984; Jonsson *et al.,* 1997). It is possible that similar behavioural and physiological responses occur in other upstream migrants, such as lamprey or eels, although this has not been empirically demonstrated. Turnpenny (1999) provides an overview of the behaviour of fish in relation to hydro plants.

Changes to the flow or hydrological regime of rivers through the use of inappropriate compensation or 'freshet' arrangements may present a significant barrier to the in-stream movement, of not only resident fish species, but migratory fish such as Atlantic salmon, eels and lamprey spp. The timing of freshet release, coupled with low compensation flows may limit access of all fish species to suitable spawning substrates (Thorstad and Heggberget, 1998; Gibbins *et al.,* 2001). This may seriously affect recruitment within some populations, and because dams and weirs tend to be located in headwater areas, the impact may be particularly serious for Multi-Sea-Winter (MSW) Atlantic salmon that are known to spawn predominantly in the upper reaches of river catchments.

The ramping rate at which river flows are altered, for example during hydro-peaking, may also result in the scouring of fish spawning areas or the stranding of migrating fish in pools (Saltveit *et al.,* 2001; Halleraker *et al.,* 2003). Stranding may leave affected fish vulnerable to predation by piscivorous birds or mammals. Baran *et al.* (1995) in a study of the impact of hydro-mediated changes in river flow regimes demonstrated that, although a reduction in fish abundance was shown by all size classes of brown trout, adult fish were impacted more than juvenile conspecifics by constant periods of reduced flow. Little is known about the impact of minimal flows on the passage of non-salmonid species of conservation concern although some information has been gathered for sea lamprey (Svensson, 2000; Ovidio and Philippart, 2002).

The ecological value of the hyporheic zone of rivers with respect to fish, particularly Atlantic salmon, recruitment has been virtually ignored with regard to the potential impact of hydropower development. Recent studies (e.g. Malcolm *et al.,* 2002, 2003a,b) suggest that watershed management strategies, including the determination of compensation flows, which focus solely on surface water characteristics, risk overlooking sub-surface processes that may be critical to the survival of fish and other in-stream fauna.

The majority of hydroelectric schemes in Scotland aim to abstract water at Q95 levels (that is, the flow that is exceeded on average for 95% of the time, based on a flow duration curve for each river using at least two years of data) (Bragg *et al.,*1999; Copestake, 2006). In many cases this is insufficient and Copestake (*op. cit.*) describes SEPA's best practice as being the establishment of a 'hands-off flow' (generally between Q95 and Q90), below which no abstraction would occur. To achieve WFD compliance, it is likely that both new and existing schemes will require some level of derogation if they are to be allowed to continue electricity generation.

Altering water levels in impounded waters during the electricity generating cycle, may directly impact fish species which spawn in the loch itself by reducing the availability or quality of in-loch spawning substrates. Drawdown at inappropriate times of the year may also reduce access by pre-spawning fish to afferent rivers or streams. Long-term studies of the impact of impoundment on fish species within the UK (e.g. Crisp *et al.,* 1983, 1990) and elsewhere in Europe (e.g. Aass *et al.,* 1989; Penczak, 1995) have demonstrated improvements in brown trout growth rates within the impounded sections. These increases

Plate 13.4 Atlantic salmon (*Salmo salar*) leaping a waterfall on the River Almond on its way upstream to spawn
© Lorne Gill / SNH

were mediated by changes in the availability of invertebrate prey organisms after impoundment, either through inundation of terrestrial habitats or through changes to invertebrate community structure. These benefits are, however, offset by long-term negative impacts on the structure of Arctic charr and brown trout populations (Aass *et al.,* 2004).

Changes to water temperature, chemistry and sediment transport within rivers and impounded standing waters can also directly impact fish populations. Impounding water or reducing flows may modify the thermal and chemical characteristics of both impounded and receiving waters. In a study of Atlantic salmon growth in receiving waterbodies below hydroschemes, Jensen (2003) suggested that although some temperature-mediated changes in the growth rate of Atlantic salmon may occur in affected areas, the scale of these impacts may be relatively minor. Long-term studies of fish populations in Cow Green reservoir and its afferent and efferent streams (e.g. Crisp, 1984; Crisp *et al.,* 1984; Crisp and Mann, 1991) provide clear evidence that impoundments can impact a range of fish species found within the UK. Studies in mainland Europe (e.g. Kruk and Penczak, 2003) suggest that temperature changes associated with impoundments may present opportunities for other species, resulting in changes to fish community structure. Petts (1984) provides a review of the impact of impounding rivers and suggests that the release of anoxic water from the hypolimnion of standing waters, or even the supersaturation of overspill and outflows (McDonald and Hyatt, 1973), can have a damaging impact on fish populations downstream of dams and impoundments. Dams and weirs can also influence sediment transport within rivers and this can impact freshwater fish by reducing the quality of spawning or nursery habitat by reducing the passage of spawning gravels or increasing the deposition rate of fine particles, such as silt (Osmundson *et al.,* 2002).

The bioaccumulation of toxins or heavy metals can also occur in areas where water is impounded for hydro (Tremblay *et al.,* 1996; French *et al.,* 1998). Several studies (e.g. Morrison and Therien, 1995; Doyon *et al.,* 1998) have shown that toxins, such as mercury, can bioaccumulate in fish which are resident within such areas. Once accumulated, toxic materials can also be transported downstream during drawdown (Shetagne *et al.,* 2000), where they can be taken up by in-stream fauna.

Invertebrates

Changes to the flow or hydrological regime of rivers can impact a range of aquatic fauna other than fish (Garcia de Jalon *et al.,* 1994). Reduction in the wetted area, particularly when associated with large and rapid flow changes, can negatively impact the extent of suitable in-stream habitats for invertebrates and result in losses in invertebrate production (Englund and Malmqvist, 1996; Parasiewicz *et al.,* 1998; Brunke *et al.,* 2000). Smith (2005) reviewed the range of fauna which can be found within the hyporheic zones of UK rivers and although relatively little is known about the hyporheic fauna of rivers within Scotland, it is logical to assume that changes to the hydrological regime of rivers will have some impact on aquatic biota which utilize this environment. The freshwater pearl mussel, an invertebrate which is listed in Annex II of the EU Habitats Directive and is a UK Biodiversity Action Plan Priority Species, merits particular mention both because of its conservation importance and its vulnerability to changes in the flow regime of rivers (Skinner *et al.,* 2003). Extreme changes in flow conditions have the capability to either strand or wash away populations.

Exposure of littoral habitats in impounded waters by controlling surface levels can dramatically alter the loch level range. Copestake (2006) suggests that 'natural' Scottish lochs have remarkably stable levels and typically vary by no more than 0.5 m. By holding back water and then releasing it in a rapid, but controlled manner, impoundment levels can vary by as much as 20 m, exposing invertebrate and plant species. Where level variations occur it is not unusual to see 'drawdown scars' around the littoral fringes of the impoundment and these areas are generally devoid of aquatic plant and invertebrate communities.

Changes to water temperature, chemistry and sediment transport within rivers and impounded standing waters can also directly affect invertebrate populations (Garcia de Jalon *et al.,* 1994). In rivers, macroinvertebrate biomass and community structure (Lauters *et al.,* 1996; Lessard and Hayes, 2003) can be affected as a result of changes in water chemistry and temperature downstream of impoundments and hydro-peaking downstream of tailraces. Brunke *et al.* (2000) suggest that flow reductions can affect macroinvertebrates by enhancing the sedimentation of fine suspended particles, so that muddy deposits cover extensive areas of the bottom, current velocities are reduced below the tolerable limits for sensitive rheophilic species and near-shore or bankside habitats are dried out and become unusable.

Reservoirs also tend to reduce the amount of suspended material which is transported downstream, and this can have a significant impact on the biomass and community structure of a range of invertebrate species (Armitage, 1978) including the freshwater pearl mussel.

Plants

Changes to the flow or hydrological regime of rivers can affect aquatic flora in a number of ways. By reducing flow, for example, sensitive in-stream flora, such as the river jelly lichen

(*Collema dichotomum*) may be left exposed, resulting in its desiccation and eventual loss. Riparian flora may also be affected, either through localized erosion at outflows or as a result of less frequent and reduced downstream flooding and spray/humidity (Englund *et al.,* 1997). Exposure of littoral habitats in impounded waters during drawdown periods can also result in the loss of sensitive plant species through perturbation of edge and marginal habitats.

Changes to water temperature, chemistry and sediment transport can also affect aquatic flora. Rorsslett and Johansen (1996), for example, found that the regulation of streamflows by hydroelectricity plants resulted in nutrient enrichment and the establishment of nuisance growths of submerged bryophytes, filamentous algae and aquatic vascular plants downstream of impoundments. Eutrophication and increases in turbidity can reduce the ability of some emergent and floating macrophytes species to survive or re-establish themselves. Macrophyte loss may have indirect impacts on fauna, such as invertebrates, fish, or birds, that may utilize macrophytes for food or shelter. The impact on plant species due to changes in water temperature, chemistry or sediment transport is not restricted to impounded waters. Holmes and Whitton (1977), for example, noted changes in the abundance of some macrophyte species in response to regulation of the River Tees after the construction of Cow Green Reservoir.

Birds

Changes to the flow or hydrological regime of rivers may directly affect those species of bird which depend on in-stream biota for food (Nilsson and Dynesius, 1994). For example, species that specialize on macroinvertebrates, such as dipper (*Cinclus cinclus*) may be affected through the loss or reduction in prey availability. Piscivorous birds, such as merganser (*Mergus serrator*), goosander (*M. merganser*) and heron (*Ardea cinerea*) may be similarly affected, although the stranding of some fish in pools may be seen as a positive, if temporary, benefit.

Altering water levels in impounded waters can also negatively affect bird species by creating a sterile margin around the edge of the water. Where the drawdown zone is wide, loss of fish, invertebrate or aquatic plant production can have knock-on effects on bird species that utilize these biota for food or, in the case of plants, shelter. Rapid changes in water level can also directly affect breeding birds such as red-throated divers (*Gavia stellata*), black-throated divers (*G. arctica*) and Slavonian grebe (*Podiceps auritus*) (Mudge and Talbot, 1993; Hancock, 2000; Hake *et al.,* 2005; Copestake, 2006).

Disturbance and direct mortality through collision with power lines associated with hydropower installations is another factor that is also worthy of consideration. Various studies (e.g. Miquet, 1990; Janss and Ferrer, 1998; Harness and Wilson, 2001; Lehman, 2001) examined the role of power lines in the increased mortality rate of raptors and black grouse (*Tetrao tetrix*). A review by Bevanger (1998) concluded that a range of bird species can be affected by power lines although Bevanger (*op. cit.*) concluded that insufficient data are available to judge the significance of mortality at the population level. Bevanger (*op. cit.*) also suggested that the cumulative effects of negative impacts on bird populations and the number of endangered or vulnerable status being killed in connection with utility structures deserves increased general awareness. Disturbance to sensitive or shy bird species may be an issue in some sites, particularly during the construction phase, leading to the abandonment of nests and the loss of young.

Mammals

Changes to the flow or hydrological regime of rivers may have a direct impact on those mammal species which depend on in-stream biota for food or utilize riparian habitats for shelter (Nilsson and Dynesius, 1994). The loss of habitat and disturbance, particularly during the construction phase, can be a major concern when considering the impact of hydro developments on mammals. Species that are more likely to be encountered are otters and water voles (*Arvicola terrestris*). However, hydropower scheme developments may also entail the construction of a variety of physical structures, such as turbine buildings, access tracks and water transfer facilities. By modifying riparian habitats or by removing trees or renovating/destroying existing structures it is possible that sensitive species, such as bats, otters or water voles, may be killed, disturbed or displaced. In some upland situations consideration should also be given to the possibility of the presence of wildcats (*Felis silvestris*). All of these species, with the exception of water voles, are afforded strict protection under the Habitats Regulations as EPS. European Protected Species are afforded strict protection from intentional or reckless disturbance and their breeding sites and resting places are protected from all types of damage or destruction.

Other ecological considerations

Natural river systems have a continuously changing set of physical characteristics to which aquatic flora and fauna have become adapted. Few rivers within the UK can be considered pristine and most have been altered in some form along at least part of their length (Gilvear *et al.*, 2002). Notwithstanding this fact, structures associated with hydroelectric schemes may have a significant impact on the physical characteristics of a river by substantially reducing the amount of suspended material which is transported downstream, by reducing water velocity, altering patterns of erosion and sedimentation particularly on shallower rivers. It can also affect the flow regime by reducing discharge overall and can alter channel form (Brandt, 2000). The primary threats to rivers and streams by hydropower development are:

- pollution (including eutrophication);
- excessive surface water abstraction;
- construction of dams and reservoirs;
- water transfer schemes between rivers;
- insensitive bank protection works; canalisation and inappropriate bank management (including overgrazing); and
- hydroelectric power scheme building development within the floodplain.

Water transfer schemes are a common feature of large scale hydroelectric schemes in Scotland. During the period 1945-1965, 28 hydroschemes linked a number of hitherto isolated waterbodies by means of 275 km of tunnel and 166 km of aqueduct within the Tummel, Affric/Beauly and Conon catchments. The transfer of water from one catchment to another may have affected the biota of receiving waterbodies through the transfer of non-native flora and fauna, the loss of genetic isolation for native species (such as Atlantic salmon, trout and Arctic charr) and by possible changes to water chemistry. For species such as freshwater pearl mussel which are highly sensitive to changes in the concentration of certain chemical determinands (such as calcium, nitrate, phosphate and BOD), transfer from one catchment to another can be a critical factor in their continued survival in some localities. In the advent of a disease or parasite outbreak, such as *Gyrodactylus salaris*, the continued transfer of water from one catchment to another may give cause for concern.

13.3.4 Landscape

Landscape character is a key consideration when considering the potential impact of any new development and considers how any one landscape is different from another on the basis of its recognizable pattern of physical and cultural characteristics (SNH, 2001b). Most landscapes are able to accommodate some form of hydroelectric development, although the

Table 13.6 Summary table of landscape issues to be considered for new hydroelectric scheme developments.

Structure	Potential Impact
Weir/Dam/Intake	• Scale, form and finish of the structure • Prominence / visibility • Landscape character change including altered flows • Character of wild land
Impoundment	• Creation of new water body: visibility and fit with landscape character • Drawdown: extent, frequency and visibility • Drawdown: effect on wild land quality
Penstock/Tunnel/Pipeline/Aqueduct	• Landscape and visual impact of a new linear feature (buried, surface or part-buried) • Disturbed corridor: both construction and linear feature • Effect on wild land • Landscape / visual impact of related features; e.g. air valves, pipe bridges, river crossings
Turbine Buildings	• Landscape / visual impact associated with location / siting of building(s) / structure(s) • Design of building(s) / structure(s) especially scale and form • Effect on wild land • Landscape / visual impact of related structures and activities; e.g. fencing, hard standing, lighting, noise and servicing
Tail Race	• Design of tail race and fit with local character especially at loch edge / river bank • Visibility and audibility of tail race
Access Tracks	• Landscape and visual impact arising from alignment, scale, associated drainage, cuttings and embankments and structures such as culverts and bridges • Effects on wild land
Transmission Lines/Grid Connection	• Landscape and visual impact of a new linear feature • Disturbed corridor: both construction and linear feature • Effect on wild land

Plate 13.5 Black-throated diver *Gavia arctica* © Laurie Campbell / SNH

suitability of individual schemes will depend on the size or scale of the operation as well as its physical location. It is clear that some landscape character types will be more able to accommodate new developments than others (LI-IEMA, 2002).

The value of Scotland's landscape is recognized by the designation of 40 National Scenic Areas (NSA) (CCS, 1978). Taken together with Areas of Great Landscape Value (AGLV) (SNH, 2002) and recent National Park designations in the Loch Lomond and Trossachs and the Cairngorms areas, landscape is now considered to be a key consideration for planning authorities.

Landscape designations do not preclude developments of any kind and Figure 13.1 shows that hydroelectric schemes are already located within areas designated as NSA, National Parks and even Designed Landscapes.

Table 13.6 provides a broad overview of the type of impacts that each of these main hydro scheme components may have on landscape character. Clearly, the severity of any impact depends on a number of factors, including:

- physical structure of the development (i.e. weirs, dams, intakes, pipelines, tunnels, air valves, open channels, fish passes, impoundments and river crossings);
- operation (i.e. altered flow regimes, water management regimes and duration);
- construction impacts (i.e. construction corridor, access, storage, lay-down areas);
- turbine house (i.e. location, tailrace, fencing, hard standing and lighting); and
- access for operation and maintenance (i.e. temporary and permanent access requirements, maintenance or tracks and built structures).

With the exception of the recently consented 100 MW Glendoe scheme, which is situated towards the western end of the Monadhliath Mountains, most new hydroelectric developments will, in terms of their installed capacity, be relatively small. This does not, however, mean that their landscape impact will be less significant. A proposal for a 3.55 MW scheme at Shieldaig in Wester Ross, for example, included the impoundment of four lochs within the Wester Ross NSA. Inundation of existing lochs and drawdown during electricity generating periods may have left drawdown scars and this would have a direct visual impact and a perceived negative effect on the quality of the wild land experience in this remote landscape. In addition to impoundment impacts, this proposal would have entailed the construction of a number of access tracks, dams and pipelines and also acoustic disturbance from the proposed extensive use of helicopters during the construction phase of the development.

Most, but not all, new small-scale hydroschemes are located in relatively remote areas of the countryside, making connection to the National Grid or other recipients difficult to achieve without the use of overland transmission lines. Such linear structures can have a considerable visual impact in their own right especially in areas hitherto unaffected by such developments.

13.4 Discussion

According to Reid *et al.* (2005), the growth of environmental awareness during the 20th century has led the public to scrutinize the environmental costs and benefits of renewable energy generation. This scrutiny is tempered by a greater awareness of the global concerns over the impact of greenhouse gas emissions and changes to the UK energy policy (Pillai *et al.*, 2005).

It has long been recognized that hydropower schemes may affect aquatic habitats and landscape quality within Scotland (SNH, 2001a, b; Reid *et al.*, 2005). Whilst there is a perception that all impacts are negative, this is not always the case. The linkage between hydroschemes and fisheries is an example whereby it can be argued that hydro has, to some extent, delivered some significant natural heritage gains. The SEERAD Fisheries Research Laboratory at Pitlochry, for example, owes its origins to the Brown Trout Research Laboratory which was set up at that site by the North of Scotland Hydro Electricity Board in 1948. This facility now provides freshwater fisheries advice to Scottish Ministers and plays a key role in the dissemination of scientifically-based fisheries management to the general public. Whilst most of this research has focused on Atlantic salmon and other salmonid species, such as sea trout and brown trout, it has made a valuable contribution to our understanding of the ecology of other Scottish freshwater fish species.

In addition to providing the basic infrastructure for the FRS Freshwater Laboratory, almost all of the fish counters which are currently operational within Scotland are associated with hydropower schemes (Eatherley *et al.*, 2005). The installation of counters at hydro dams is not a mandatory requirement for hydro operators but some of these, for example at Spey Dam, Pitlochry, Lairg, Awe Barrage, Orrin, Aigas and Kilmorack, continue to provide valuable, fisheries-independent, information with regard the status of migratory salmonid stocks within some of the most important Atlantic salmon rivers in Scotland.

The relationship between hydro operators and other stakeholders varies depending on location and the range of interests involved. Anglers, for example may be unhappy with current compensation flow arrangements within some areas, but this may be offset by the provision of freshets and other releases of fresh water during electricity generation.

Canoeists may also be unhappy at the loss of good quality white water as well as the experience of wild land or access, through the placement of physical obstructions or reduced flows. Whilst it is difficult to compensate for the loss of the wild land experience, impacts in some areas have been offset by the creation of new waterbodies, through impoundments, or the creation of reliable and challenging runs through the regular release of freshets or dam releases. Examples of areas where such arrangements are in place include the Tummel, Awe and the River Leven (at Kinlochleven).

Large scale hydroelectric projects, such as the large water transfer schemes at Tummel, Affric/Beauly and Conon have been around for many years and have, themselves become part of the Scottish landscape to many members of the public. The fish pass and dam at Pitlochry has, for example, become a major tourist attraction in its own right.

The various large water transfer schemes were completed at a time when there was no need to produce an Environmental Impact Assessment, thus it is impossible to determine what have been the real ecological impacts of these schemes. Such a situation would not have been allowed to occur if the same proposals were under consideration today. Pillai *et al.* (2005) correctly concluded that the approval procedure for new schemes means that a much broader range of environmental factors is now being considered than in the past. This reflects a more complex domestic legislative process which is, in turn, being driven by European Community environmental law. The recent refusal by Scottish Ministers to grant consent for the Shieldaig and Slattadale Hydroelectric Scheme proposal lends credence to the view that environmental, including landscape, concerns are now a key element of the decision-making process. A review of this case, and the process which led to its refusal, is provided by Pillai *et al.* (*op. cit.*).

Modern schemes, which have recently undergone, or are undergoing, the S. 36 consent process are guided by the provision of comprehensive scoping advice from Government Agencies such as SNH (SNH, 2001b) and SEPA (see Copestake, 2006), as well as current EIA Regulations. This ensures that adequate baseline information is gathered, and impacts assessed, *before* developments are considered by relevant planning authorities.

Although natural heritage designations and EU conservation directives have played a key role in protecting many valuable species and habitats within Scotland, the development and transposition in to Scottish law of the Water Framework Directive is without doubt the most holistic water management legislation to come into force in modern times. A key requirement of the WFD is the creation of River Basin Management Plans and these identify both the pressures on individual waterbodies and measures for minimizing their impact. The ecological status for each waterbody is set by comparing its current condition to a set of reference values with the aim of achieving good ecological status by 2015. For existing schemes, particularly the long-established water transfer schemes, it may be possible to see alternative objectives if the programme of measures designed to bring the waterbody up to good ecological status is considered to be disproportionately expensive (Copestake, 2006). Therefore, for existing hydroelectric schemes, the target for heavily modified waterbodies may be to achieve the best possible 'ecological potential' with targets consistent with the purpose for which the water is being used. At the very least, hydropower operators must establish operating practices which minimize ecological impacts and maximize environmental benefits.

The WFD has, as one of its core requirements, a commitment to adhere to the obligations of the EU Habitats and Birds Directives and domestic conservation legislation.

In Scotland, the WEWS Act and the CAR Regulations will be the primary tools for ensuring that the natural heritage is a key consideration in the management of existing and future hydroscheme developments.

Hydropower generation is clearly here to stay. It makes a valuable contribution to the UK's energy policy, contributing up to 11% of Scotland's electricity. It is also clear, however, that the benefits associated with this form of 'clean' and 'renewable' electricity generation also occur, perhaps ironically, at a cost to the environment. This cost can, however, be minimized through the careful and sensitive siting of new developments. Technological improvements will play a part but the key driver for future improvements will, undoubtedly, be the Water Framework Directive.

References

Aass, P., Nielsen, P. and Brabrand, A. (1989). Effects of river regulation on the structure of a fast-growing brown trout *(Salmo trutta L.)* population. *Regulated Rivers: Research & Management.* **3**: 255-266.

Aass, P., Jensen, C. S., L'Abee-Lund, J. H. and Vollestad, L. A. (2004). Long-term variation in the population structure of Arctic charr, *Salvelinus alpinus*, & brown trout, *Salmo trutta*. *Fisheries Management & Ecology.* **11**: 125-134.

Alabaster, J. S. (1990). The temperature requirements of adult Atlantic salmon, *Salmo salar* L., during their upstream migration in the River Dee. *Journal of Fish Biology.* **37**: 659-661.

Armitage, P. D. (1978). Downstream changes in the composition, numbers, & biomass of bottom fauna in the tees below Cow Green Reservoir & in an unregulated tributary Maize Beck, in the first five years after impoundment. *Hydrobiologia.* **58**: 145-156.

Armstrong, J. D., Kemp, P. S., Kennedy, G. J. A., Ladle, M. and Milner, N. J. (2003). Habitat requirements of Atlantic salmon & brown trout in rivers & streams. *Fisheries Research.* **62**: 143-170.

Armstrong, G., Aprahamian, M., Fewings, A., Gough, P., Reader, N. and Varallo, P. (2004). *Fish passes: Guidance Notes On The Legislation, Selection & Approval Of Fish Passes In England And Wales.* Environment Agency Fish Pass Manual ver. 1.1. 308pp.

Baran, P., Delacoste, M., Dauba, F., Lascaux, J. M., Belaud, A. and Lek, S. (1995). Effects of reduced flow on brown trout *(Salmo trutta* L.) populations downstream dams in French Pyrenees. *Regulated Rivers: Research and Management.* **10**: 347-361.

Beech, M. H. (1984). Fish pass design - criteria for the design and approval of fish passes and other structures to facilitate the passage of migratory fish in rivers. *Fisheries Research Technical Report., MAFF Directorate Fisheries Research., Lowestoft.* **78**: 46pp.

Berry, J. (1955). Hydro-electric developments and nature conservation in Scotland. *Proceedings of the Royal Philosophical Society of Glasgow.* **77**: 23-36.

Bevanger, K. (1998). Biological and conservation aspects of bird mortality caused by electricity power lines: A review. *Biological Conservation.* **86**: 67-76.

Bragg, O. M., Black, A. R. and Duck R.W. (1999). *Anthropogenic impacts on the hydrology of rivers and Lochs: Literature Review and Proposed Methods.* Scotland and Northern Ireland Forum for Environmental Research [SNIFFER] Report No W98(50) I1, 111pp.

Brandt, S. A. (2000). Classification of geomorphological effects downstream of dams. *Catena.* **40**: 375–401.

British Hydropower Association. (2005). *A Guide to UK Mini-Hydro Developments.* Wimbourne, Dorset, UK: British Hydropower Association.

Brunke, M., Hoffmann, A. and Pusch, M. (2000). The impacts of flow reduction on aquatic invertebrates in the lowland River Spree, Germany. *Wasser und Boden.* **52**: 33-41.

Cada, G. F. (2001). The development of advanced hydroelectric turbines to improve fish passage survival. *Fisheries*. **26:** 14-23.

Carr, J. (2000). Atlantic salmon (*Salmo salar* L.) smolt migration patterns in the dam-impacted St. John River system. In: *Advances in Fish Telemetry* (Moore, A, and Russell, I. Eds), pp. 48-72. Publ. CEFAS, Lowestoft.

Chanseau, M. and Larinier, M. (1999). The behaviour of returning adult Atlantic salmon (*Salmo salar* L.) in the vicinity of baigts hydroelectric plant on the pau river as determined by radio telemetry. *Bulletin Francais de la peche et de la pisciculture.Paris.* **353-354:** 239-262.

CCS. (1978). *Scotland's Scenic Heritage.* Countryside Commission for Scotland Publ. 97pp.

Clay, C. H. (1995). *Design Of Fishways and other Fish Pass Facilities.* Second edition. London: Lewis Publishers. pp. 248.

Copestake, P. (2006). Hydropower and environmental regulation – A Scottish perspective. *Ibis.* **148:** 169–179.

Cooper Committee. (1942). *Hydro-Electric Development in Scotland.* Command Paper Cmd 6406, HMSO Edinburgh.

Coutant, C. C. and Whitney, R. R. (2000). Fish behavior in relation to passage through hydropower turbines: A review. *Transactions of the American Fisheries Society.* **129:** 351-380.

Crisp, D. T. (1984). Effects of Cow Green Reservoir upon downstream fish populations. *Freshwater Forum.* **52:** 47-62.

Crisp, D. T. and Mann, R. H. K. (1991). Effects of impoundment on populations of bullhead *Cottus gobio* L. and minnow, *Phoxinus phoxinus* (L.), in the basin of Cow Green Reservoir. *Journal of Fish Biology.* **38:** 731-740.

Crisp, D. T., Mann, R. H. K. and Cubby, P. R. (1983). Effects of regulation of the River Tees upon fish populations below Cow Green Reservoir. *Journal of Applied Ecology.* **20:** 371-386.

Crisp, D. T., Mann, R. H. K. and Cubby, P. R. (1984). Effects of impoundment upon fish populations in afferent streams at Cow Green Reservoir. *Journal of Applied Ecology.* **21:** 739-756.

Crisp, D. T., Mann, R. H. K., Cubby, P. R. and Robson, S. (1990). Effects of impoundment upon trout (*Salmo trutta*) in the basin of Cow Green Reservoir. *Journal of Applied Ecology.* **27:** 1020-1041.

Doyon, J., Schetagne, R. and Verdon, R. (1998). Different mercury bioaccumulation rates between sympatric populations of dwarf and normal lake whitefish (*Coregonus clupeaformis*) in the La Grande complex watershed, James Bay, Quebec. *Biogeochemistry.* **40:** 217-233.

Eatherley, D.M.R., Thorley, J.L., Stephen, A.B., Simpson, I., MacLean, J.C. and Youngson, A.F. (2005). *Trends in Atlantic Salmon: The Role of Automatic Fish Counter Data in their Recording.* Scottish Natural Heritage Commissioned Report No. 100 (ROAME No. F01) 65pp.

Elder, H.Y. (1965). Biological effects of water utilisation by hydro-electric schemes in relation to fisheries with special reference to Scotland. *Proceedings of the Royal Society of Edinburgh.* **69B:** 246-271.

Englund, G., Jonsson, B. and Malmqvist, B. (1997). Effects of flow regulation on bryophytes in north Swedish rivers. *Biological Conservation.* **79:** 79-86.

Englund, G. and Malmqvist, B. (1996). Effects of flow regulation, habitat area and isolation on the macroinvertebrate fauna of rapids in north Swedish rivers. *Regulated Rivers: Research and Management.* **12:** 433-445.

French, K., Anderson, M., Scruton, D. and Ledrew, L. (1998). Fish mercury levels in relation to characteristics of hydroelectric reservoirs in Newfoundland, Canada. *Biogeochemistry.* **40:** 217-233.

Garcia De Jalon, D., Sanchez, P. and Camargo, J. A. (1994). Downstream effects of a new hydropower impoundment on macrophyte, macroinvertebrate and fish communities. *Regulated Rivers: Research and Management.* **9:** 253-261.

Gibbins, C. N., Soulsby, C., Jeffries, M. J. and Acornley, R. (2001). Developing ecologically acceptable river flow regimes: A case study of Kielder Reservoir and the Kelder water transfer system. *Fisheries Management and Ecology.* **8:** 463-485.

Gilvear, D. J., Heal, K. V. and Stephen, A. (2002). Hydrology and the ecological quality of Scottish river ecosystems. *Science of the Total Environment.* **294:** 131-159.

Gowans, A.R.D. (1999). Movements of adult Atlantic salmon (*Salmo salar* L.) in relation to hydroelectric schemes in Scotland. *University of Aberdeen: PhD Thesis.* 145 pp.

Hake, M., Dahlgren, T., Åhlund, M., Lindberg, P. and Eriksson, M.O.G. (2005). The impact of water fluctuation on the breeding success of the black-throated diver *Gavia arctica* in southwest Sweden. *Ornis Fennica.* **82:** 1–12.

Halleraker, J. H., Saltveit, S. J., Harby, A., Arnekleiv, J. V., Fjeldstad, H. and Kohler, B. (2003). Factors influencing stranding of wild juvenile brown trout (*Salmo trutta*) during rapid and frequent flow decreases in an artificial stream. *River Research and Applications.* **19:** 589-603.

Hancock, M. (2000). Artificial floating islands for nesting Blackthroated Divers *Gavia arctica*. Scotland: construction, use and effect on breeding success. *Bird Study.* **47:** 165–175.

Hansen, M.M. (2002). Estimating the long-term effects of stocking domesticated trout into wild brown trout (*Salmo trutta*) populations: an approach using microsatellite DNA analysis of historical and contemporary samples. *Molecular Ecology.* **11:** 1003-1015.

Harness, R. E. and Wilson, K. R. (2001). Electric-utility structures associated with raptor electrocutions in rural areas. *Wildlife Society Bulletin.* **29:** 612-623.

Hendry, K. and Cragg-Hine, D. (2003). *Ecology of the Atlantic salmon.* Conserving Natura 2000 Rivers, Ecology Series No. 5 English Nature, Peterborough. 32 pp.

Holmes, N. T. H. and Whitton, B. A. (1977). The macrophytic vegetation on the River Tees in 1975: Observed and predicted changes. *Freshwater Biology.* **7:** 43-60.

ICES/EIFAC. (2004). Report of the ICES/EIFAC Working Group on Eels (WGEEL). 22–26 November 2004 Galway, Ireland.

Janss, G. F. E. and Ferrer, M. (1998). Rate of bird collision with power lines: Effects of conductor-marking and static wire-marking. *Journal of Field Ornithology.* **69:** 8-17.

Jensen, A. J. (2003). Atlantic salmon (*Salmo salar*) in the regulated River Alta: Effects of altered water temperature on parr growth. *River Research and Applications.* **19:** 733-747.

Johnson, F.G. (1994). Hydro-electric generation. In: *The Fresh Waters of Scotland: A national resource of International Significance.* (Maitland, P.S., Boon, P.J. and McLusky, D.S. Eds) pp. 297-316. John Wiley and Sons, Chichester 639pp.

Jonsson, N., Jonsson, B. and Hansen, L.P. (1997). Canges in the proximate composition and estimates of upstream migration and spawning in Atlantic salmon *Salmo salar*. *Journal of Animal Ecology.* **66:** 425-436.

Jungwirth, M., Schmutz, S. and Weiss, S. (Eds). (1998). *Fish Migration and Fish Bypasses.* Oxford: Fishing News Books. 438 pp.

Kruk, A. and Penczak, T. (2003). Impoundment impact on populations of facultative riverine fish. *International Journal of Limnology.* **39:** 197-210.

Lauters, F., Lavandier, P., Lim, P., Sabaton, C. and Belaud, A. (1996). Influence of hydropeaking on invertebrates and their relationship with fish feeding habits in a Pyrenean river. *Regulated Rivers: Research & Management.* **12:** 563-573.

Larinier, M., Porcher, J.P. and Travade, F. (2002). Fishways: Biological basis, design criteria and monitoring. *Bulletin Francais de la Pêche et de la Pisciculture.* **364:** 208pp.

Lehman, R. N. (2001). Raptor electrocution on power lines: Current issues and outlook. *Wildlife Society Bulletin.* **29:** 804-813.

Lenthall, J. (2004). *Best Value and Biodiversity in Scotland: A Handbook of Good Practice for Public Bodies.* HMSO, Edinburgh 74pp.

Lessard, J. L. and Hayes, D. B. (2003). Effects of elevated water temperature on fish and macroinvertebrate communities below small dams. *River Research and Applications.* **19:** 721-732.

LI-IEMA. (2002). Guidelines for Landscape and Visual Impact Assessment. SPON Press, London. 166pp.

MacDonald, J.R. and Hyatt, R.A. (1973). Supersaturation of nitrogen in water during passage through hydroelectric turbines at Mactaquac Dam. *Journal of Fisheries Research Board Canada.* **30:** 1392-1394.

MacKenzie Committee. (1962). *Electricity in Scotland (Report on the Generation and Distribution of Electricity in Scotland).* Command Paper Cmnd 1859, HMSO, Edinburgh.

Maitland, P.S. (2003). *Ecology of the River, Brook and Sea Lamprey.* Conserving Natura 2000 Rivers, Ecology Series No. 5 English Nature, Peterborough. 52 pp.

Malcolm, I. A., Soulsby, C. and Youngson, A. F. (2002). Thermal regime in the hyporheic zone of two contrasting salmonid spawning streams: Ecological and hydrological implications. *Fisheries Management and Ecology.* **9:** 1-10.

Malcolm, I. A., Soulsby, C., Youngson, A. F. and Petry, J. (2003a). Heterogeneity in ground water-surface water interactions in the hyporheic zone of a salmonid spawning stream. *Hydrological Processes.* **17:** 601-617.

Malcolm, I. A., Youngson, A. F. and Soulsby, C. (2003b). Survival of salmonid eggs in a degraded gravel-bed stream: effects of groundwater-surface water interactions. *River Research and Applications.* **19:** 303-316.

Mathers, R.G., De Carlos, M., Crowley, K. and Ó Teangana, D. (2002). A review of the potential effect of Irish hydroelectric installations on Atlantic salmon (*Salmo salar*) populations, with particular reference to the River Erne. *Biology & Environment: Proceedings of the Royal Irish Academy.* **102B:** 69-79.

McGinnity, P., Prodohl, P., O' Maoileidigh, N., Hynes, R., Cotter, D., Baker, N., O'Hea, B. and Ferguson, A. (2004). Differential lifetime success and performance of native and non native Atlantic salmon examined under communal natural conditions. *Journal of Fish Biology.* **65:** 173-187.

Miquet, A. (1990). Mortality in black grouse *Tetrao tetrix* due to elevated cables. *Biological Conservation.* **54:** 349-355.

Morrison, K. and Therien, N. (1995). Changes in mercury levels in lake whitefish (*Coregonus clupeaformis*) and northern pike (*Esox lucius*) in the LG-2 reservoir since flooding. *Water, Air, & Soil Pollution.* **80:** 819-870.

Mudge, G.P. and Talbot, T.R. (1993). The breeding biology and causes of failure of Scottish black-throated divers *Gavia arctica.* *Ibis.* **135:** 113–120.

Murray, W.H. (1962). *Highland landscape: A Survey.* Report commissioned by by the National Trust for Scotland.

Nilsson, C. and Dynesius, M. (1994). Ecological effects of river regulation on mammals and birds: A review. *Regulated Rivers: Research & Management.* **9:** 45-53.

Osmundson, D. B., Ryel, R. J., Lamarra, V. L. and Pitlick, J. (2002). Flow-sediment-biota relations: Implications for river regulation effects on native fish abundance. *Ecological Applications.* **12:** 1719-1739.

Ovidio, M. and Philippart, J. (2002). The impact of small physical obstacles on upstream movements of six species of fish. *Hydrobiologia.* **483:** 55-69.

Parasiewicz, P., Schmutz, S. and Moog, O. (1998). The effect of managed hydropower peaking on the physical habitat, benthos and fish fauna in the RIver Bregenzerach in Austria. *Fisheries Management and Ecology.* **5:** 403-417.

Payne, P. (1988). T*he Hydro: A. Study of the Development of the Major Hydro-Electric Schemes Undertaken by the North of Scotland Hydro Electric Board.* Aberdeen, UK: Aberdeen University Press.

Penczak, T. (1995). Food consumption by fish populations in the Warta River, Poland, before and after impoundment. *Hydrobiologia.* **302:** 47-61.

Petts, G.E. (1984). *Impounded Rivers: Perspectives for Ecological Management.* Wiley, Chichester, 326 pp.

Pillai, A., Reid, C.T. and Black, A.R. (2005). Reconciling renewable energy and the local impacts of hydro-electric development. *Water Law Review.* **7:** 110-123.

Reid, C.T., Pillai, A. and Black, A.R. (2004). Environmental controls on hydroelectric schemes in Scotland. *Water Law.* **6:** 238-241.

Reid, C.T., Pillai, A. and Black, A.R. (2005). The emergence of environmental concerns: hydroelectric schemes in Scotland. *Journal of Environmental Law.* **17:** 1-22.

Rorslett, B. and Johansen, S.W. (1996). Remedial measures connected with aquatic macrophytes in Norwegian regulated rivers and reservoirs. *Regulated Rivers: Research & Management.* **12:** 509-522.

Salford Civil Engineering Limited. (1989). *Small Scale Hydroelectric Generation Potential in the UK.* Salford Civil Engineering Limited Report to the Department of Energy , Report Number ETSU-SSH-4063-P2.

Saltveit, S. J., Halleraker, J. H., Arnekleiv, J. V. and Harby, A. (2001). Field experiments on stranding in juvenile Atlantic salmon (*Salmo salar*) and brown trout (*Salmo trutta*) during rapid flow decreases caused by hydropeaking. *Regulated Rivers: Research & Management.* **17:** 609-622.

Schetagne, R., Doyon, J. and Fournier, J. (2000). Export of mercury downstream from reservoirs. *Science of the Total Environment.* **260:** 135-145.

Scottish Executive. (1999). *National Planning Policy Guidance; NPPG 14 Natural Heritage.* HMSO, Edinburgh. 24pp.

Scottish Executive. (1999). *Planning Advice Note; PAN 58 Environmental Impact Assessment.* HMSO, Edinburgh. 57pp.

Scottish Executive. (2000). *National Planning Policy Guidance; NPPG 6 Natural Heritage.* HMSO, Edinburgh. 23pp.

Scottish Executive. (2000). *Planning Advice Note; PAN 60 Planning for Natural Heritage.* HMSO, Edinburgh. 43pp.

Scottish Executive. (2002). *Planning Advice Note; PAN 45 Renewable Energy Technologies.* HMSO, Edinburgh. 58pp.

Scottish Executive. (2003). *Securing a Renewable Future: Scotland's Renewables Energy.* HMSO, Edinburgh. 22pp.

Scottish Executive. (2004). *A Strategy for the Conservation and Enhancement of Biodiversity in Scotland.* HMSO, Edinburgh. 58pp.

Scottish Executive Environment Group. (2006). *Implementing the Water Environment and Water Services (Scotland) Act 2003: Consequential Amendments to the Electricity Act 1989, Existing Schemes & Local Enactments - A Policy Statement.* Scottish Executive Environment Group, March 2006, 9pp.

SEERAD. (2000). *Habitats and Bird Directives: June 2000.* Nature conservation: implementation in Scotland of EC Directives on the Conservation of Natural Habitats and of Wild Flora and Fauna and the Conservation of Wild Birds ('The Habitats and Birds Directives'). Revised. *Guidance Updating Scottish Office Circular No. 6/1995.* Edinburgh, UK: Scottish Executive.

Scottish Hydro-Electric. (1992). *Hydro-Electric and the Environment.* SHE, Perth.

Skinner, A., Young, M. and Hastie, L. (2003). *Ecology of the Freshwater Pearl Mussel.* Conserving Natura 2000 Rivers, Ecology Series No. 5 English Nature, Peterborough. 16 pp.

SEPA. (2002). The future of Scotland's Waters, Guiding principals on the technical requirements of the Water Framework Directive. Stirling, UK: Scottish Environmental Protection Agency.

SEPA. (2004). *Consultation on the Scottish River Basin Management Planning Strategy.* Stirling, UK: Scottish Environmental Protection Agency.

SEPA. (2005). Scotland River Basin District, characterisation and impact analysis required by article 5 of the Water Framework Directive. Stirling, UK: Scottish Environmental Protection Agency.

Smith, G. W., Johnstone, A. D. and F. Shearer, W. M. (1996). *The behaviour of returning adult Atlantic salmon* (Salmo salar L.) *at a Borland lift fish pass as determined by radio telemetry.* SOAFD Fisheries Research Services Report No. 7/96.

Smith, J.W.N. (2005). *Groundwater–Surface Water Interactions in the Hyporheic Zone.* Environment Agency Science Report SC030155/SR1, 71pp.

SNH. (2001a). *Natural Heritage Futures: Fresh Waters.* Scottish Natural Heritage Natural Heritage Futures Series 36pp.

SNH. (2001b). *Guidelines on the Environmental Impacts of Wind farms and Small Scale Hydroelectric Schemes.* Scottish Natural Heritage, Battleby.

SNH. (2002). *Natural Heritage Zones: A National Assessment of Scotlands Landscapes.* Report to Scottish Natural Heritage 445pp.

SNH. (2004). Renewables Trends in Scotland: Statistics and Analysis. Scottish Natural Heritage Internal Report 27pp.

SNIFFER. (2004). *WFD 29: Management Strategies and Mitigation Measures Required to Deliver the Water Framework Directive for Impoundments.* Edinburgh, UK: SNIFFER.

Solomon, D.J., Sambrook, H.T. and Broad, K.J. (1999). *Salmon migration and river flow: results of tracking radio tagged salmon in six rivers in South West England.* Environment Agency R&D Publication 4. 110pp.

Struthers, G. (1996). *Hydro-electric Development in Scotland and its Effects on Fish.* Hydro-Electric, Perth, Scotland. 70pp.

Svensson, B. S. (2000). Hydropower and instream flow requirements for fish in Sweden. *Fisheries Management and Ecology.* **7:** 145-155.

Thorstad, E. B. and Heggberget, T. G. (1998). Migration of adult Atlantic salmon (*Salmo salar*); the effects of artificial freshets. *Hydrobiologia.* **371-372:** 339-346.

Tremblay, A., Lucotte, M. and Rheault, I. (1996). Methylmercury in a benthic food web of two hydroelectric reservoirs and a natural lake of Northern Quebec (Canada). *Water, Air, & Soil Pollution.* **91:** 255-269.

Turnpenny, A. W. H. (1999). Mitigation measures for migratory fish at hydro plants. *International Journal on Hydropower & Dams.* **6:** 83-88.

UK Steering Group. (1995). Biodiversity: The UK Steering Group Report. Volume 2 Action Plans. HMSO, London. 324 pp.

Webb, J. (1990). *The behaviour of adult Atlantic salmon ascending the Rivers Tay and Tummel to Pitlochry dam.* Scottish Fisheries Research Report No. 48.

14 Environmental Impacts from Bioenergy – A View from Sweden

Tomas Käberger – *Associate Professor, International Institute for Industrial Environmental Economics, Lund University, PO Box 196, SE-221 00 Lund, SWEDEN.*

Summary

1. In Sweden bioenergy has grown into the second largest source of energy, and is contributing to reducing emissions of CO_2 and improving the security of energy supply. Usage in 2003 was 378 PJ (105 TWh), or 42 GJ/capita.

2. When a tree is harvested for the purpose of providing wood products or paper, only half of the biomass ends up as the desired end product, the other half is available as by-products for energy purposes. After the wood has served as a building material or the fibres have been recycled several times as paper, most of the energy may still be recovered.

3. Utilization of by-products has provided a new and important source of income in the forestry sector. Today, the bioenergy market is vital to the economic competitiveness of the forest industry in general and sawmills in particular.

4. Prior to this expansion, environmental concerns were voiced regarding several perceived risks associated with bioenergy: some of the more important were local air pollution, increased local transport of fuel, forestry practices threatening biodiversity and, in addition, new risks to labour. The early environmental concerns have now been resolved: local air pollution has been managed by using raw biofuels only in efficient high-power boilers, while refined wood pellets are increasingly used for the more difficult small-scale applications such as heating individual houses; transport to large district heating plants in cities is often made using rail or ship. The increased use of bioenergy has been achieved during a period when forestry has become more aware and respectful of ecological values and mechanization has reduced labour risks.

5. Attention is now focused on multi-functional energy forestry, such as when *Salix* spp. plantations are used to develop wildlife havens or treating sewage water or sewage sludge. The bioenergy sector, perhaps more than other parts of forestry and agriculture, is developing systems for recycling of nutrients.

Käberger, T. (2008). Environmental Impacts from Bioenergy – A View from Sweden. In *Energy and the Natural Heritage*, ed. by C.A. Galbraith and J.M. Baxter. TSO Scotland, Edinburgh. pp. 185-194

14.1 Significant increase in bioenergy utilization

The driving forces encouraging modern bioenergy systems have gathered strength during the last few decades. From the early 1970s, there has been an interest in Sweden in reducing dependence of imported oil. At the time, energy savings, energy efficiency, renewable energy, coal, and nuclear power were all favoured options, however, the risks and costs of nuclear power that were highlighted in a national referendum in 1980 resulted in that option being no longer considered viable. Paradoxically, however, the ultimate decommissioning of nuclear power was preceded by a doubling in capacity; but this was not a problem for the development of bioenergy generation as its initial market was mainly in the heating sector.

The next decade started with the introduction of high carbon taxes on fossil fuels in the heating sector. This tax was introduced on the basis of an unholy alliance between the electricity companies – hoping to create a market for the significant over-capacity in electricity generation due to the rapid expansion in nuclear power generation capacity – and the environmental movement, both hoping that the result would be reduced carbon emissions, greater energy efficiency and more renewable energy generation (Käberger, 2002). Since the year 2000, evolving geopolitical conflicts have increased the urgency of concerns about security of supply of oil and gas throughout Europe. The overall result has been an acceleration in the rate of development in the bioenergy sector in Sweden and elsewhere in Europe. Bioenergy supply capacity has increased from 40 TWh in 1970 to 105 TWh in 2003 (Figure 14.1). In response to growing demand, the rate of increase has

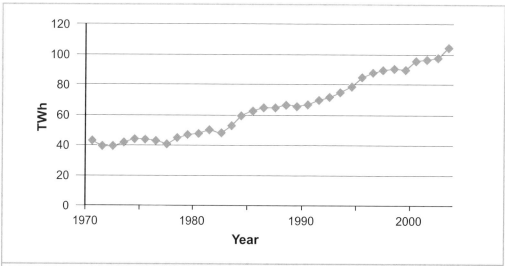

Figure 14.1 Bioenergy use in Sweden from 1970 to 2003. Data 1970-2002, based on Energy facts and figures published yearly by the Swedish Energy Administration. (www.stem.se), for 2003 via Ministry of Finance Personal Communication.

grown: on average, the bioenergy use has increased by 2 TWh per year during the last 30 years, by 2.5 TWh per year during the last 20 years, and by 3 TWh per year during the last 10 years. This rate of increase is equivalent to the output from one new nuclear power station added every year. In fact, in 1970 bioenergy supplied about 40 TWh more than

Measures of Bioenergy use in Sweden 2003		
Energy 105 TWh	Energy per capita 12 MWh/capita	Average power per capita 1.3 kW/capita
378 PJ	48 GJ/capita	Share of total energy use: 20%

nuclear energy: during the following decades 12 nuclear reactors were added, but there were only two years when nuclear power supplied more energy than bioenergy in Sweden, and by the year 2000, bioenergy was once again supplying 40 TWh more energy than nuclear power.

To further illustrate this, it should be noted that more nuclear electricity is produced per capita in Sweden than in any other country in the world. Disregarding the transport sector, Swedish bioenergy supply exceeded oil at the turn of the century and became the largest source of energy in Sweden, and if the use of oil for transport is disregarded, bioenergy is the largest source of energy in Sweden. In Finland, bioenergy generation includes a significant share from peat; including peat in the total means that, bioenergy generation for Finland surpassed the total oil use in 2003.

14.2 Large, but what is it?

Most of the biomass used for energy purposes in 1970 came from residues in the pulp industry. Black liquor, bark and other residues were burned as substitutes for oil to provide heat to the industry itself, while reducing the problem of waste disposal.

Plate 14.1 Field of short-rotation coppice willow adjacent to the E.ON UK's biomass power station at Steven's Croft, near Lockerbie © Phil Baarda

In the 1980s residues in the sawmills and wood industry were increasingly utilized for energy purposes, and in the 1990s foresters started to collect branches and tops while logging. EU legislation has also increased the requirement to burn biomass waste for energy utilization rather than sending it to landfills.

Initially, the pulp- and paper-industry was both producing and using fuel as a substitute to fossil fuels for production of heat and power. There was also an early market for suppliers of equipment among farmers using wood from their own forests, and sawmills using their own residues to produce the heat they needed.

Despite being weak, a tax incentive created to encourage bioenergy use resulted in district heating plants turning to bioenergy, thus creating a market for the excess residues that could not be utilized in the forest industries. District heating-networks were built in Sweden from the late 1960s, mainly by municipal energy companies. Low electricity prices, due to over-capacity after the nuclear expansion, meant there was only limited interest in electricity production from biomass. Instead the priority was to maximize total energy efficiency. As a result, technologies such as smoke-stack condensation were developed, making it possible to utilize the energy otherwise lost as moisture and released as water vapour through chimneys.

From 1990 the carbon tax on fossil fuels was sufficient to encourage substitution of coal in existing district heating plants and, sometimes, even of oil with wood powder or oils from biomass. Since 1990 virtually all new heat generation capacity has been based on both large and small scale biomass.

Improved energy efficiency of houses created an environmental challenge to the bioenergy industry. Burning wood efficiently and meeting good environmental performance standards requires a combination of high temperature and sufficient air supply. Traditional wood logs are so large that the heat released during combustion is larger than the heat requirement of a well-insulated, single-family house. Two solutions have been developed. The first relies on heat storage in a water tank: the wood fired boiler is operated at full power for a few hours, the heat accumulates in the tank and is then released to the house at a controlled rate. The

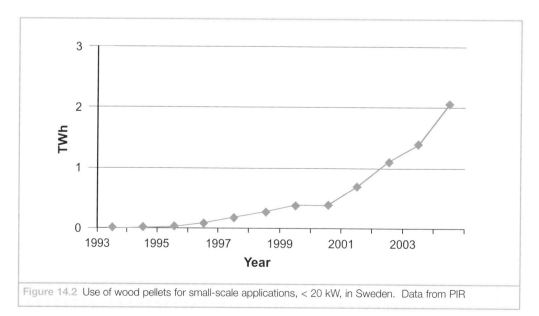

Figure 14.2 Use of wood pellets for small-scale applications, < 20 kW, in Sweden. Data from PIR

Plate 14.2 Domestic wood pellet burning furnace designed to power central heating and hot water boiler.
© Martin Gaywood

second solution is based on smaller pieces of wood, wood pellets, that can be efficiently combusted at low power. In addition to being useable on a small scale, low power application, pellets provide opportunities for storage, transport and automatic handling superior to any unrefined biofuel (Various, 2004).

Small-scale wood pellet use has accelerated during recent years. While only a few hundred pellet stoves substituting for, or supplementing direct electric heating existed in the mid 1990s, more than 3,500 were installed in 2003. A similar increase has occurred for installations of pellet burners replacing oil-burners in conventional central heating systems. The resulting increase in pellet use for small-scale applications is shown in Figure 14.2. Larger quantities are used in district heating plants.

14.3 Relations with the forest industry

The major share of the bioenergy market is based on residues from the forestry sector and used for heating in industry, district heating systems and in small-scale applications. Bioenergy does not compete with the forest industry: instead the energy sector has become a key contributor in ensuring the continuing competitiveness of the Swedish forest industry in general and the sawmill industry in particular. Traditionally, only half of the above-ground biomass of a tree cut in the forest was used for timber and paper production; the other half was discarded as residue at different stages of the production process. As the bioenergy market started paying for these residues, the value of the standing crop of the forests increased. To the sawmills, the bioenergy market has become vital for their continuing competitiveness: such that income from selling traditional residues to the energy sector has been larger than profits for many years. Faced with increasing competition from Eastern Europe and America it is likely that Swedish sawmills would have closed if the energy market had not provided this additional income.

The Scottish forestry sector could also potentially benefit from similar harvests during the coming two decades if, and only if, modern sawmills and a bioenergy market are established simultaneously. In the old industry there is one group of factories that will compete rather than work in synergy with the bioenergy industry, and that is the chipboard factories. In Sweden most of these have transformed into producing wood pellets instead of chipboards.

During the development of the Swedish bioenergy industry, the role of the Swedish Bioenergy Association, SVEBIO, was crucial. Unlike many similar organizations, the bioenergy association has been vertically integrated, organizing the complete supply chain

Plate 14.3 Branches and tops of trees cut for timber or pulpwood are bundled for transport to energy plants © Tomas Käberger

from forest owners and farmers to producers of boilers and combustion equipment, and fuel traders to district heating and energy companies. As a result the organization has been an efficient forum for the development and distribution of new technologies and business concepts. SVEBIO has also served as a source of information to society at large. Sometimes the capacity to provide information has been very important politically as analysis of political proposals has required information from many companies and resources for analysis. The vertical integration has also meant that the organization has not acted to reduce competition. A very important consideration for the long-term success of the development of the bioenergy sector was the openness to imported biofuels: Swedish fuel suppliers have at different times suggested restrictions on imports, citing security of supply as well as the dubious environmental benefits of unfamiliar imported biomass such as olive nuts or recycled fuels. However, the bioenergy association has always been in favour of unrestricted imports as this freedom of supply has been of vital importance for maintaining the willingness of interested parties to invest in biomass dependent heat and co-generation plants. The opportunity to import biofuels has provided an important reduction in price uncertainty for investors; in the end, there has always been a small but healthy international trade - the order of magnitude of net imports has been 5% of total bioenergy use (Ericsson and Nilsson, 2004) - but this has not deterred a fast-growing demand for fuels from Swedish suppliers.

14.4 New developments

Energy crops make up only some 15,000 ha of land, contributing less than one percent to the bioenergy supply. However, as the demand for bioenergy increases, so will the demand for energy plantations, in particular in those European countries with less extensive forest industries. Increasing oil prices have made automotive fuel production from biomass more appealing and economically viable. In Sweden an ethanol market has been developed initially based on ethanol from the forest industry. One plant producing ethanol from grain has added significant capacity, although most of the ethanol used as automotive fuel is imported.

Ethanol as an automotive fuel has been favoured with exemptions from the general fuel tax. The first ethanol users were captive fleets of buses; then a series of some 250 flexible fuel Ford Taurus vehicles were imported from the US. When the ethanol-from-grain plant was built, fuel distribution companies in the region of the production plant started blending ethanol into petrol up to 5%. Now, such blending is done throughout the country, mostly relying on imported sugarcane-based ethanol produced at low economic cost in Brazil which despite the long transportation distance shows good environmental life cycle performance.

The number of ethanol vehicles has increased dramatically during recent years as more than 10,000 Ford Focus cars with flexible fuel engines have been sold. In 2004 SAAB announced it would introduce an FFV-model in 2005, and Volvo have said that they will also have vehicles that can run on any mixture of ethanol and petrol on the market by 2005. Several other FFVs are available in the Brazilian and US markets and are expected to arrive in the Swedish market as a result of growing demand.

The policy support for vehicles falling under definitions of 'environmental cars' has been orchestrated at different levels. In addition to the tax rebate on the fuel, there are favourable tax rules for such 'environmental cars' as company cars, and in some of the major cities in Sweden local regulation provide favourable parking rules for these vehicles.

14.5 Environmental issues

14.5.1 Opportunities

Recently the Swedish Radiation Protection Agency prepared legislation requiring the bioenergy industry to contribute to the on-going decontamination of areas of Sweden after the Chernobyl accident. In some regions in Sweden, the fall-out from the accident, almost 20 years ago, was so high that remaining radioactive caesium may still require restrictions on the use of meat from animals reared here. As caesium is taken up by the trees and subsequently concentrated in the ash after combustion, long-term storage of such ash will act to remove significant quantities of radioactive caesium from regions of high fall-out. The bioenergy industry is agreeable to implementing the legislation, but finds it unfair that they should be expected to bear the cost when the pollution was caused by the operators of the nuclear reactor.

There are several other opportunities for the use of bioenergy systems in helping reach environmental objectives while reducing dependence on unsustainable sources of energy. Significant areas of agricultural land have accumulated undesirably high amounts of cadmium due to prolonged use of inorganic fertilizers. Some variants of *Salix* spp. have the capacity to accumulate cadmium and planting such *Salix* spp. as an energy crop and storing the ash after combustion will contribute to cadmium decontamination of agricultural land (Berndes *et al.*, 2004).

A pioneering system-development has been undertaken by the energy company in Enköping, located by Lake Mälaren, some 70 km west from Stockholm. The sewage treatment plant of the city faced more stringent demands on the water released into the Lake. The conventional solution involving concrete and chemical treatments would require significant investment and on-going operating costs: instead, the neighbouring energy company together with the farmer next to the co-generation plant developed an ecological solution. The water from the sewage treatment plant is used to irrigate and fertilize a *Salix* sp. plantation thus utilizing the undesirable nutrients to increase productivity. The sewage treatment plant avoided unnecessary investment, the farmer got a profitable crop, and the energy company had a source of fuel established within a few hundred metres of the co-generation plant.

When establishing energy plantations there may be opportunities to achieve other environmental or landscape goals simultaneously. A *Salix* sp. plantation may act as a wind-break, serve as erosion control, reduce nutrient run-off from agricultural land, or serve as a visual barrier. Introducing *Salix* sp. plantations in agricultural landscapes may provide new habitats, in particular for birds and mammals, thus increasing biodiversity – and creating opportunities for recreation (Börjesson *et al.,* 2002; Berndes and Börjesson, 2004).

14.5.2 Local environmental and health effects

Incomplete combustion of fuels leads to emissions of hydrocarbons and particles, and is associated with various health risks and also is subject to environmental regulation. The continued use of old types of wood burning practices may still be a considerable problem in villages and towns, especially when combined with frequent atmospheric temperature inversions. With modern large-scale combustion plants, the emissions are under strict control with negligible external impacts. As all the large plants have been built since modern technologies and environmental regulations were introduced, local pollution from these plants poses no concerns. However, there are still thousands of old-type wood-burning systems in operation, but as the modern equipment is not only environmentally superior and also more convenient and fuel efficient, the incentive to modernize is there. The kind of equipment described above, heat accumulating tanks and modern pellet equipment, are all contributing to a dramatic reduction in local pollution: the relation between the best and worst is in the order of a factor of 1,000 in emissions of hydrocarbons.

However, there is new evidence that the risks of old-type equipment may not be as high as once thought, provided good birch wood is used. The chemical composition of smoke particles is such that the health effects may be expected to be less severe than effects of particles from other sources (Kjällstrand and Petersson, 2001).

Plate 14.4 A modern wood burning stove © Tomas Käberger

14.5.3 Sustainability issues

Sustainability of any operation is key to the ultimate success of the process. A fundamental condition is that the forestry or agriculture delivering the biomass should be sustainable under material flow- as well as biodiversity criteria. Swedish forestry practices are not perfect, but the environmental organizations agree that there has been measurable improvement in practices thus preserving habitats for biodiversity during the decades when bioenergy utilization has also increased. Collecting branches and tops from trees logged has no additional negative ecological effects. However, if acting separate from the primary harvesters, it is necessary that bioenergy entrepreneurs have the same level of knowledge so as to protect valuable habitats in the forests.

With all harvesting practices, nutrients are removed from the soil. Recycling of nutrients from harvested food or from biomass used for materials have both proved difficult due to contamination during use. Biomass harvested for energy purposes, however, is usually kept uncontaminated. Recycling of ash after suitable stabilization is therefore fully possible, and the degree of recycling will be close enough to 100 percent for all nutrients except nitrogen. Often, the reduction of nitrogen in combustion, and the resulting net removal of nitrogen from forest soils may in some parts of Sweden be seen as an advantage as it compensates for the overload caused by air-pollution (Lundborg, 1997). If, on the other hand, additional nitrogen is needed, nitrogen fertilizers may be produced using a fraction of the energy supplied by the bioenergy system.

Ash recycling is carried out by only a small proportion of bioenergy systems in Sweden. An incentive for the practice comes from recycling being a requirement for the voluntary environmental labelling system for electricity in Sweden (Käberger, 2003). Recommendations on how to recycle ash have been provided by the National Board on Forestry (Skogsstyrelsen, 2001), and a project intended to promote the practice is running in cooperation between several authorities, energy companies and forest owners (RecAsh, 2006).

Net CO_2 effects of bioenergy systems are simple in general but complicated in detail. It is generally sufficient to see that as long as the biological source of the biomass to be converted to energy is managed in a sustainable fashion, the net carbon balance with the atmosphere will be constant, and the bioenergy system will be neutral to climate. But there can be complications. One set of issues that may be relevant to peat-systems as well as systems using wet biomass is the emission of methane: as methane is a stronger greenhouse gas than CO_2, avoiding or increasing methane emissions may have significant impacts on the performance of the bioenergy system.

Biomass may be combusted in such a way that the carbon that plants have removed from the atmosphere is stored underground. Under a system of economic incentives to make carbon sequestration economically viable for fossil fuels, biomass based energy systems may also benefit from economic compensation for removing carbon from the atmosphere. That compensation may be of the same order of magnitude as the payments for electricity and heat delivered (Obersteiner *et al.*, 2001).

Conclusion

In Sweden bioenergy use has increased rapidly and is now a major source of energy. Development has occurred in symbiosis with the forest industry, and bioenergy systems may be utilized to achieve other objectives than increasing renewable energy supply. Modern technologies have reduced local air-pollution while long-term sustainability can be achieved provided forestry and agricultural practices are well managed.

References

Berndes, G. and Börjesson, P. (2004). Low cost biomass produced in multifunctional plantations – the case of willow production in Sweden. 2nd World Conference and Technology Exhibition on Biomass for Energy, Industry and Climate Protection, Rome, Italy, 10-14 May 2004.

Berndes, G., Fredriksson, F. and Börjesson, P. (2004). Cadmium accumulation and *Salix* based phytoextraction on arable land in Sweden. *Agriculture, Ecosystems and Environment.* **103**(1): 207-223.

Börjesson, P., Berndes, G., Fredriksson, F. and Käberger, T. (2002). Multifunktionella bioenergiodlingar. Slutrapport (Multifunctional bioenergy plantations. Final report, in Swedish). Environmental and Energy Systems Studies, Dept. of Technology and Society, Lund University, Sweden.

Ericsson, K. and Nilsson, L.J. (2004). International Biofuel Trade – A Study of the Swedish imports. *Biomass and Bioenergy.* **26**: 205-220.

Käberger, T. (2002). Swedish Nuclear Power and Economic Rationalities. *Energy and Environment.* **30**: 185-200.

Käberger, T. (2003). Environmental labelling of electricity delivery contracts in Sweden. *Energy Policy.* **31**: 633-640.

Kjällstrand, J. and Petersson, G. (2001). Phenolic antioxidants in wood smoke. *Journal of the Science of the Total Environment.* **277**: 69-75.

Lundborg, A. (1997). Reducing the Nitrogen Load: Whole-tree harvesting. *Ambio.* **26**: 387-393.

Obersteiner, M., Azar, C., Kauppi, P., Mollersten, K., Moreira, J., Nilsson, S., Read, P., Riahi, K., Schlamadinger, B., Yamagata, Y., Yan, J. and van Ypersele, J.P. (2001). Managing Climate Risk. *Science.* **294:** 786-787.

RecAsh. (2006). http://www.recash.info/news.asp?lang=en; accessed 04 August 2006.

Skogsstyrelsen. (2001). Rekommendationer vid uttag ar skogsbränsle och kompensationsgödsling. Meddelande 2001:2. Jönköping.

Swedish Energy Agency. (2004). *Energiläget 2004,* Eskilstuna.

Various. (2004). Pellets 2002. The first world conference on pellets. *Biomass and Bioenergy.* **27** (6): 513-693.

15 Onshore Windfarms Landscape Visual and Cumulative Impacts – The SNH Approach

Laura Campbell – *Scottish Natural Heritage, 16/17 Rubislaw Terrace, Aberdeen AB10 1XE.*

Summary

1. Onshore windfarms on a modern, commercial scale are large engineering undertakings, often in difficult terrain and conditions.
2. The landscape and visual effects of onshore windfarms can be considerable and may be controversial.
3. Many aspects need to be examined when assessing a windfarm's impacts on an area's landscape character and visual amenity.
4. There is often much that can be done to reduce the negative impacts of windfarms provided an appropriate location is selected in the first place. Factors such as the layout, number and size of turbines, and the alignment of access tracks, can often be altered to lessen negative impacts.
5. Cumulative landscape and visual impacts are complex to assess and present. The decisions about when an area's capacity is reached are difficult to make.
6. SNH's aim is to encourage the right windfarm in the right location.

15.1 Introduction

This chapter is about the landscape and visual impacts of onshore windfarms in Scotland, and the role of Scottish Natural Heritage, the government's natural heritage adviser, in addressing these. Cumulative effects are considered, as are guidance and policy relating to landscape and visual issues. This chapter is divided into four main sections: firstly, an outline of the context, secondly a description of current, commercial windfarms and their typical impacts on landscape character and visual amenity. Thirdly, cumulative impacts are discussed and fourthly, an outline of SNH's role and involvement in windfarm casework, policy, research and guidance is presented.

15.2 Context

SNH is a government body responsible to Scottish Government Ministers and through them to the Scottish Parliament. Its remit includes habitats, species, landscape, access and recreation. Its advice on landscape issues is based on a landscape character approach, as required in national planning guidance (Scottish Office, 1999) and in common with other

Campbell, L. (2008). Onshore Windfarms Landscape Visual and Cumulative Impacts – The SNH Approach. In *Energy and the Natural Heritage*, ed. by C.A. Galbraith and J.M. Baxter. TSO Scotland, Edinburgh. pp. 195-204 parts of the UK. In principle, SNH supports onshore wind power as one measure in helping to achieve renewable energy production targets set by government. However, such support comes with the caveat that appropriate natural heritage issues need to be taken into account and negative impacts on them minimized.

The number of onshore windfarms, and applications for them, has increased greatly in recent years. In the late 1990s, only one or two windfarms existed in Scotland, together with a small number of single turbines, for example on Fair Isle and at Findhorn on the Moray Firth. At the end of 2004 perhaps about 30 windfarms had been, or were being, constructed and about 250 were at various stages of the planning process (see Figure 12.3).

Evolving technologies have resulted in much larger turbines than those built or even envisaged several years ago. The size of proposed windfarms, in terms of energy output, turbine numbers and their extent, has also increased greatly; and those windfarms that were built in the late 1990s now seem comparatively small. In Scotland, as elsewhere, windfarms have implications for the appearance and character of landscapes both now and into the future. Attitudes towards the potential changes vary from strict opposition to strong support. Such opinions are often firmly held and proposals for windfarm developments can generate robust debate.

15.3 Windfarm developments

Onshore windfarms involving a number of turbines are a relatively new type of development; traditional windmills were much smaller (up to approximately 24 metres high for some of the tallest) and they tended to occur singly rather than in groups. The unprecedented type and scale of modern windfarms have contributed to the strength of views often held about this form of development.

Essentially, a windfarm consists of a group of wind turbines. The number of turbines varies from small groups of three or four, up to several hundred in the largest, currently proposed developments. Modern wind turbines are of a fairly standard design, having three rotating blades vertically mounted on a solid tower (Figure 15.1). The alternative designs, including two-bladed machines, horizontally revolving blades, and lattice towers tend to be less popular than this simple, sculptural form. Despite their relatively standard design, wind turbines can vary considerably in size. The most recent generation of commercial turbines measure up to 100 – 140 metres to the tip of the blades at their highest

Figure 15.1 Standard wind turbine design and indication of scale © Claire McDougall / SNH

rotation. The height to the top of the tower, also known as the hub, or nacelle height, is about 70 metres, with blade lengths typically being 30 to 40 metres. The increasing size of turbines offers greater efficiency and savings: fewer turbines are needed to produce the same amount of electricity. With an increase in turbine and windfarm size, however, the greater

Access tracks   Large borrow pit

Sub-station building   Turbine foundation

Figure 15.2 Visual impacts associated with windfarms © SNH

generally the potential for adverse landscape and visual impacts.   Large turbines may not always be compatible with their surroundings.   In addition, where there are proposals to extend the earlier generation of windfarms, a contrast in size between old and new turbines, and differences in their layout, will be disconcerting.

Wind turbines themselves are not the only components of windfarms.   Ancillary equipment, such as access tracks and electricity transmission lines, is needed and can also be highly visible (Figure 15.2). Access tracks are required to connect the windfarm to the main road together with a network of service tracks between each turbine. These tracks must be wide enough and of sufficiently shallow gradients to allow access for the large vehicles needed to prepare foundations and to transport and erect turbine components. When the construction period is over, the width of tracks can often be reduced as maintenance vehicles are usually smaller than construction equipment. This can allow some track restoration work, resulting in reduced landscape and visual impacts.

The remoteness of many windfarms means relatively long access tracks need to be constructed. The requirement for a considerable amount of road-building material necessitates the digging out on-site of 'borrow pits', which may be large. Further construction impacts include excavations for the turbine foundations; forest clearance, fencing, or additional ground preparation may also be needed.

A connection to the national grid is necessary in all cases. Generally, each turbine is linked to the windfarm sub-station by underground cables that run beneath or alongside the access tracks. The sub-station itself is a building similar in size to a small house and from this power lines may run overhead, usually strung between wooden poles rather than pylons, to connect with the national grid. The increasing number of windfarms has brought about a need for new or upgraded transmission lines to distribute the electricity. As a generalization, the windiest locations are distant from the main centres of population and most conventional power stations. The national grid network of electricity distribution lines is not optimally spread to service such locations. Proposals to upgrade some of the main overhead power lines are themselves controversial. Even if different routes are not used, new pylons can be much taller than the existing ones. This degree of change contributes to the strong feelings some people have about such developments.

15.4 Landscape and visual impacts of windfarms

An assessment of landscape and visual impacts of a proposed windfarm development is usually carried out as part of an Environmental Statement that accompanies a planning application. The standard methodologies for these assessments are contained within the publication "*Guidelines for Landscape and Visual Impact Assessment*" (LIIEMA, 2002). As with other subjects in environmental assessment, the underlying concept for landscape and visual impact assessment is that the significance of an impact depends on the magnitude of the change and the sensitivity of the host environment. Generally, the greater the sensitivity and the larger the proposed change the more significant the likely impacts are assessed as being. Impacts on landscape character and visual amenity are separate, but related, concepts.

Landscape impacts

Perhaps most obviously, impacts on the landscape include those that affect its physical elements. These can be divided into three main categories: landform, landcover, and settlement. In the case of a windfarm development, landform can be modified by access tracks where cuttings and embankments are needed to achieve suitable gradients to allow the delivery of turbine components and the cranes needed to position them. Landcover can change, for example where tree or forest felling is required. This may be necessary not just to provide clear space for turbines, but also to reduce the effects that adjacent woodland can have on turbine performance by making air flows more turbulent. There are various ways in which settlement can be affected, including the requirement to maintain a minimum distance between turbines and residents, and also the windfarm's relationships to other built features in the landscape.

Other aspects of landscape, in addition to its physical features, also need to be considered. These can include cultural and historical aspects; how the landscape is experienced; and whether it is valued or designated. Landscape character is concerned with identifying the key features comprising a landscape and how these combine to form areas of distinct and discrete character. It describes the pattern of elements that constitute a particular area and how it is perceived; its 'sense of place' and local identity.

Assessing impacts on landscape character involves determining whether a particular development would be appropriate or damaging in the landscape. For example, would the size and layout of turbines be appropriate in the landscape? Or would they conflict with its scale or pattern, or how it is experienced? In large-scale landscapes, such as wide uplands or gently rolling hills, large turbines may correspond well with the simple expanse. Fewer, larger turbines tend to be easier to design in simple, harmonious ways that do not seriously detract from the landscape. However, in smaller-scale or more intricate landscapes, or where domestic buildings or other human-scale artefacts exist, very large turbines are likely to appear out-of-place. They can contrast too strongly with other landscape elements, as their size becomes over-dominant when seen in relation to buildings whose dimensions are known. Turbines may not be suitable at all in an area valued for its wild land qualities.

Plate 15.1 Crystal Rig wind farm on the horizon in the eastern Lammermuir Hills, as seen from near North Berwick, 20 Km away © John Baxter

Visual impacts

Visual impacts are defined as changes in the appearance of the landscape as the result of development (LIIEMA, 2002). They are regarded as positive or negative, or in other words beneficial or detrimental. The scale of visual impact varies with the sensitivity of the landscape and the number and sensitivity of viewers. All other things being equal, the more people that see a new development the greater the likely impacts are assessed as being. Thus, a trunk road or a railway may be regarded as a more sensitive viewpoint than a minor road. But the sensitivity of viewers is equally important.

Residents are regarded as being highly 'sensitive', as their views of a development will persist and occur every day. In contrast, travellers are considered as being 'less sensitive' because they are transient and their view of the development would be of much shorter duration. Within this category, tourist routes would be ranked as more sensitive than non-designated roads. The angle of view to the development also affects sensitivity: oblique views may be rated as less sensitive than straight ahead views. Whether the structures are silhouetted on a sky-line or not also needs to be considered. The reasons why people are in an area are also relevant. Thus, identified or popular viewpoints and routes for walkers, and especially those designed to encourage users to enjoy the landscape, rate as highly sensitive. Participants in formal sports might be ranked as less sensitive as their attention is – or is assumed to be – elsewhere. Workers, finally, are generally rated as least sensitive, for the same reason: they are not expected to be looking at the view. So an industrial estate or office is considered to be a less sensitive viewpoint than a residential area or a footpath.

Magnitude of change

The level of change caused by the proposed development is also relevant when assessing both landscape and visual effects. Very generally, the bigger the change the greater the likely impacts. But the context is also important, together with factors such as the relationship with other landscape features; so magnitude of change is not a straightforward linear relationship. For example, a single small wind turbine (low magnitude) in an undeveloped or pristine landscape (high landscape sensitivity, even if it would not be seen by many people) could result in a large change to the character of that landscape.

Cumulative impacts

Cumulative effects result from two or more windfarms being seen at the same time or in sequence. These are, inevitably, more likely to occur as the number of windfarms increases. They can arise in a single view, or when looking around from a single viewpoint, perhaps from the top of a hill. When developments are seen in sequence, even if not in a single glance - as when travelling along a route - repeated sighting of windfarms may reinforce and add to the impact of seeing a single development. Cumulative impacts raise specific issues and can be difficult to assess. 'Multi-layered' environmental assessments can become very complex as they try to indicate areas from which more than one windfarm could be seen, and also identify from where which windfarms would be visible. Sequential viewpoints can be even harder to assess. But cumulative impacts also raise, more fundamentally, the question of 'when is enough enough?'. Is there a point at which a given landscape or area could reach capacity? And, if so, how do we judge when that point is likely to be reached? This is an ongoing problem and challenge to which there is as yet no simple answer.

15.5 Roles of SNH

SNH, as the government adviser on natural heritage issues, has specific roles to play in the consents system for windfarm approvals. With regard its landscape remit, SNH has published its Landscape Policy Framework. (SNH, 2005). This clarifies SNH's approach to landscape matters, including the use of landscape character.

SNH produced a renewable energy policy in 2001 (SNH, 2001b). This recognizes the value that renewables technologies can have in reducing dependence on fossil fuels. Whilst noting potential impacts on the natural heritage, SNH seeks a strategic approach to guide renewable energy developments towards the locations where adverse impacts can be minimized.

SNH roles in consents systems

There are several ways and stages at which SNH contributes to windfarm consents systems:

Casework

One of the main strands of SNH involvement with windfarms is through consultations on individual cases. Permission is needed for windfarm developments, and this is sought from local authorities or, for larger schemes of more than 50 MW, directly from the Scottish Government. SNH has a role as the natural heritage adviser to the Government, local authorities, developers and the public. It is, accordingly, consulted on applications for developments likely to have natural heritage impacts. In addition, SNH is a statutory consultee, and as such it has to be formally consulted, for all planning applications that are accompanied by an Environmental Statement. Most windfarms fall into these categories.

Policy

SNH often contributes to responses to draft renewables policies. This includes national guidance and also individual local authorities' planning policies. The experience accrued from involvement in casework across Scotland is essential in ensuring consistent, practical policy advice.

Research and guidance

SNH has commissioned several research projects, often in partnership with others, examining various aspects of windfarm developments. These seek to develop national guidance and policy, and disseminate and promote good practice. For example, photo-montages are one of the main methods used by both the public and decision-makers to judge the acceptability of a proposal, and it is important that they are not misleading. SNH is well-placed to contribute to this debate and, along with industry and local authority representatives, it has commissioned research into best practice. A first guide was produced in 2002, and was updated in 2006, (University of Newcastle, 2002; Horner, MacLennan and Envision, 2006).

Standard methodologies

As part of its national role, SNH contributes to the development and use of standard methodologies. This is invariably in collaboration with other relevant bodies such as planning authorities and windfarm industry representatives. The use and advocacy of standard, agreed methodologies for describing and assessing landscape and visual impacts has been established by the *Guidelines for Landscape* (LIIEMA, 2002) and *Visual Impact Assessment* and *Landscape Character Assessment Guidance for England and Scotland* (Countryside Agency & SNH, 2002).

Guidance

SNH's involvement in the planning and consents systems means that considerable experience of various types of windfarms has been gained. This has helped SNH to formulate and contribute to guidance in addition to general methodologies on landscape and visual impact assessment. SNH's *"Guidelines on the Environmental Impacts of Windfarms and Small-scale Hydroelectric Schemes"* (SNH, 2001a) describes environmental factors relevant to windfarm design. For national natural heritage interests, SNH produced Strategic Locational Guidance in 2002. This provides information about natural heritage sensitivities and designations. It provides a starting point to indicate where particular sensitivities may lie, but does not, and cannot, replace individual and other appropriate assessments. SNH has also produced advice on the scoping of cumulative landscape and visual impact assessments (SNH, 2003). This remains informal although it has been developed in consultation with the industry and with local authorities.

In partnership with the relevant local authorities, SNH commissioned four pilot studies which attempted to define landscape capacities for windfarms at a regional scale. The pilot areas were Ayrshire and the Clyde Valley, Argyll and Bute, East and North Highland and Moray, and the Western Isles (Land Use Consultants & Argyll and Bute Coucil, 2002; Macaulay Land Use Research Institute & Edinburgh College of Art, 2003; Benson *et al.*, 2004; Land Use Consultants, 2004). The findings and methodologies of these innovative reports were appraised, and it was found that they helped to identify sensitivity to change rather than the maximum recommended amount of windfarm development. This is partly because of the complexities involved even in defining, rather than identifying, landscape and visual capacity. There have also been a few studies that focus on particular areas, such as parts of the Ochil Hills, where there are groups of applications; and other studies that focussed on a few specific scenarios which included clustering versus dispersal of development. These types of approach may be more practical. Several local authorities have produced renewable energy strategies which aim to guide developments to more appropriate locations. In the absence of regional targets or other strategic frameworks for wind power provision, these studies and strategies help provide a context for decision-making.

15.6 Acknowledgements

The opinions expressed in this paper are those of the author and do not necessarily reflect those of SNH. The author gratefully acknowledges the contributions of Emma Jordan for Figure 15.3 and Clare McDougall for Figure 15.2. She is also grateful to Nigel Buchan, Krystyna Campbell and Jenny Simmonds, all of SNH, for help with drafts of this paper. Any remaining errors are the fault of the author alone.

References

Benson, J.F., Scott, K.E., Anderson, C., Macfarlane, R., Dunsford, H. and Turner, K. (2004). *Landscape Capacity Study for onshore wind energy development in the Western Isles. SNH Commissioned Report* No 042 (ROAME N0. F02LC04).

Countryside Agency & Scottish Natural Heritage. (2002). *Landscape Character Assessment Guidance for England and Scotland.* SNH, Perth & CA, Cheltenham.

Horner, Maclennan and Envison. (2006). *Visual Representation of Windfarms – Good Practice Guidance.* SNH, Battleby, Perth.

Land Use Consultants for Scottish Natural Heritage & Argyll and Bute Council. (2002). *Assessment of the sensitivity of landscapes to windfarm development in Argyll and Bute.* SNH, Perth.

Land Use Consultants. (2004). *Ayrshire and Clyde Valley windfarm landscape capacity study. SNH Commissioned Report No 065* (ROAME No. F01AA309c).

Landscape Institute & Institute of Environmental Management and Assessment. (2002). *Guidelines for Landscape and Visual Impact Assessment.* 2nd edition. Spon Press, London.

Macaulay Land Use Research Institute & Edinburgh college of Art. (2003). *Study into landscape potential for wind turbine development in East and North Highland and Moray. SNH Commissioned Report No 070* (ROAME No. F02AA302).

Scottish Executive. (2002). *Planning Advice Note 45 Renewable Energy Technologies.* Scottish Executive, Edinburgh.

Scottish Natural Heritage. (2001a). *Guidelines on the Environmental Impacts of Windfarms and Small Scale Hydroelectric Schemes.* SNH, Perth.

Scottish Natural Heritage. (2001b). *SNH's Policy on Renewable Energy.* Policy Note Series Policy Statement No. 2. SNH, Perth.

Scottish Natural Heritage. (2003). *Cumulative Effect of Windfarms SNH Guidance.* SNH, Perth.

Scottish Natural Heritage. (2005*). Policy Statement No 05/07 SNH's Landscape Policy Framework.*

Scottish Office. (1999). *National Planning Policy Guideline NPPG 14 Natural Heritage.* Scottish Office, Edinburgh.

University of Newcastle. (2002). *Visual Assessment of Windfarms Best Practice.* SNH Commissioned Report F01AA303A.

Plate 15.2 Creag Meagaidh © Lorne Gill, SNH

16 Effects of Terrestrial Wind Farms on Birds and Upland Habitats

D. Philip Whitfield – *Scottish Natural Heritage, 2 Anderson Place, Edinburgh EH6 5NP.*
Current address: Natural Research (Projects) Ltd, Banchory Business Centre, Burn O'Bennie Road, Banchory, Aberdeenshire AB31 5ZU.

Andrew M Coupar – *Scottish Natural Heritage, Great Glen House, Leachkin Road, Inverness IV3 8NW.*

Summary

1. The main potential negative effects of terrestrial wind farms on birds and upland habitats are outlined. For birds these are fatality through collision with turbine blades and displacement from the environs of turbines through disturbance. Habitats suffer direct loss beneath the footprint of the infrastructure and indirect losses through soil disturbance and changes to hydrology.

2. Understanding and predicting the effects of wind farms on birds is hampered for many reasons: this review concentrates on some. It is widely accepted that Before-After-Control-Impact (BACI) studies are desirable to provide rigorous conclusions on wind farm effects yet they are relatively uncommon due largely to practical difficulties: greater cooperation between stakeholders is probably required to circumvent this shortfall.

3. Too few of the numerous studies on wind farm – bird interactions are accessible to a wide audience; still fewer are published in the peer-reviewed scientific literature, bringing numerous difficulties to all parties interested in the wind energy industry, exacerbated by the apparent complexity of the issues. Readily available, independent and authoritative studies of habitat impacts are almost non-existent. Developers are therefore encouraged to publish more of the studies that they commission and the wider research community encouraged to engage in this extremely significant yet relatively untapped field.

4. The potential beneficial effects of wind energy developments, when coupled with targeted habitat management, are noted as an alternative land use for those bird species which do not appear unduly influenced by wind farm effects but which may be poorly-served by existing land uses. Evaluating these biodiversity trade-offs is another area for future research.

Whitfield, D.P. & Coupar, A.M. (2008). Effects of Terrestrial Wind Farms on Birds and Upland Habitats. In *Energy and the Natural Heritage*, ed. by C.A. Galbraith and J.M. Baxter. TSO Scotland, Edinburgh. pp. 205-220

16.1 Introduction

Other chapters in this volume have covered the environmental and political drivers behind increasing the contribution of 'clean' and renewable sources to Scottish energy production, with the goal of environmental gains through decreased CO_2 emissions (Sprent *et al.*, 2008; Todd and Band, 2008). In Scotland, terrestrial (onshore) wind farms form the bulk of novel renewable energy initiatives, resulting in a number of issues relating to the potential effects of terrestrial wind farms on birds and habitats. Rather than reiterate the environmental benefits accrued by wind energy, such aspects are noted only where they are directly relevant to carbon cycles in habitats. Whilst the focus is on the evidence and arguments surrounding some of the potential negative effects of wind energy production, the widely accepted positive effects should not be forgotten, including the potentially beneficial habitat creation opportunities presented by wind farm construction, which are not often acknowledged. Nevertheless, by describing some of the potential environmental drawbacks of onshore wind energy generation, this provides a reminder of the need for the correct balance to be struck (Todd and Band, 2008): maximization of beneficial reductions in CO_2 emissions through novel developments should also aim to minimize any adverse immediate impacts on the natural heritage.

Detailed reviews of the impacts of wind farm – bird interactions are available elsewhere (e.g. Erickson *et al.*, 2001; Bern Convention, 2003), hence, the focus here on the need for rigorous impact research and the difficulties created by a poor scientific publication history of wind farm – bird studies, in order to encourage high standards and an improved knowledge-base. The implications of wind farm construction for Scotland's habitats are reviewed and the significance of key habitats and the main issues affected by wind farms are described, giving special prominence to arguments for and against wind farm construction on blanket bog.

16.2 Wind farms and birds

There are four main potentially adverse impacts of wind farms on birds (Bern Convention, 2003; Band *et al.*, 2007):

- mortality through collision with moving turbine (rotor) blades;
- displacement of birds from an area in or around the wind farm site through disturbance (indirectly equivalent to habitat loss);
- displacement of birds from an area beyond the wind farm site by a 'barrier effect' in which displacement from the wind farm prevents birds using other areas which were formerly accessed through the wind farm site before development;
- direct habitat loss and fragmentation through the construction of wind farm infrastructure.

Collision with power lines and electrocution at power poles are secondary impacts if connection of the wind farm to the power grid is above ground, but they are potential problems common to many forms of electricity generation (Erickson *et al.*, 2001), and so are not dealt with here. It is important to note, nevertheless, that wind farms are often constructed in more remote locations or at high points in the landscape that may bring unique difficulties for associated power lines.

Plate 16.1 (left) Golden plover (*Pluvialis apricaria*) a bird of the uplands © Lorne Gill and (right) White-tailed eagle (*Haliaeetus albicilla*); its numbers are slowly increasing across Scotland © Lorne Gill

Direct habitat loss through wind farm construction is generally considered inconsequential, as construction usually only involves loss associated with turbine bases and maintenance tracks (Percival, 2000). Inappropriate siting of a development may lead to loss of limited nest site habitat, however, and for small species with small home ranges direct habitat loss may result in destruction of a substantial part or all of an individual's home range. Further exceptions could include particularly large wind farms or, where wind farms are built on peatland habitats where construction may interfere with the hydrological processes that maintain the peatland (Parkyn *et al.*, 1997) and damage an area even wider than the wind farm area itself.

Disturbance during construction is short-term and usually can be readily counteracted by timing construction outwith sensitive periods for birds. Hence, most potential problems for birds posed by wind farms involve the risks of post-construction displacement through disturbance and turbine collision mortality, and so most studies of wind farm – bird interactions deal with these issues.

Collision mortality and displacement through disturbance are mutually antagonistic risks: when one risk decreases, the other risk increases (Band *et al.*, 2007). Hence, some adverse impact can always potentially occur. Consequently, adverse effects are more likely when a wind farm is larger and/or when the bird interest is greater, and there is a clear consensus that sensitive planning of wind farm location is fundamental to avoiding deleterious effects (e.g. NWCC, 2000; Bern Convention, 2003). A further consequence of the ubiquitous potential risks that a wind farm may pose is that ornithological assessments of wind farm proposals must be rigorous.

Ornithological assessments of wind farm proposals can also be informed by the results of previous studies of wind farm impacts: such studies have been reviewed several times recently (e.g. Gill *et al.*, 1996; Erickson *et al.*, 2001; Bern Convention, 2003). No generalized conclusions were reached by these reviews because it was apparent that displacement was an issue for some species at some sites, but was not a serious issue in several other cases. Similarly, collision fatalities occurred at several sites, infrequently involving relatively high numbers, but occurred only occasionally or not at all for some species at other sites.

Safe conclusions are also hampered by a marked shortage of studies published in the scientific peer-reviewed literature, thus potentially reducing confidence in the credibility of studies. This shortage is readily apparent from the sources in reference lists of reviews, and although globally there have been hundreds of studies of the effects of onshore wind farms on birds, only a handful have appeared in the scientific literature (e.g. Winkelman, 1985; Osborn *et al.*, 1998, 2000; Leddy *et al.,* 1999; Larsen and Madsen, 2000; Barrios and Rodríguez, 2004; de Lucas *et al.*, 2004; Everaert and Stienen, 2006). For UK wind farms, on our current knowledge, only one site-based study of effects has been published (Meek *et al.*, 1993), and this involved a small number of turbines.

The importance of the peer-review process is heightened by many potential methodological pitfalls in wind farm studies. Displacement effects are best studied with a BACI (Before-After-Control-Impact) design (Green, 1979; Anderson *et al.*, 1999), which involves survey of bird numbers or behaviour at the wind farm (impact) site and a similar reference (control) site before and after construction. BACI protocols have been followed by several studies, though not all (e.g. Gill *et al.*, 1996; Bern Convention, 2003); those that have been unable to adhere to a BACI design are less reliable, but may still be revealing nevertheless. As changes in bird numbers or behaviour on a wind farm site can be influenced by a number of factors other than the influence of the wind farm itself, these additional factors should be accounted for. This can be done by the use of a good reference site where the influence of the additional factors change in tandem with those on the wind farm site. Results will also be most reliable when collected over a number of years because, for example, bird abandonment of a wind farm site through disturbance may be temporary due to habituation or, on the other hand, there may be a time lag in an effect of displacement due to site-faithful, long-lived birds. Most, if not all, BACI wind farm studies are conducted by incorporating the impact assessment process for a developer's development proposal. At least in the UK, planning authorities cannot impose the need for a reference site away from the development site to be studied simultaneously, and developers may be unwilling or unable to fund additional studies away from the development site, for a variety of reasons, such as unsympathetic neighbouring landowners and uncertainty over approval of the proposal. The desirability of BACI studies is thus hindered practically and so probably requires a strategic overview of research needs and stakeholder-partnership initiatives to be fulfilled, potentially funded by setting aside some of the subsidies/profits which the drive for renewable energy developments can generate.

Searches for victims of collision with rotor blades can underestimate fatalities if there are no calibration studies of (and corrections for) sources of error:

- search error (observers do not find all corpses which are present);
- removal error (corpses may be removed before searched for, by scavengers, for example);
- crippling error (birds may die outside of the search area if they are fatally wounded); and, in some cases -
- 'habitat' error (some habitats may not be searchable) (Gauthreaux, 1996).

Several recent studies have acknowledged these problems and have accounted for most or all of them (e.g. Johnson *et al.*, 2000; Smallwood and Thelander, 2004). Early studies were less aware, however, and consequently many do not provide reliable estimates of collision mortality: Winkelman (1995) reported that of 108 European studies, only three had produced reliable collision mortality estimates. For the UK, Percival (2000) reviewed several studies (the majority available only as reports to development companies) and indicated that collision fatality estimates were low. However, as Gill *et al.* (1996) point out, at least some of these studies did not calibrate their search efforts for potential errors and so are "best regarded as anecdotal". Lowther (2000) also offered similar criticisms of some of the reports. The only study in Percival's (2000) review that is in the public domain, and so readily available for independent scrutiny, is that of Meek *et al.* (1993): these authors openly acknowledged that searches for collision victims were 'casual' and so Percival's (2000) derivation of a collision fatality rate, without referring to this strong caveat, was inappropriate. It may be safest to conclude that, like most other European studies, most early UK studies at wind farms may not have provided reliable collision fatality estimates.

As pointed out by several authors, most recently Smallwood and Thelander (2004), discussion of collision fatality rates (or, indeed, any other potential effects of wind farms) should be made in the context of information on bird activity levels since the intensity of effect is liable to be influenced, at least crudely, by the level of bird activity. A number of authors have also indicated the importance of site topography, weather, species and season in accounting for differences in collision fatalities (e.g. Barrios and Rodríguez, 2004), serving to emphasize the need for several studies in order to increase our understanding of and ability to predict collision fatality. A difficulty here is that research on the potentially large number of influential factors on collision fatality requires good numbers of strike victims and many or most modern wind farms where methodological awareness has circumvented search biases do not apparently result in such numbers (Erickson *et al.*, 2001). Clearly, it is of overriding importance that wind farms should not be located where they kill large numbers of birds but this overriding goal results in few studies of influences on collision fatality and thus, ironically, reduced understanding of where wind turbines should best be located. By a similar token, post-construction research is far less likely to occur at a wind farm where very few collision fatalities are anticipated because such research is not deemed cost-effective and planning authorities may have greater difficulty in imposing a post-construction 'monitoring' condition on developers. A small individual site effect may be seen to justify an absence of post-construction study but cumulatively across many such sites these effects may impact a population and hence the absence of post-construction study, even at low-risk sites, is a serious obstacle to assessing cumulative impacts.

Uncertain reliability presents difficulties for wind farm studies because the degree of impact seems species-, site-, and location-specific, so that differences in impact can be apparent within wind farm sites (e.g. Hunt, 2002; Smallwood and Thelander, 2004) as well as between sites (e.g. Erickson *et al.*, 2002). Whereas relatively high rates of collision per turbine have been recorded for golden eagles (*Aquila chrysaetos*) at Altamont Pass, California (Smallwood and Thelander, 2004), collision rates at Foote Creek Rim, Wyoming (Young *et al.*, 2003a, b) were lower than expected based on differences in eagle use of the two sites (Johnson *et al.*, 2000; Erickson *et al.*, 2002). The location of turbines away from 'hotspots' of eagle activity at Foote Creek Rim (Erickson *et al.*, 2002) may explain the difference between the sites. Moreover, the lack of a displacement effect at one site does not necessarily mean that there will be no effect at another. For example, USA studies imply that pairs of golden eagles may not be displaced by operational wind farms (Johnson *et al.*, 2000; Hunt, 2002), whereas initial results at a Scottish wind farm are more suggestive of displacement (Walker *et al.*, 2005). The difference may lie in a prolonged history of human persecution and greater use of remote areas away from human influence for eagles in Scotland.

Of course, an absence of publication in the scientific literature does not inherently mean that a study has limited scientific credibility. For instance, the recent studies of collision mortality at Altamont (Hunt, 2002; Smallwood and Thelander, 2004) have been transparently conducted to accepted standards (Anderson *et al.*, 1999), and have considerably advanced the research field. These recent studies at Altamont, and much other ornithological research at USA wind farms, are available on the internet, which both allows rapid access to research results in a field where the pace of development is fast and circumvents another difficulty associated with not publishing in the peer-reviewed literature: inaccessibility. At least in the UK, most wind farm studies occur only as 'confidential' reports to development companies and so present difficulties to all stakeholders by not being in the public domain:

- Inaccessibility is problematic for independent review and hinders learning.
- The use of confidential reports in Environmental Impact Assessments (EIAs), which is not wholly justified by a need to protect rare species, increases the time taken by planning authorities and their advisers to source reference material and makes their acceptability as supporting arguments problematic, regardless of their scientific validity, if accessibility is open to some developers but not others.
- Material necessary for other developers to conduct cumulative effect studies may be difficult to source; moreover, public EIAs only outline projected effects and not the actual/observed effects documented by post-construction research that are necessary for realistic cumulative studies.
- Several wind farms in Scotland are associated with positive habitat enhancement measures as 'mitigation', but these cannot be appreciated or accounted for if reports on such management are confidential.

Consequently, while recognizing the importance of not publicly releasing any information which may potentially bring harm to a species (notably if it may identify nest sites of rare or protected species), we would encourage developers to publicize the results of impact studies and habitat enhancement work. The use of positive management measures to enhance bird populations away from wind farms may not always be appropriate as 'mitigation'. Nevertheless, such measures are to be encouraged whenever appropriate as part of the development process, even if not strictly required to counteract any predicted detrimental effects, because they offer a clear way ahead for dispelling any arguments on the net benefits of terrestrial wind farm development to birds.

16.3 Upland habitats affected by wind farms

Given that the main extent of semi-natural terrestrial habitats in Scotland is in upland areas (Ratcliffe and Thompson, 1988), an inevitable consequence of much wind farm development is the loss, damage or alteration of this resource. The upland habitats most frequently affected are:

Plate 16.2 Turbine base excavation in blanket bog. Causeymire Wind Farm, Caithness. Courtesy of npower renewables © David Shaw, SNH.

- grassland;
- dry heath;
- wet heath;
- blanket bog.

Occasionally montane and woodland habitats also may be affected. Less extensive but widespread upland habitats, such as springs, flushes, rock and scree, also occur on most upland wind farm sites. Freshwater habitats - streams, rivers, lochans and lochs, are key features on many sites, both in their own right and for the species they support: they are not, however, considered further here, nor are individual species dependent on freshwater or terrestrial habitats.

The uplands also support extensive areas of plantation forestry (Averis *et al.*, 2004). This seems to be an increasingly popular choice for wind farm proposals, possibly in recognition of the importance of safeguarding semi-natural habitats. Developing such sites is not without its difficulties as discussed below.

16.4 Determining the significance of upland habitats

Before the significance of the impacts of a wind farm development can be evaluated, it is necessary to determine the significance of the habitats affected – the so called 'valued ecological receptors' as they are described in Environmental Statements. Significance can vary, from 'local' - a habitat which is relatively common-place and may be heavily modified though still retaining a range of characteristic species, to 'international' - including qualifying habitats within sites designated as Special Areas of Conservation (SACs) under the EC Habitats Directive (Directive 92/43/EEC), or as Ramsar sites under the Ramsar Convention on Wetlands (IEEM, 2006). The significance of habitats is thus determined not only by their nature but also by where they occur. For example, an area of high quality habitat outwith a designated site may be less highly valued than an area of poorer quality habitat of the same type within a statutory site.

Considering the key upland habitats most typically affected by wind farms (Table 16.1), most are of significance - either international, if occurring in an SAC, or national wherever they occur and, within limits, irrespective of their condition.

The relevance of the Habitats Directive to habitats on Annex 1, but occurring outwith SACs, is still unclear. Some take the view that their presence on Annex 1 of itself confers international importance; others consider that those habitats are only of international importance when a qualifying feature of a designated site. A third interpretation is that as the Directive indicates that the designation of sites makes only a contribution to the achievement of favourable conservation status of relevant habitats, then at least a proportion of the resource outwith the designated areas must be safeguarded to achieve favourable conservation status. Thus, some proportion of Annex 1 habitats in the wider countryside must be deemed to be of international importance. This issue remains to be resolved.

Although not all montane habitats are on Annex 1 of the Habitats Directive, their significance in relation to wind farm development should not be underestimated. One of the main arguments in favour of wind power is that it will reduce greenhouse gas emissions and thus reduce the potential impacts of climate change. As montane habitats in Scotland are amongst those at most risk from climate change (Defra, 2001) it would seem particularly perverse if wind farm developments were to directly reduce their extent. This line of reasoning has already been successful in amending the proposed layout at the Millennium Wind Farm in Inverness-shire.

Plantation forestry is not normally considered to have a high ecological value. It can, however, support protected species, e.g. bats and otters, and so should not be dismissed lightly. Depending on its development, it may also still support significant elements of the habitat upon which it was planted and thus have a high restoration potential. Alternatively, there may be the potential to create habitats, such as montane scrub which, although not necessarily 'native' to the wind farm site, would contribute to restoring a much diminished

Table 16.1 Relevance of national and international instruments to the evaluation of key upland habitats.

	Annex 1 of EC Habitats Directive	UKBAP priority habitat ww.ukbap.org.uk/genpagetext.aspx?id=91
Grassland	some	some
Dry heath	all	all
Wet heath	most	all
Blanket Bog	all	all
Montane	most	some

Plate 16.3 Turbine location following construction (See Plate 16.2) and habitat restoration. Causeymire Wind Farm, Caithness. Courtesy of npower renewables © npower renewables

national resource. However, ground preparation and tree growth may have irreversibly altered the original soil structure and function, and any subsequent wind farm development might contribute to further instability.

16.5 Impacts of wind farm construction and operation on key upland habitats

The main impacts of wind farms on habitats occur during the construction phase, the duration of which is largely dependent on the size of the development. Current proposals typically anticipate from nine months to 2-3 years to construct. This contrasts with the operational phase, which is normally expected to be 25 years. Impacts on habitats on this

Table 16.2 Main impacts of wind farm construction and operation on key habitats of national and international importance. (✔) indicates impacts for wet heath are minor relative to those for blanket bog.

Impact	Dry heath	Wet heath	Blanket bog
Direct habitat loss	✔	✔	✔
Indirect loss due to soil disturbance	✔	✔	✔
Indirect loss due to hydrological disturbance	✔	✔	✔
Fragmentation	✔	✔	✔
Loss/change due to associated changes in land management	✔	✔	✔
Erosion potential	✔	✔	✔
Loss of stored carbon		(✔)	✔
Loss of capacity to store carbon		(✔)	✔

timescale are harder to predict but are generally considered to be less significant than those experienced during construction. The scale and significance of impacts (Table 16.2) relate not only to the size of the development, but also to site layout, construction techniques, the micro-siting of individual elements and other mitigation measures undertaken.

16.6 Direct losses

The main direct habitat losses result from track construction, borrow pits, turbine foundations, crane hard standings, works compounds (which may include concrete batching plants) and materials lay-down areas. The areas of loss are often greater than is initially apparent from reference to the dimensions of the various components. For example, a turbine base may comprise a concrete plinth 11 m x 11 m, but this requires the excavation of a pit considerably in excess of that, particularly if in an area of deep peat. Furthermore, should the pit fill up with water seeping in from the surrounding peat mass it may require to be pumped out into settlement lagoons, the construction of which may result in further habitat loss.

The favoured method for track construction is to excavate down to a mineral base and build the track on that. On level ground with no or little peat, disturbance to the habitat should not extend much beyond the running surface and any associated drainage, but when cutting across a slope, some 'cut and fill' will be required, extending the area of impact (Scottish Natural Heritage, 2006).

Where it is necessary for tracks to cross peat, floating roads are sometimes proposed as an alternative to excavation. There is no agreed depth of peat required for floating roads, with some proposed on as little as 50 cm and others restricted to areas with at least 2 m of peat. Of equal, if not greater, significance is the consistency of the peat. It is not possible to float a track on very fluid peat – an alternative route should be sought.

Direct loss of wet heath, dry heath and blanket bog is contrary to the objectives of the UK Biodiversity Action Plan (UKBAP) and consequently, the objectives of the Scottish Biodiversity Strategy (Scottish Executive, 2004).

16.7 Indirect losses

Although floating tracks can reduce the area of direct habitat loss to only a little over the width of the running surface, they do cause additional indirect impacts by compressing the peat beneath them, thus reducing the hydraulic conductivity and hence the flow of water across the line of the track. The impact of this alteration of the natural hydrology is difficult to quantify, but it is likely to result in some upslope areas retaining water, with downslope areas receiving less through-flow than previously. The significance to habitats and plant communities of these changes has to be considered in the context of importance of ground water movements relative to atmospheric inputs.

Indirect losses of habitat also result through changes in the nature of the habitat: these may be changes from one habitat type to another or to the condition of the habitat. Revegetation of track verges, turbine bases, crane hardstandings, etc. is often proposed and undertaken as mitigation for the direct losses associated with their construction. Such practices are generally welcomed as they reduce the potential for erosion. However, the vegetation that subsequently grows is unlikely to be the same as that which was there originally, with a trend towards drier, more nutrient-dependent communities, e.g. wet heath replacing blanket bog, dry heath replacing wet heath and grassland replacing dry heath. Such trends are again contrary to the objectives of the UKBAP.

16.8 Fragmentation

Tracks of one sort or another have been built through the Scottish uplands for generations. Traditionally their purpose was to facilitate travel from one place of residence or business to another (Aitken, 1984). The nature of windfarm tracks is, however, quite different from anything that has gone before as they require a high-density network, sometimes completely isolating relatively small areas of heath or bog from the larger areas of which they once formed a part. The implications of this are uncertain. For heathland habitats, a 4 - 5 m wide running surface is unlikely to be a significant barrier to the movement of most organisms or plant propagules. It thus seems likely that there is little genetic isolation. The same is true for blanket bog (but see Wilson and Provan, 2003), but for this habitat there may also be the issue of hydrological isolation which is likely to demonstrate any effects over much shorter timescales. Long term monitoring of habitats and the species they support is required to determine whether fragmentation resulting from track construction and use results in significant loss or change.

16.9 Management change

The construction of a wind farm is often accompanied by other changes in land use. Of most relevance here are changes in agricultural and/or sporting use. Irrespective of the nature and magnitude of the change, it will almost certainly result in changes in grazing regimes with consequent changes in habitat condition. There may also be changes in associated management, for example muirburn. These changes may be beneficial to the habitats and species they support or may be detrimental. Only detailed monitoring can inform that assessment. Many wind farm applications now include proposals for long term management plans devised to enhance the natural heritage of the site or an even wider area through a range of management practices, e.g. altered grazing regimes, blocking of ditches. Such proposals are to be welcomed, but it should be remembered that the habitat losses that are an inevitable consequence of wind farm construction are not the only way of securing these wider "improvements" in the condition of upland habitats. More research is required to evaluate the relative merits of the loss of habitat extent and improved habitat condition.

16.10 Carbon budgets

The apparent contradiction between wind farms as devices to reduce greenhouse gas emissions, and wind farms on blanket bogs causing a loss of stored carbon and carbon fixation capacity, has not gone unnoticed. Also, establishing the total carbon 'cost' of a wind farm, including all elements of manufacture and construction and the 'savings' through reduced carbon emissions resulting from wind-generated electricity replacing fossil fuel-generated electricity, is extremely difficult. However, a few key figures (Scottish Natural Heritage, 2003) illustrate the overall message from any such comparison:

- carbon fixation by a typical area of bog is ~2.5 tC/ha/yr;
- carbon stored in peat is typically ~55 kg/m^3 ;
- carbon emitted in typical grid-mix supply is 407 tC/MW.

The carbon savings of wind-generated electricity over traditional means are so great that on most sites, and probably all, total loss of all peat would still be insufficient to negate them. Thus, while it still makes sense to keep the carbon costs of a site as low as possible, the case cannot be made that wind farms should avoid blanket bogs because the carbon budget will inevitably be unfavourable.

16.11 Erosion

Another argument presented for wind farms avoiding blanket bog is the erosion risk. Blanket bog erosion is a widespread phenomenon in upland Scotland (Coupar *et al.,* 1997), though there remains much uncertainty as to its causes. It is, however, generally accepted that it can occur naturally and that areas that were once eroded can revegetate naturally. It is also widely understood that erosion can be exacerbated, and prevented from recovering, by activities such as muirburn, heavy grazing, trampling and drainage.

In relation to wind farms the main concern is that excavating turbine bases, road construction and associated drainage, etc., destabilize an inherently unstable medium – saturated peat. In particular, it is suggested that disturbing the hydrological integrity of a peat mass, for example by cutting through 'peat-pipes' (natural water drainage channels within the peat deposit), will cause changes in water movement, the consequences of which are impossible to predict.

In October 2003 a major bog-slide at the wind farm construction site at Derrybrien in County Galway, Ireland, appeared to confirm these concerns. Construction was underway in an area of deep peat from which plantation forestry had been partially removed, when a large volume of peat flowed downhill blocking a road and finally reaching a loch resulting in the death of thousands of fish (www.imcg.net/imcgnl/nl0404).

Whatever the precise cause of the Derrybrien bog-slide, and there have been numerous investigations, the wind farm industry now takes this whole issue much more seriously. Assessing the risk of bog-slides and describing the mitigation measures to control their impacts is now expected as part of the Environmental Impact Assessment process for any wind farm proposal involving areas of deep peat. Guidance recently published by the Scottish Executive (2006) should help to ensure a greater degree of consistency of approach than has been the case hitherto.

16.12 Conclusions

Despite many studies having been conducted on the effects of wind farms on birds very few are readily accessible and even fewer have been published in the peer-reviewed scientific literature. While the 'grey literature' undoubtedly has a role in furthering understanding of wind farm – bird interactions, notably in potentially allowing quick access to full research results in a field which advances rapidly, far too few results are published in the peer-reviewed literature or are otherwise accessible and demonstrably robust scientifically. A major recommendation is therefore that wind farm studies commissioned by developers are made more readily accessible and subjected to peer-review. The accepted importance of BACI studies to understanding wind farm effects on birds is unlikely to be fully realized if developers are left to their own devices and not assisted or required to implement them: a strategic overview of research needs and greater cooperation between parties with an interest in understanding wind farm effects are thus also required.

For species where there is a reasonable degree of confidence that properly planned wind farms may only exceptionally have detrimental impacts (e.g. hen harrier *Circus cyaneus*: Madders and Whitfield, 2006; Whitfield and Madders, 2006), if coupled with targeted habitat management, wind energy developments may provide a land use preferable to some existing alternatives.

With respect to habitats, there remains a need for greater consistency in the evaluation of habitat importance and in determining likely impacts. However, as for the birds, the latter will only come about when more information appears in the public domain and more independent studies are carried out which assess the real impacts of different construction methodologies across a wide range of sites and over meaningful timescales.

References

Aitken, R. (1984). Scottish mountain footpaths: a reconnaissance review of their condition. Countryside Commission for Scotland, Perth.

Anderson, R.L., Morrison, M., Sinclair, K. and Strickland, D., (with Davis, H. and Kendall, W.). (1999). *Studying Wind Energy/Bird Interactions: A Guidance Document*. National Wind Coordinating Committee, c/o RESOLVE, Washington DC. [Available from www.nationalwind.org/pubs]

Averis, A.M., Averis, A. B.G., Birks, H.J.B., Horsfield, D., Thompson, D.B.A. and Yeo, M.J.M. (2004). *An Illustrated Guide to British Upland Vegetation*. Joint Nature Conservation Committee, Peterborough.

Band, W., Madders, M. and Whitfield, D.P. (2007). Developing field and analytical methods to assess avian collision risk at wind farms. In: de Lucas, M., Janss, G.F.E. and Ferrer, M. (eds). *Birds and Wind Power: Risk Assessment and Mitigation*. Quercus, Madrid. pp259-275.

Barrios, L. and Rodríguez, A. (2004). Behavioural and environmental correlates of soaring-bird mortality at on-shore wind turbines. *Journal of Applied Ecology*. **41**: 72-81.

Bern Convention (Convention on the Conservation of European Wildlife and Natural Habitats). (2003). *Windfarms and Birds: An analysis of the effects of windfarms on birds, and guidance on environmental assessment criteria and site selection issues*. T-PVS/Inf (2003) 12. Convention on the Conservation of European Wildlife and Natural Habitats (Standing Committee), Council of Europe, Strasbourg.

Coupar, A., Immirzi, P. and Reid, E. (1997). The nature and extent of degradation in Scottish blanket mires. In Tallis, J.H., Meade, R. and Hulme, P.D. (eds). *Blanket Mire Degradation: Causes, Consequences and Challenges*. Macaulay Institute, Aberdeen.

de Lucas, M., Janss, G.F.E. and Ferrer, M. (2004). The effects of a wind farm on birds in a migration point: the Strait of Gibraltar. *Biodiversity & Conservation*. **13**: 395-407.

Defra. (2001). Literature review of the implications of climate change for species, habitats and the wider UK countryside. [Available from www.defra.gov.uk/wildlife-countryside/ewd/rrrpac/lreview.index.htm]

Erickson, W.P., Johnson, G.D., Strickland, M.D., Young, D.P., Sernka, K.J. and Good, R.E. (2001). *Avian Collisions with Wind Turbines: A Summary of Existing Studies and Comparisons of Avian Collision Mortality in the United States*. NWCC c/o RESOLVE Inc., Washington, DC and LGL Ltd., King City, Ontario. [Available from http://www.west-inc.com/wind_reports.php]

Erickson, W., Johnson, G., Young, D., Strickland, D., Good, R., Bourassa, M., Bay, K. and Sernka, K. (2002). *Synthesis and comparison of baseline avian and bat use, raptor nesting and mortality information from proposed and existing wind developments*. Final report by WEST Inc. prepared for Bonneville Power Administration, Portland, Oregon. [Available from http://www.west-inc.com/wind_reports.php]

Everaert, J. and Stienen, E.W.M. (2006). Impact of wind turbines on birds in Zeebrugge (Belgium): significant effect on breeding tern colony due to collisions. *Biodiversity & Conservation* doi 10.1007/s10531-006-9082-1.

Gauthreaux, S.A. (1996). Suggested practices for monitoring bird populations, movements and mortality in wind resource areas. *Proceedings of the National Avian-Wind Power Planning Meeting II, Palm Springs, CA, 1995*, pp. 80-110. NWCC c/o RESOLVE Inc., Washington, DC and LGL Ltd., King City, Ontario. [Available from http://www.west-inc.com/wind_reports.php]

Gill, J.P., Townsley, M. and Mudge, G.P. (1996). *Review of the impacts of wind farms and other aerial structures upon birds.* Scottish Natural Heritage Review No. 21, Edinburgh.

Green, R. H. (1979). *Sampling design and statistical methods for environmental biologists.* Wiley, New York.

Hunt, W. G. (2002). *Golden eagles in a perilous landscape: predicting the effects of mitigation for wind turbine blade-strike mortality.* Consultant Report 500-02-043F to California Energy Commission, Sacramento, California. [Available from www.energy.ca.gov/reports/2002-11-04_500-02-043F.PDF]

IEEM. (2006). Guidelines for ecological assessment in the United Kingdom. [Available from www.ieem.org.uk/ECIA.htm]

Johnson, G.D., Young, D.P., Erickson, W.P., Clayton, E., Derby, C.E.M. and Good, R.E. (2000). *Wildlife monitoring studies SeaWest windpower project, Carbon County, Wyoming 1995-1999.* Final report by WEST Inc. prepared for SeaWest Energy Corporation, San Diego, California and Bureau of Land Management, Rawlins District Office, Rawlins, Wyoming. [Available from www.west-inc.com/wind_reports.php]

Larsen, J.K. and Madsen, J. (2000). Effects of wind turbines and other physical elements on field utilization by pink-footed geese (*Anser brachyrhynchus*): a landscape perspective. *Landscape Ecology.* **15**: 755-764.

Leddy, K.L., Higgins, K.F. and Naugle, D.E. (1999). Effects of wind turbines on upland nesting birds in conservation reserve program grasslands. *Wilson Bulletin.* **11**: 100-104.

Lowther, S. (2000). The European perspective: some lessons from case studies. *Proceedings of the National Avian-Wind Power Planning Meeting III, San Diego, CA, May 1998*, pp. 115-124. NWCC c/o RESOLVE Inc., Washington, DC and LGL Ltd., King City, Ontario. [Available from http://www.nationalwind.org/publications/wildlife.htm]

Madders, M. and Whitfield, D.P. (2006). Upland raptors and the assessment of wind farm impacts. *Ibis.* **148** (Suppl. 1): 43-56.

Meek, E.R., Ribbands, J.B., Christer, W.G., Davey, P.R. and Higginson, I. (1993). The effects of aero-generators on moorland bird populations in the Orkney Islands, Scotland. *Bird Study.* **40**: 140-143.

NWCC (National Wind Coordinating Committee). (2000). *National Avian-Wind Power Planning Meeting IV, Carmel, CA, May 2000: Meeting Summary.* NWCC c/o RESOLVE Inc., Washington, DC and LGL Ltd., King City, Ontario. [Available from http://www.nationalwind.org/publications/wildlife.htm]

Osborn, R.G., Dieter, C.D., Higgins, K.F. and Usgaard, R.E. (1998). Bird flight characteristics near wind turbines in Minnesota. *American Midland Naturalist.* **139**: 20-38.

Osborn, R.G., Higgins, K.F., Usgaard, R.E., Dieter, C.D. and Neiger, R.D. (2000). Bird mortality associated with wind turbines at the Buffalo Ridge Wind Resource Area, Minnesota. *American Midland Naturalist.* **143**: 41-52.

Parkyn, L., Stoneman, R.E. and Ingram, H.A.P. (eds). (1997). *Conserving Peatlands.* CAP International, Wallingford.

Percival, S.M. (2000). Birds and wind turbines in Britain. *British Wildlife.* **12**: 8-15.

Ratcliffe, D.A. and Thompson, D.B.A. (1988). The British Uplands: their ecological character and international significance. In Usher, M.B. and Thompson D.B.A. (eds). *Ecological change in the uplands*, Blackwell Scientific Publications, Oxford.

Scottish Executive. (2004). *Scotland's Biodiversity: It's in Your Hands.* Scottish Executive, Edinburgh.

Scottish Executive. (2006). Peat landslide hazard and risk assessments: best practice guide for proposed electricity generation developments. [Available from www.scotland.gov.uk/Resource/Doc/161862/0043972.pdf]

Scottish Natural Heritage. (2003). Technical Guidance Note: Windfarms and Carbon Savings. [Available from http://www.snh.org.uk/pdfs/polstat/caf.pdf]

Scottish Natural Heritage. (2006). Tracks in the Scottish Uplands: Good Practice Guide. Scottish Natural Heritage, Battleby.

Smallwood, K.S. and Thelander, C.G. (2004). *Developing methods to reduce bird mortality in the Altamont Pass Wind Resource Area.* Final Report by BioResource Consultants to the California Energy Commission, Public Interest Energy Research-Environmental Area, Contract No. 500-01-019. [Available from www.energy.ca.gov/pier/final_project_reports/500-04-052.html]

Sprent, J., Clift, R. and Ekins, P. (2008). Climate Change: The Need to Alter Our Patterns of Energy Generation and Use. In C.A. Galbraith & J.M. Baxter (eds). *Energy and the Natural Heritage.* TSO Scotland, Edinburgh.

Todd, I. and Band, B. (2008). Renewable Energy – Overview, Trends and Challenges. In C.A. Galbraith & J.M. Baxter (eds). *Energy and the Natural Heritage.* TSO Scotland, Edinburgh.

Walker, D., McGrady, M., McCluskie, A., Madders, M. and McLeod, D.R.A. (2005). Resident Golden Eagle ranging behaviour before and after construction of a windfarm in Argyll. *Scottish Birds.* **25**: 24-40.

Whitfield, D.P. and Madders, M. (2006). *A review of the impacts of wind farms on hen harriers Circus cyaneus and an estimation of collision avoidance rates.* Natural Research Information Note 1 (revised). Natural Research Ltd, Banchory. [Available from www.natural-research.org]

Wilson, P.J. and Provan, J. (2003). Effect of habitat fragmentation on levels and patterns of genetic diversity in natural populations of the peat moss *Polytrichum commune. Proceedings of the Royal Society, London Series B.* **270**: 881-886.

Winkelman, J.E. (1985). Bird impact by middle-sized wind turbines on flight behaviour, victims, and disturbance. *Limosa.* **58**: 117-121.

Winkelman, J.E. (1995). Bird/wind turbine investigations in Europe. *Proceedings of the National Avian-Wind Power Planning Meeting, Denver, CO, July 1994*, pp. 110-140. NWCC c/o RESOLVE, Washington, DC and LGL Ltd., King City, Ontario. [Available from http://www.nationalwind.org/publications/wildlife.htm]

Young, D.P., Erickson, W.P., Good, R.E., Strickland, M.D. and Johnson, G.D. (2003a). *Avian and bat mortality associated with the initial phase of the Foote Creek Rim windpower project, Carbon County, Wyoming. November 1998 – June 2002.* Final report by WEST Inc. prepared for Pacificorp Inc., Portland, Oregon & SeaWest Windpower Inc., San Diego, California. [Available from www.west-inc.com/wind_reports.php]

Young, D.P., Erickson, W.P., Strickland, M.D., Good, R.E. and Sernka, K.J. (2003b). *Comparison of avian responses to UV-light-reflective paint on wind turbines. Subcontract report July 1999 – December 2000.* National Renewable Energy Laboratory, Colorado. [Available from www.nrel.gov/publications]

Golden eagle at eyrie © Laurie Campbell/SNH

17 Marine Renewables – The Available Resource and How to Tap it

Ian Bryden – *The Robert Gordon University, Aberdeen AB11 6TF.*
Current address: Institute for Energy Systems, University of Edinburgh, Kings Buildings, Edinburgh EH9 3JL.

Summary

1. The potential and range of renewable marine energy sources are summarized. The marine resource around Scotland is seen as a significant and yet largely untapped source of energy.
2. The rapidly developing technologies to harness wave and tidal current power are reviewed. The not inconsiderable technological challenges are discussed together with the potential environmental implications both for marine habitats and species.
3. The opportunities for Scotland to be at the forefront of marine renewables technological development through the work of the European Marine Energy Centre (EMEC) are highlighted. The challenge remaining for Scotland is to fully exploit these new technologies and develop the infrastructure to deliver the resulting power to the grid.

17.1 Introduction

The British Isles are located between the north-east Atlantic Ocean and the North Sea. This location has resulted in a west facing coastline exposed to high energy waves driven on-shore by the predominant westerly winds that blow over the Atlantic fetch. In addition, the islands are surrounded by a complex structure of amphidromic systems that drive tidal currents, which in places are accelerated by various sounds and narrows.

In the 1970s wave power was seriously suggested as an alternative to fossil and nuclear power and there was a major UK government funded programme of research and development. This ended in the mid 1980s when political priorities and cheap oil suggested that marine energy sources represented, at best, a long term option for energy production. Attitudes to energy, however, have now changed from those of the 1980s. Global climate change is no longer seen as a purely academic concern. The enhanced greenhouse effect driven by human induced emission of gases is widely accepted by scientists and many politicians as a major threat to future development (Bryden and Robertson, 2004) . Increasingly, sceptical voices are being regarded as driven by non-scientific principles. In addition, there are concerns about national and global long- term energy security. In terms of world fuel availability, social and economic development will

Bryden, I. (2008). Marine Renewables – The Available Resource and How to Tap it. In *Energy and the Natural Heritage*, ed. by C.A. Galbraith and J.M. Baxter. TSO Scotland, Edinburgh. pp. 221-228 depend on sustainable sources of energy. The "proved reserves" of oil, for example, were estimated in 2004 to be equivalent to 41 years of present consumption (BP, 2004). This does not, of course, mean that oil will run out in 2045. "Proved reserves" refer to the quantity of oil which could be economically developed assuming present technology, prices and, of course, knowledge about the size of resource stocks. Even though, however, there is no prospect of immediate drastic decline of world oil production, local production in the UK is under more immediate pressure. The same information source estimated the UK proved reserves to be equivalent to only 5.4 years of production! The equivalent figures for natural gas production were 67.1 years for the world and 6.1 years for the UK.

The wind industry offers the prospect of a sustainable energy resource and the UK represents one of the windiest land masses in the world. There is, however, growing concern by many organizations about the impact of wind development on local environments and communities. Nevertheless the industry does represent the most developed section of the non-hydro renewable community and must, surely, play a major part in the development of long term energy security.

Given the new political and social environment of the 21st century, perhaps marine energy could form part of a new, growing energy industry for the UK. Wave energy research is, once again, receiving funding from public and private sources and the extraction of energy from tidal currents is also receiving serious consideration.

17.2 Status of the marine sector

Wave power is now reaching the stage of full scale commercial prototype testing, with full size devices being tested in many parts of the world. The European Marine Energy Centre (EMEC) in Orkney (www.emec.org.uk see Chapter 20) has been established to facilitate the systematic evaluation of devices in representative Atlantic conditions and is an important development in the creation of a wave power generation industry. Developers are able to connect their devices into the electrical grid and test them for electrical behaviour as well as marine performance. EMEC is also working to develop an equivalent facility for evaluating tidal current power generation devices.

Although developers of marine energy systems now have full scale devices, the industry is not yet able to compete economically with onshore wind and this represents the greatest challenge to the developing industry over the next few years.

17.3 Wave power
17.3.1 Size of the wave resource

There is still no consensus on the size of the harnessible UK wave energy resource. Determination of a national wave resource requires much more than integrating time averaged estimations of the power incident towards the coastline. Even the methodologies used to assess the resource are subject to some controversy. A report by the Scottish Executive (Snodin, 2001) suggested that the UK resource could exceed 45TWhrs/annum, available for under 7p/KWhr. This analysis drew upon models of the underlying wave energy distribution, taking into account areas not available due to environmental and navigational constraints; the greatest uncertainties in the analysis lay, however, not in knowledge of the underlying wave climate but in the costing of the technology itself.

Figure 17.1 LIMPET – oscillating column device on the coast of Islay (image reproduced with the permission of Wavegen Ltd)

17.3.2 Technical options

The critical parameter for wave development relates to the device location. The deep water to the west of the UK offers substantial energy opportunities. It also, however, presents major technical problems such as device survivability and connection to the grid. Devices mounted on the coastline itself will be more accessible for maintenance and connection but the resource is far more limited.

The best known technologies used for coastal generation are the oscillating water column and the tapered channel (TAPCHAN). The LIMPET (www.wavegen.co.uk), is an oscillating column device rated at 500KW installed on the island of Islay in the Inner Hebrides (Figure 17.1). A demonstration tapered channel device (Falnes, 1992) with rated output of 350 KW operated at Toftesfallen, 40km north-west of Bergen in Norway between 1985 and the early 1990s.

Deep water devices under development and which have reached large scale prototype testing include:

- Pelamis (www.oceanpd.com), which is an articulated cylinder structure rated at 750KW. It has been developed by Ocean Power Development Ltd and is presently under test at EMEC, (Figure 17.2).
- Wave Dragon (www.wavedragon.net), which is a floating device that uses the energy in waves to lift water into an elevated pond before generating electricity by passing it back to sea level through a low head turbine. It has some similarity with the coastal TAPCHAN concept. Wave Dragon has been tested extensively in Denmark in 2003 and 2004.
- The Archimedes Wave Swing (www.waveswing.com), which is a large device rated at 2MW. This consists of a float which is driven by the waves to oscillate vertically and drive a novel linear generator. This was installed in Portuguese waters in 2004.

There are numerous other devices at various stages of full scale testing including the Aquabuoy (www.finavera.com) and the Powerbuoy (www.oceanpowertechnologies.com).

17.3.3 Environmental issues

The extraction of energy from waves will alter the nature of sediment transportation and deposition. In deep water, this might be of minimal importance but could be of some concern for coastal and near coast developments. More significant might be the level of infrastructure associated with the installation and operation of wave technology. Coastal stations, in particular, will involve large scale modification to the environment, which might be detrimental.

Offshore developments, if not carefully located, could prove to be hazards to other users of the sea. Impact and interaction with shipping must be a factor in planning any wave power generation development.

Maintenance of both coastal and offshore devices will result in increased industrial activity, which might be considered detrimental to local communities. The increase in employment and, of course, the net reduction in greenhouse gas emissions must be considered in mitigation.

Figure 17.2 Pelamis wave energy converter © Pelamis Wave Power

17.4 Tidal current power

17.4.1 The tidal current resource

The resource has been frequently misunderstood and all too often the superficial similarity with wind has been over-emphasized. Early analyses used methods appropriate to wind farm assessment to suggest that the energy from tidal currents could be predicted in terms of number of devices per unit area of sea bed (DTI, 1993). This is not appropriate and recent analysis recognizes that it is more appropriate, in relatively simple channel geometries at least, to consider the energy flux through sections perpendicular to the flow. Any such analysis must also consider the effect of energy extraction on the nature of the hydraulic environment itself and how this may reduce current speed. The most recent analysis, which took account of both these principles, suggests that the achievable UK tidal stream resource is about 22TWhr/annum (Carbon Trust Marine Energy Challenge, 2004).

It is interesting to note that, although the raw tidal current resource is smaller than that for wave, the resource is concentrated into a relatively small number of very large sites, which could offer the prospect overall of less expensive development. In addition, the much greater predictability of tidal currents is a major attraction, when compared to the random nature of both wave and wind as energy sources. The prospect of linking tidal devices to short term energy storage (Bryden and MacFarlane, 2000) could offer real opportunities for flexible and dependable generation.

17.4.2 Technical options

In principle, the extraction of energy from tidal currents has a high degree of similarity with the extraction of energy from the wind. There are some very fundamental differences, however, which have significant influence on the design of tidal current turbines.

A wind turbine might be exposed to wind speeds up to 75m/s in extreme situations, yet still be expected to deliver electricity from wind speeds less than 10m/s. The most extreme tidal environments, which have been identified as candidate sites for development, have reported current speeds up to 7m/s, but with 'extreme' speeds during spring tides of 3m/s being much more common.

Typically, for most likely locations, a tidal current turbine of a particular chosen power output will be substantially smaller than an equivalently rated wind turbine. The horizontal forces on a tidal device will, however, be substantial. This poses challenges to the designer, especially considering the known difficulties in installing seabed hardware in extreme tidal current conditions. This issue has been one of the dominant factors in the design of tidal current systems. Most devices presently under consideration are sea bed mounted and rely either on foundation pillars drilled or piled into the sea bed or upon gravity to maintain their position and oppose the flow induced forces and moments. Alternative approaches based upon the use of buoyant moored support have also been suggested. In any case the installation of the device and subsequent access for maintenance will be a challenge, especially as the period of slack water in any tidal cycle, in many locations, can be very short.

As with wave power, large scale commercial prototypes have been tested. These include:

- The SeaFlow device (Bryden and MacFarlane, 2000), installed in the Bristol Channel in 2003. It is a horizontal axis device, with a rated power output of 300KW, mounted on a vertical pillar fixed into the sea bed.

Figure 17.3 The Sea Snail being prepared for launch © Ian Bryden

- The Stingray system (www.engb.com), which was tested in Yell Sound, Shetland during 2002 to 2004 used a unique linear foil system. This took advantage of the hydrodynamic lift on a variable pitch, horizontal foil to drive a hydraulic power take-off system.
- The Hammerfest Strom (www.tidevannsenergi.com) system is a sea bed mounted horizontal axis system which was installed in Norway in 2003.

There are other devices and demonstration projects in the development phase such as:

- The Hydroventuri (www.hydroventuri.com) system, which uses the differential pressure within a venturi contraction to generate power.
- The Lunar Energy device (www.lunarenergy.co.uk) which is a bed mounted horizontal axis device in a protective and flow enhancing cowl.
- The TiDel (www.smdhydrovision.com) system which uses twin horizontal axis turbines mounted on a cable moored submerged platform.

The Sea Snail system (www.rgu.ac.uk) developed by the author, is not a tidal energy device in itself but is a mobile support platform designed to hold tidal energy technology firmly onto the sea bed without using complex and costly fixing technology or excessively heavy ballast (Figure 17.3). Instead it utilizes the hydrodynamic down force on reversible pitch foils to provide a secure frictional mounting.

17.4.3 Environmental issues

Many of the issues associated with tidal current extraction mirror those for wave power. Installation of most systems will likely involve preparation of the sea bed, although the Sea Snail has been developed to allow installation with minimal bed preparation.

There has been some concern about the influence of energy extraction on local current speeds, although research suggests that between 10% and 20% of the kinetic energy flux can be extracted without causing measurable reduction in flow speeds outside of the immediate wake behind devices (Bryden and Melville, 2004). The predicted reduction in flow speed as a function of kinetic energy extracted in a simple constrained channel (Figure 17.4) shows that the extraction of 20% of the kinetic energy flux will reduce the speed by approximately 6%, which would be at the limits of easy measurability with most tidal flow speed instrumentation.

While it would appear that marine creatures could impact on the blades of a tidal turbine, there has not yet been any experimental study on this. Theoretical considerations suggest, however, that the prospect of impact for any creature smaller than the turbine radius is minimal. This should be a matter for further research.

17.5 The economic challenges to development

Marine resource development is not yet sufficiently advanced to offer commercial profitability. As a result of developer determination and the activities of EMEC, it is likely that some of the technological concepts presently under development will offer the prospects of positive investment return in the future. In 2003, the Scottish Executive, commissioned a study of the prospects for the development of a Scottish marine renewable industry. In the resulting report of the Marine Energy Group (MEG) (MEG, 2004), it was observed that the direct cost of wave and tidal current generation, at present, was between 7 and 15p/KWhr. This could, however, fall considerably as the scale of installed technology increased. The variation of direct cost against installed capacity for the wind industry (Figure 17.5) suggests that, if the example of wind power is repeated, the cost of generation will decrease as the installed capacity of devices is increased. Until, of course, a sufficient number of devices are installed; the cost of generation will be too high for economic return on investment.

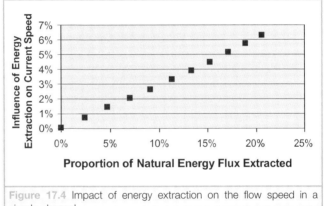

Figure 17.4 Impact of energy extraction on the flow speed in a simple channel

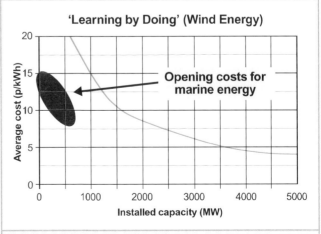

Figure 17.5 Cost Capacity experience with the wind industry [diagram reproduced from MEG (2004)]

The MEG (2004) report suggested that marine renewable energy could offer Scotland the opportunity of a new industry directly employing up to 7000 personnel by 2020 and generating 10% of Scotland's electricity and this could be achieved with an investment of £156 million, which would allow the realization of commercially attractive investment and subsequent growth. Who will pay for the installation of devices prior to the achievement of commercially attractive generation? Extrapolation into the UK and Europe would be a difficult, but enlightening, exercise.

17.6 Conclusions

Marine renewable technology appears to offer prospects for long term, sustainable energy supply. The economic prospects appear to be considerable and, if care is taken in the development of the resource, the environmental and social impact could be minimal in comparison with environmental benefits from reduced CO_2 emissions.

Acknowledgements

The Author would like to thank the Forum for Renewable Energy in Scotland, the Robert Gordon University and the Engineering and Physical Sciences Research Council for their support of research into marine renewable energy. He would also like to request that all those in the debate on renewable energy and the enhanced greenhouse effect base their arguments on fact rather than prejudice.

Postscript. It should be noted that in the three years since this chapter was written some of the science has been surpassed in this rapidly changing field. For up-to-date information on the current science see www.supergen-marine.org.uk

References

BP. (2004). 53rd Statistical Review of World Energy 2004. BP Global Reports.

Bryden, I. G. and MacFarlane, D. (2000). The Utilisation of Short Term Energy Storage with Tidal Current Generation Systems. *Energy: The International Journal,* 25, Pergamon ISSN 0360-5442 893-907.

Bryden, I. and Melville, G. (2004). 'Choosing and Evaluating Sites for Tidal Current Development'. Proceedings of the Institute of Mechanical Engineers, Vol 218, Part A: J.Power and Energy, p567-578, Professional Engineering Publishing Limited, London, UK, ISSN 0957-6509.

Bryden, I.G. and Robertson, P. K. (2004). Global Climate Change – The Conflicting Arguments. *Houston Geological Society Bulletin*, December, p37-49.

Carbon Trust Marine Energy Challenge. (2004). UK, Europe and global tidal stream energy resource assesment, 2004, 107799/d/2100/05/1

DTI. (1993). "Tidal Stream Energy Review T/05/00155 REP. Binnie and Partners, Sir Robert McAlpine & Sons Ltd and IT Power Ltd.

Falnes, J. (1992). Review of Wave Energy Research in Norway. Workshop on Wave Energy R & D held at Cork, EUR Rep. No. 15079 EN.

Marine Energy Group, (MEG). (2004). Harnessing Scotland's Marine Energy Potential. Scottish Executive Publications.

Snodin, H. (2001). Scotland's Renewable Resource, 2850/GR/04, 2001. Scottish Executive, Edinburgh.

18 Marine Renewable Energy Technologies – Natural Heritage Impacts

Alexander J. Downie*+ – *Scottish Natural Heritage, 2 Anderson Place, Edinburgh EH6 5NP.*
*Current address: *SEPA, *Clearwater House, Heriot-Watt Research Park, Avenue North, Riccarton, Edinburgh EH14 4AP.*

Victoria Copley – *Natural England (formerly English Nature), Slepe Farm, Arne, Wareham, Dorset BH20 5BN.*

Zoë Crutchfield – *Joint Nature Conservation Committee, Dunnet House, 7 Thistle Place, Aberdeen AB10 1UZ.*

Sarah Wood – *Countryside Council for Wales, Maes-y-Ffynnon, Ffordd Penrhos, Bangor, Gwynedd LL57 2DW.*

Summary

1. The statutory nature conservation agencies (the Country Agencies) in the UK (Scottish Natural Heritage (SNH), Natural England (NE) formerly English Nature (EN), Countryside Council for Wales (CCW), Environment and Heritage Service (EHS), and the Joint Nature Conservation Committee (JNCC)) are frequently asked to comment on the potential effects of a wide range of maritime civil engineering projects on the natural heritage, including landscape, issues. Consequently they may use this experience as a starting point to answer questions relating to possible impacts of new technologies.

2. There is an increasing interest in the development of renewable energy technologies, particularly power generation from resources such as wind, waves and tides but should these technologies be viewed as simply another form of maritime civil engineering? Most assessments of the environmental impacts of marine renewable technologies, especially at the commercial operation phase, are still based upon prediction and best estimates rather than on solid experience and measured effects.

3. Details of technological developments and known environmental impacts are greatest concerning offshore wind farms. Monitoring of existing and proposed schemes is, therefore, required if the accuracy of future assessments is to be improved. A provisional ranking of the major technologies, from of least to most potential natural heritage impacts, has been undertaken by SNH, thus: offshore wave, tidal stream,

Downie, A.J., Copley, V., Crutchfield, Z. & Wood, S. (2008). Marine Renewable Energy Technologies – Natural Heritage Impacts. In *Energy and the Natural Heritage*, ed. by C.A. Galbraith and J.M. Baxter. TSO Scotland, Edinburgh. pp. 229-240

+The views expressed in this chapter are those of the author and his affiliated organization at the time of writing and are not necessarily the views of his current employer.

shoreline wave, offshore wind farm, tidal barrage/impoundment. The location of individual developments is likely to have the biggest influence on this ranking.

4. This chapter seeks to examine whether marine renewable technologies possibly create specific natural heritage impacts additional to what we know already from other engineering developments. The marine renewables industry is at a relatively early stage of development, with developers keen to promote the environmentally friendly elements of their technologies. This means that, at this early stage, there is the potential to influence the way schemes are designed, implemented and sited. Guidance is required on the range of issues that should be considered in scoping maritime renewable energy projects.

18.1 Introduction

Within the UK the statutory nature conservation agencies (Scottish Natural Heritage (SNH), Natural England (NE), Countryside Council for Wales (CCW), and the Joint Nature Conservation Committee (JNCC)), also known collectively as the Country Agencies, are charged with providing advice, through a number of statutory and non-statutory consultation procedures, on the potential effects of civil engineering developments on the natural heritage. This role is performed by the Environment and Heritage Services in Northern Ireland. The increasing interest in the development of renewable energy technologies, particularly power generation from resources such as wind, waves and tides, is causing these agencies to question whether or not these new technologies should be viewed simply as another form of maritime civil engineering.

The very strong interest in the development of renewable energy technologies in general, and particularly generation from marine systems, is being encouraged by fiscal and environmental policy initiatives at a global, UK, individual country and even regional level to increase the proportion of electricity produced by renewable technologies. DTI's *Atlas of UK Marine Renewable Energy Resources* (DTI, 2004) states that:

> "... There is a growing expectation that the energy resources created by the dynamics of the marine environment will be able to make a real and measurable contribution to the Renewables Agenda over the next 10 years, both nationally and globally ...".

The objectives here are to try to identify the potential interactions between the construction and operation of such civil engineering developments and the marine and coastal environment, and to assess the importance of each interaction in terms of scale, type of development and the habitats and species involved. In particular this chapter seeks to examine whether marine renewable technologies possibly create specific natural heritage impacts when compared with other engineering developments.

As a means of separating these emerging technologies the Country Agencies tend to categorize them into: shoreline wave; offshore wave; tidal stream (marine currents); tidal barrage/impoundment; offshore wind farm. We acknowledge that other technological types exist, such as thermal, but are not aware that such concepts are being developed for use in the marine environment.

18.2 Background

The Country Agencies have been providing comment on the potential effects of a wide range of maritime civil engineering projects on natural heritage issues, including landscape, for many years. Research has been commissioned to help formulate advice, both specific and generic, to provide best practice guidance for staff use in development proposals (Eno, 1991; Arup Enviromental, 1993; Davies and Wilson, 1995; Masters and Gee, 1995; Hill *et al.*, 2001; Scott Wilson and Downie, 2003; Stone, 2003; Scott *et al.*, 2004). Consequently we will use this research and past experience as a starting point to answer questions relating to possible impacts of new technologies where we have no other information to go on. Previous work commissioned by the Country Agencies has also provided information relating to the vulnerability of habitat types to generic damage from different civil engineering processes (Holt *et al.*, 1995; Walker, 1997), as shown in Table 18.1 relating to coastal habitat types.

Table 18.1 Vulnerabilities of coastal habitat types to generic impacts from civil engineering processes (after Walker (1997))

GENERIC IMPACTS	HABITAT TYPE					
	Rocky shores	Shingle shores	Sandy shores	Sand dunes	Estuaries and Mudflats	Saltmarsh
Damage to topography	X	X		X	X	X
Damage to soils		X		X		X
Visual impacts	1	2	2	2	X	X
Changes in drainage		X	X	X		X
Changes in ecology	1	X	X	X	X	X
Changes in sediment transport	X	X	X	X	X	X
Contaminant release	X	X	X	X	X	X

X Potential damage, which may occur as a result of a construction process.
1 Damage may be minimized by use of natural topography or materials.
2 Damage may be minimal if construction can be buried.

The following illustrate some of the lessons already learned from experience of other civil engineering developments:

- the structure and location of many developments are the two factors most important in determining the scale of eventual environmental impact arising both from construction and operation;
- detailed predictive hydrodynamic models should be employed to determine the relative impacts of different design constructions;
- environmental baseline conditions at sites should be thoroughly reviewed in advance of developments taking place;

- the lowest environmental impacts are observed where water flows closest to baseline conditions are maintained; and
- the potential consequences of any future developments should be carefully addressed and accurately monitored.

The Country Agencies work together, through the inter-agency Marine Industries Working Group, to address the need to provide, as far as it is possible, consistent advice on International and UK-wide issues. Additionally, participation in UK-wide collaborative projects such as *MarLIN* (see www.marlin.ac.uk) and in particular the work of the Biology and Sensitivity Key Information Sub-programme (Hiscock and Tyler-Walters, 2003), will help to identify the likely sensitivity of biotopes and species to natural events and human activities.

Marine Renewable Energy and the Natural Heritage: an overview and policy statement (SNH, 2004) attempts to identify potential impacts of marine renewable developments and includes a series of tables of principal impacts and potential mitigation measures for underwater cabling, offshore wind farms, offshore wave, tidal stream, shoreline wave, and tidal barrage developments – an example, modified for the purposes of this chapter, is given in Table 18.2.

Table 18.2 Principal potential impacts identified for marine tidal stream devices. (After SNH, 2004)

	Impact detail	Construction	Operation
Hydrology	Attenuation of tidal currents and impact on sedimentation patterns		X
Water quality	Leakage of hydraulic fluids		X
	Leakage of pollutants in accidents	X	X
	Erosion of sacrificial anodes		X
	Use of antifoulants		X
Marine habitats	Loss of habitats for turbine bases		X
	Smothering of habitat and changes in food sources	X	X
Marine species	Underwater noise impacts on marine mammals and fish		X
	Collision risk with marine mammals		X
Birds	Underwater collision risk for deep-diving species		X
Landscape/seascape	Impact on landscape/seascape of any superstructure		X
Fisheries	Exclusion area for use of nets	X	X
Navigation	Risk to cargo shipping – loss of goods and oil pollution	X	X

The nature conservation guidance (Defra, 2005) describes the many ways in which wind farms *may* affect the marine environment and provides suggested mitigation measures to offset them. In addition, participation in external groups such as COWRIE (Collaborative Offshore Wind Research Into the Environment), the Offshore Energy Strategic Environmental Assessment (SEA) Steering Group and the Department of Trade and Industry (DTI) run UK Offshore Renewable Energy Environmental Forum allows the Agencies to participate in discussions with regulators and developers of the marine renewables industry as well as non-governmental organizations (NGOs), such as the Royal

Society for the Protection of Birds (RSPB) and the Marine Conservation Society (MCS), at a relatively early stage of project development. Participation in international events such as the three workshops run in Belgium under the OREO WIND project has allowed exchange of information and experience at a European level, in particular with respect to looking at offshore wind farms and designated areas; national planning procedures for offshore wind energy in the EU; and Natura 2000 implications for development of wind energy (Peterson and Neuman, 2004).

18.3 Review of environmental impacts

Commissioned research into environmental impacts has shown, not unexpectedly, that marine renewable energy developments of different types have a number of common features, e.g. moorings or foundations, transmission cables to land. Whilst any listing of environmental impacts by type would be repetitive, the nature of the impact(s) is often quite different: e.g. wave power farms are likely to change the wave regime more compared to offshore wind farms whilst offshore wind farms are more likely to have an impact on birds compared to the other technology types.

With respect to specific protection or conservation measures, for instance in relation to a development within a marine protected area or Natura site, or one having an impact on a species subject to special protection, these were not included in this general overview of the significance of impacts. If any special protection provisions apply, then the significance of impacts must be assessed against any specific tests relating to that form of protection, e.g. the development may be subject to stringent analysis to ensure that it does not adversely affect the particular marine natural heritage interests safeguarded by the site.

SNH has gone further than most of the other Country Agencies by attempting, even at this early stage of the development of the technologies, to suggest a hierarchy in terms of the potential likely significance of their marine and coastal natural heritage impacts (see Figure 18.1). For the purposes of this chapter we have modified this somewhat to give a more UK-wide perspective.

It is important to note that wind farms, and other renewable projects, may have a role to play in recovery of degraded marine environments. It could be possible to offset some of the potentially negative impacts of marine renewable technologies by managing other potentially damaging activities in and around the sites (for example by establishing exclusion areas for mobile fishing gear or adopting wind farm sites as protected areas).

To date most assessments of the environmental impacts of marine renewable technologies, especially at the commercial operation phase, are still based upon prediction and best estimates rather than on solid experience and measured effects. It is only very recently that actual observations have begun to be fed back from the commercial operation phase of large demonstration projects, as was reported at Billund, Denmark in the 2004 conference *"Offshore Wind and the Environment"*.

A notable feature to date has been the exceptional size and scale of the renewable technology structures being proposed. For example, proposals so far have included:

- wind turbines of 150m or higher (above the sea surface);
- wave devices the size of three railway carriages, some 150m long and 3.5m in diameter with a displacement of 700 tonnes (including ballast);

- subsurface tidal stream structures 20m high, weighing 120t, with 2+m high nacelles incorporating three rotating blades each of 10m diameter from blade tip to hub mounted on nacelle.

LEAST PERCEIVED NATURAL HERITAGE IMPACT

Offshore wave devices appear to offer major generation opportunities in return for relatively limited natural heritage impacts, particularly if moored (rather than bottom-founded) devices can be developed, if sited well offshore and outwith valued seascapes and important areas for wildlife, and provided that risks in relation to navigation and shipping can be adequately addressed.

Tidal stream (marine current) devices, provided they are not sited in confined high current velocity channels likely to be of natural heritage value, also appear to offer significant generation opportunities in return for limited natural heritage impacts, especially if they are below surface and allow sufficient navigational clearance.

Shoreline wave devices may have a significant impact on coastal landscapes. Shoreline wave devices are most appropriate where such built development on the shoreline is compatible with the existing nature of shoreline development or coastal protection works; or elsewhere where any adverse impacts on the landscape or wild qualities of an undeveloped coast can be justified with reference to the quantity of energy capture or the experimental value of the device.

Offshore wind farms are potentially likely to have an appreciable impact on the natural heritage, in terms of species (notably birds), landscape, and the pollution consequences from navigational risk accepting that they are possibly less of a hazard than low-in-the-water devices. In general, landscape and visual impacts as viewed from land will diminish with distance from the coast, though this may be less true within enclosed waters or estuaries.

Tidal barrage/impoundment schemes are likely to have major impacts on the natural heritage, particularly of shoreline soft sediment habitats. Small-scale schemes, and tidal generators installed within an existing barrier or causeway, may have more limited impacts.

MOST PERCEIVED NATURAL HERITAGE IMPACT

NOTE: All the technology types may be expected to be comparable in terms of transmission line impacts.

Figure 18.1 Suggested hierarchy of potentially significant impacts of marine renewable technologies on the natural heritage. (After SNH Policy Statement No. 04/01)

Figure 18.2 North Hoyle offshore wind farm, Wales © Sarah Wood, CCW

When taken in combination with the areas these schemes are proposed to cover, e.g. wind farm sites of 250-300 turbines in an area of approx. 245 km², this is development on a scale the Country Agencies have never come across before with maritime civil engineering projects and more importantly perhaps, one that is happening very rapidly. The UK agencies are not alone in this assessment, for example The German Advisory Council on the Environment highlighted it as an issue of concern in their report concerning marine environment protection for the North and Baltic Seas (SRU, 2004).

The speed of offshore wind farm development in particular is unprecedented compared to other maritime civil engineering developments. For example in November 2003, North Hoyle, Wales became the UK's first major offshore wind farm (see Figure 18.2). All the more remarkable when it is considered that the first round of offshore wind farm development was only announced in 2000/01. To date 12 of the 18 projects proposed under Round One (http://www.thecrownestate.co.uk/34_r1_windfarm_locations_map_04_08_13.pdf) have gained all the necessary statutory consents to enable construction and operation, e.g. following on from North Hoyle the wind farm development at Scroby Sands, East Anglia, is now constructed and operational and others will quickly follow.

Further offshore wind farms (and other technologies) cannot be considered without understanding how the electricity generated will be transmitted back to the national grid. Work is also underway investigating the potential of converting the energy into a chemical fuel such as hydrogen (http://www.friendsofscotland.gov.uk/education/renewable.html).

Whilst issues such as possible cabling effects are not new, the number of new cables being suggested for deployment in 'green sea sites', as a result of recent offshore wind farm developments is unprecedented in terms of scale and speed of deployment. Additionally such developments are being proposed at a time when although there is raised concern with respect to the effects of cabling on electro-sensitive species, the effects remain largely unquantified, especially with respect to their significance. Work in this area has been commissioned by COWRIE (CMACS, 2003), which reported that the current state of knowledge was too variable and inconclusive to make an informed assessment of any possible environmental impact of electromagnetic fields (EMF) in the range of values likely to be detected by organisms sensitive to electric and magnetic fields. Therefore modelling and direct measurement of the electric and magnetic field components of EMF was undertaken. COWRIE has commissioned further work, to follow-up on these results from the first phase.

There are new features presented by these proposed developments that are novel both in terms of their design and their potential operational environmental impact(s), namely:

1. Visual impact of fields of rotating turbine blades above the surface of the sea.
2. Visual impacts on a scale not seen before from these new energy developments.
3. Addition of noise to the marine environment from renewable energy developments, possibly dispersed around much of the coast of the UK.
4. Fields of rotating turbine blades below the surface of the sea.
5. Fields of wave dampening devices with the potential to alter the wave exposure patterns in some areas.
6. The suggestion that tidal energy extraction could change the underlying hydraulic characteristics of tidal environments through local slowing of the tidal flow, which could have an influence on marine life in areas concerned. (http://newsvote.bbc.co.uk /mpapps/pagetools/print/news.bbc.co.uk/1/hi/scotland/3580484.stm).
7. Artificial substrates being created on a scale not seen before, sometimes in areas of known low natural biodiversity.

18.4 Conclusions

Whilst marine renewables are to some extent 'just another form of maritime civil engineering project' and we can apply experience from other sectors, especially from the marine construction point of view, there are aspects of renewables that set them apart. We have greatest (but still little) experience in offshore wind projects and this has highlighted specific natural heritage impacts, especially with respect to birds, marine mammals and seascape. There are also the more generic issues raised by offshore wind farms such as the scale and speed of proposed development which have no precedent. Taking the more global view also presents us with a new dilemma in that the Government will have to make hard decisions on how to deliver different targets (for example those set at the World Summit on Sustainable Development, Johannesburg for biodiversity and the Kyoto Agreement for climate change).

Developers are keen to promote the environmentally friendly elements of their technologies but in scoping future maritime renewable energy projects it is important that guidelines such as Defra (2005) are applied consistently.

The use of these new technologies means there is the potential for large scale, significant cumulative impacts. These cumulative impacts can have international considerations, something that was the subject of the OREO WIND project (http://www.imieu.org), which concluded amongst other things that:

1. Little is known about the environmental impacts of the offshore wind farms and to date, across Europe as a whole, there has been little strategic coordination of their location.
2. There is a need for more guidance on how to judge significance of environmental impacts.
3. Judgement of cumulative cross-border environmental impacts of these offshore wind farms may turn out to be as important a task as the judgement of local environmental impacts of projects.

The UK perhaps is in the lead in Europe in developing a strategic approach to marine renewable development projects through the DTI-led work on SEA for offshore wind, which is providing a positive contribution to the assessment of the environmental impacts of proposed new developments. At present greatest concern is voiced regarding the possible environmental impact of offshore wind farms. There are very few operational offshore wind farms, but many being proposed. It is important to maximize the learning from those that are already operational, such as the demonstration projects at Horns Rev and Nysted in Denmark and the wind farms currently completed in the UK, namely North Hoyle and Scroby Sands. It is also possible to extrapolate from our experience in other marine sectors (especially oil and gas) and onshore wind to identify *potential* impacts and be reasonable in our assessments of these. We are doing this in conjunction with the industry and regulators, as well as other stakeholders (Harley *et al.*, 2001).

A need has been identified to balance the long term view, i.e. the potentially significant contribution to offsetting potential impacts of climate change, with local, regional and sometimes international impacts on internationally important features. To help formulate our advice there is a need for a greater amount of predictive modelling to be undertaken such as determining the relative hydrodynamic impacts of different designs of wind farm arrays. At present final array designs tend to be chosen more for a combination of operational performance of the turbines and their visual impact. All modelling and predictions also need to take into account natural changes, as well as those caused by renewables. If we do not know the details of natural change then the models and any other predictions could be of limited value; comprehensive monitoring of existing and new schemes is required if the accuracy of future assessments is to be improved.

Whilst the SNH ranking of technologies may not be perfect it does provide a basis for discussion. It should be noted that the issue of siting of individual developments is likely to have the biggest influence on this ranking. As with other maritime civil engineering developments, discussions at an individual case level may lead to the identification of sites, habitats or species of concern with respect to possible impacts from the proposal. Given the above factors, it is important to seek to minimize uncertainty for the industry whilst also helping to ensure that it is sustainable. We can do this by identifying important and/or sensitive features in the maritime environment, a feature of the work of the *MarLIN* project.

Further, key issues that need to be considered include:

- Electromagnetic effects on fish from underwater cables (all technologies).
- Underwater noise and its effects on marine mammals and fish (in particular for offshore wind and tidal stream).

- Impacts on tidal channel habitats (in particular for tidal stream).
- Changes in sedimentation, scour and dispersal (all technologies).
- Cable laying and landfalls (all technologies).
- Bird displacement and collision risk (in particular for offshore wind).
- Landscape and visual impacts (all offshore devices).
- Use of antifouling paints (all technologies).
- Creation of artificial reefs (in particular for offshore wind).

It remains to be seen how well we learn from operational developments in the UK since the speed and scale of offshore wind development are unprecedented. It is important that we maximize the opportunities to learn lessons from the Round One wind farm sites and apply the knowledge learned to current and future proposals. Many of the other marine renewable devices are still being tested, some but not all, at the European Marine Energy Centre (EMEC), Orkney. Government needs to take a balanced view concerning the possible mix of technologies that could eventually be deployed. There is a need to match the best technology type to the best location.

Acknowledgements

Thanks to Katie Gillham, SNH for her comments on the drafts of this chapter.

References

Arup Environmental. (1993). A review of the construction effects of marine civil engineering: Stage 1 report. *Scottish Natural Heritage Review* No 20.

CMACS. (2003). *A baseline assessment of electromagnetic fields generated by offshore windfarm cables.* COWRIE Report EMF - 01-2002 66. Prepared by: Centre for Marine and Coastal Studies, Centre for Intelligent Monitoring Systems, Applied Ecology Research Group (University of Liverpool) and ECONNECT Ltd. http://www.thecrownestate.co.uk/1351_emf_research_report_04_05_06.pdf

Davies, G.J. and Wilson, J.L.J. (1995). Wildlife sensitivity criteria for oil and gas developments in Great Britain. *Joint Nature Conservation Committee Report* No. 206.

Defra. (2005). *Nature Conservation Guidance on Offshore Windfarm Development: A guidance note for developers undertaking offshore windfarm developments.* www.defra.gov.uk/wildlife-countryside/ewd/windfarms/windfarmguidance.pdf

DTI. (2004). *Atlas of UK Marine Renewable Energy Resources: Technical Report.* A report for the Department of Trade and Industry produced by ABPmer, The Met Office, Garrad Hassan, Proudman Oceanographic Laboratory, Southampton.

Eno, N.C. ed. (1991). *Marine conservation handbook.* - 2nd edition. English Nature, Peterborough.

Harley, M., Drewitt, A., Gilliland, P., Cleary, B., Langston, R., Southgate, M., Marsh, R., Burges, D., Marais, M. and Shears, C. (2001). *Wind farm development and nature conservation: a guidance document for nature conservation organisations and developers when consulting over wind farm proposals in England.* English Nature, Royal Society for the Protection of Birds, British Wind Energy Association, Sandy.

Hill, M., Briggs, J., Minto, P., Bagnall, D., Foley, K. and Williams, A. (2001). Guide to Best Practice in Seascape Assessment. Maritime Institute, Dublin.

Hiscock, K. and Tyler-Walters, H. (2003). *Assessing the sensitivity of seabed biotopes to human activities and natural events.* Scottish Natural Heritage, Edinburgh. http://www.marlin.ac.uk/PDF/Biotope_sens_brochure.pdf

Holt, T.J., Jones, D.R., Hawkins, S.J. and Hartnoll, R.G. (1995). The sensitivity of marine communities to man-induced change – a scoping report. *Countryside Council for Wales Science Report* No. FC 73-01-96.

Masters, D. and Gee, K. (1995). Criteria for identifying the critical environmental capital of the maritime zone: a discussion paper. *English Nature Research Report* No. 136.

Peterson, H. and Neuman, F. (2004). *NATURA 2000 Implications for Development of Wind Energy. A follow-up Topical Expert Workshop. Brussels, 20 and 21 November 2003.* OREO WIND workshop report. http://www.imieu.org.

Scott, K.E., Anderson, C., Benson, J.F., Dunsford, H. and Macfarlane, R. (2004). *An Assessment of the Sensitivity and Capacity of the Scottish Seascape in Relation to Offshore Windfarms.* Report to Scottish Natural Heritage from Landscape Research Group, University of Newcastle.

Scott Wilson and Downie, A.J. (2003). A review of possible marine renewable energy development projects and their natural heritage impacts from a Scottish perspective. *Scottish Natural Heritage Commissioned Report F02AA414.*

SNH. (2004). *Marine renewable energy and the natural heritage: an overview and policy statement.* Scottish Natural Heritage Policy Statement No. 04/01. http://www.snh.org.uk/pdfs/polstat/mrp.pdf

SRU. (2004). *Marine Environment Protection for the North and Baltic Seas. Special Report. February 2004.* Nomos Verlagsgesellschaft, Baden-Baden.

Stone, C.J. (2003). The effects of seismic activity on marine mammals in UK waters, 1998-2000. *Joint Nature Conservation Committee Report* No. 323.

Walker, F.D.L. (1997). Civil engineering in the Scottish coastal environment: a review of impacts and good practice. *Scottish Natural Heritage Review No. 66.*

The mountains of North Harris from Uig © Lorne Gill/SNH

19 The North Harris Trust: Community-Environment-Renewables – Getting the Balance Right

David Cameron – *The North Harris trust, The Old Hostel, Tarbert, Isle of Harris HS3 3BG.*

Summary

1. The North Harris Trust has the challenge of balancing the need to stimulate economic activity and improve the social life of the community with the need to protect the fragile environment.
2. Renewables developments are seen as a real opportunity and the development of a small (three turbine) wind farm site is a realistic possibility.

19.1 Community

North Harris is the more mountainous northern part of the Isle of Harris in the Outer Hebrides. It is an area of approximately 22,250 ha of which some 8,100 ha are subject to crofting tenure. Scenically superb, very attractive to climbers, naturalists, walkers, anglers and to the 800 or so people who manage to make a living on the North Harris Estate.

The population of the whole island of Harris in the 1991 Census was 2240, a decline of 14.5% in the ten years since 1981. This can be compared with the overall Outer Hebrides figure of a 6% decline. There is a significant annual excess of deaths over births and a large gap of 18 to 25 year olds who leave to find employment elsewhere. Perhaps the situation can be emphasized by the fact that North Harris has seen the closure of four primary schools outside the main village of Tarbert in the last 50 years – not by choice – there were no children to go to the schools!

So by most measurements, North Harris isn't doing very well, but statistics aren't everything and when the North Harris Estate came up for sale in April 2002, the community strongly supported an attempt to purchase the land and assets (less Amhuinnsuidhe Castle and the associated salmon fishing) from the then owner. Eleven months of negotiation later, the ownership passed to the North Harris Trust and nine democratically elected directors were given the responsibility of running the Estate for the benefit of the community. The John Muir Trust are also represented on the Board of the Trust as is the present owner of Amhuinnsuidhe Castle.

The Trust will probably be rightly judged on its success in stimulating economic activity, improving the social life of the community, creating employment and reversing the statistics of decline.

Cameron, D. (2008). The North Harris Trust : Community-Environment-Renewables – Getting the Balance Right. In *Energy and the Natural Heritage*, ed. by C.A. Galbraith and J.M. Baxter. TSO Scotland, Edinburgh. pp. 241-244

19.2 Environment

North Harris has outstanding natural heritage, the facts and figures illustrate the wealth of environmental riches. The north-west area comprises 63% of the Estate and is designated SSSI, SPA and SAC. The area has 10 European Directive habitats out of 77 listed for the UK. It also has priority habitats listed in the UK Biodiversity Action Plan. Four species which require protection under by the EC Habitats and Species Directive are found on the Estate and a further six bird species are Annex 1 species and recognized by the EC as requiring special protection under the Birds Directive; North Harris has one of the most concentrated populations of golden eagles anywhere. The landscape speaks for itself and if you look at www.north-harris.org the photos are worth a thousand words. Beyond the statistics, it is worthwhile to contemplate that at the same time as the fish, animals and birds have thrived in this wonderful landscape living beside the community of North Harris, the people haven't quite done as well.

19.3 Renewables

An audit of all possible renewable opportunities across the Estate was carried out in 2004. Hydro, tidal, wave, solar, off-shore and on-shore wind, and biomass were all looked at from a technical feasibility point of view.

The majority of these types of renewable energy production are beyond the financial means of the North Harris Trust, or are many years away. However, on-shore wind and biomass were flagged up as being worthy of further investigation. They could provide an income for the Trust which fitted the criteria which were established by community consultation during the buy-out process.

The biomass project is on-going with the Community Energy Unit of HIE and the Scottish Agricultural College. It is hoped that the Trust may be able to provide land for trial sites to grow willow and/or poplar on a three year rotation cropping pattern. It may also be able to heat some of its property using the wood produced from the trial.

The on-shore wind study identified three possible sites for between one and four turbines and further more detailed investigations are underway to develop one of the sites.

19.4 The balance

Starting from the premise that the community of North Harris would like to do more than just survive, but would like to reverse decades of decline in population, provide employment and variety of work, highlight possible crofting income improvement, create business opportunities, find a way of making available low-cost housing and thereby encourage the return of young people, it is clear that for this to happen, something fundamental has got to change. The catalyst for this can be the ownership of the land and assets by the community. The Trust has inherited a fragile situation. Income comes mainly from the one source and should that source fail for reasons over which the community has no control, it will be difficult if ever to achieve their ambitions.

The Trust needs to find a reliable source of revenue which it can own, develop and control with the approval of the community. One such opportunity is the development of a small site for one to three wind-turbines. The Trust hopes to build, develop, manage and own it with the income being ploughed back into other areas of community life which do not have a profit element.

Money is needed to improve the housing owned by the Trust, to maintain paths through some of the most beautiful areas of Scotland, to support development ideas from people in the community, and to stabilize the historic remnants of the Bunavoneadar Whaling Station from falling into the sea to name but a few.

Getting the balance right means that every attempt will be made by the community through the North Harris Trust to continue to care for our environment.

Planning for the wind turbine(s) and indeed any other development will be undertaken in such a way that there will be a minimum of impact to bird, and other animal and human presence. However, at the end of the day, it is essential that the social and economic benefits to the people of North Harris gets the highest priority.

OpenHydro's open centre turbine tidal power test rig in Orkney © EMEC

20 Management of Environmental Issues at the European Marine Energy Centre (EMEC), Orkney

Kirsten M. Geddes – *MARECO Consultants Ltd., Brig O'Waithe, Stenness, Orkney KW16 3ET.*

Liz Foubister – *Aurora Environmental, 8 Garson Place, Strauness, Orkney KW16 3EE.*

Jennifer Norris – *EMEC Ltd., Old academy, Back Road, Strauness, Orkney KW16 3AW.*

Summary

1. Marine renewables have the potential to cause environmental effects, and therefore require assessment and management.
2. EMEC has a key role in the development of environmental standards in the marine renewable industry.
3. Procedures developed at EMEC can help to ensure that best practice is carried forward into full scale commercial developments.
4. It is essential that experience gained at EMEC feeds back into the development of environmental standards for the marine renewables industry as a whole.

Global climate change is now widely accepted as one of the most serious threats facing the world's environment, economy and society. The UK government's commitment to the Kyoto Protocol demands a measurable reduction in greenhouse gases, particularly CO_2 within a defined timescale. The UK's energy industries are the largest single contributors to UK greenhouse gas emissions, contributing over a third (54 million tonnes) of the total amount of CO_2 emitted in the UK (DTI, 2003). A reduction in greenhouse gas emissions is therefore closely related to switching from traditional sources of power generation to clean, sustainable alternatives.

To achieve this the UK is committed to using alternative and renewable sources of energy which will reduce the dependence on fossil fuels, cut CO_2 emissions to the atmosphere and bring a diversity and security of supply to the UK's energy infrastructure. The UK has set an ambitious target of 20% renewables generation by 2020 (DTI, 2003), with the recent ICCT report (January 25, 2005) recommending that all G8 nations should adopt national targets of at least 25% of electricity from renewables by 2025.

Geddes, K.M., Foubister, L. & Norris, J. (2008). Management of environmental issues at the European Marine Energy Centre (EMEC), Orkney. In *Energy and the Natural Heritage*, ed. by C.A. Galbraith and J.M. Baxter. TSO Scotland, Edinburgh. pp. 245-250

The Scottish Executive, however, has gone a step further and set aspirational renewable energy targets of 18% by 2010 and 40% by 2020 (Scottish Executive, 2003). These targets are unlikely to be met through increasing hydroelectric and onshore wind generation alone. The emerging wave and tidal energy conversion technologies are therefore likely to play a crucial role in reducing CO_2 emissions and creating a sustainable energy future for the UK.

Scotland possesses a huge renewable energy resource both in terms of wind (offshore and onshore) and in coastal wave and tidal capacity. As a nation there is the potential to generate far in excess of the energy currently required. Wave and tidal power alone, although still in the developmental stages, have the capacity to generate over 21.5 GW – enough power to meet Scotland's current energy needs and more (Garrad Hassan and Partners Ltd, 2001).

In this context Highlands and Islands Enterprise (HIE), in collaboration with its funding partners, set up the European Marine Energy Centre (EMEC) to progress testing and full scale commissioning within the marine renewables industry.

EMEC was established in 2003 to provide marine renewables developers from Europe and beyond with a world class testing facility for their devices. The location of the facility in Stromness, Orkney was chosen due to the excellent oceanic wave regime, strong tidal currents and proximity of existing grid connection. These factors, coupled with local facilities and expertise in the renewables and environmental sectors, provide EMEC with the ideal set of conditions to become a 'centre of excellence' both in the provision of test facilities and in the setting of environmental standards.

EMEC provides multiple grid-connected berths, full electrical and SCADA infrastructure, data centre and offices, as well as independent validation services. In addition to the device test berths, EMEC also provides meteorological and wave data – transmitted to the data centre respectively by a MiniMet station and two waverider buoys. The centre also operates CCTV monitoring of the test site, allowing visual monitoring of devices from the offices in the data centre.

Renewable energy is generally viewed as an environmentally beneficial method of generating power. However, although renewable technologies do not generally involve the net use of finite resources or emit greenhouse gases, there is the potential for environmental impacts; particularly connected with the installation of devices and associated infrastructure. The benefits in terms of reduced emissions have to be balanced against other effects, including wider impacts which may not initially be anticipated, such as those on biodiversity.

EMEC, as the first centre of its kind in the world, has a key role in the development and establishment of high standards of environmental performance in the marine renewables industry. EMEC's stewardship in the implementation of environmental standards will ensure that environmental considerations are incorporated at an early stage in the design and development of devices, leading to best practice being carried forward into commercial scale developments. To further ensure that environmental issues are at the centre of decision making, EMEC has adopted an Integrated Management System (IMS) which demonstrates its clear commitment to standards of quality, health, safety and the environment (QHSE). This system has been developed to meet the requirements of the internationally recognized ISO 14001 and to ensure the highest standards of environmental performance at the centre.

From its initial development, EMEC has maintained that the testing facilities should strive to minimize its impact on the environment. The choice of site for the wave test

Figure 20.1 Wave test site building, Billa Croo, Orkney, built to merge into landscape © EMEC

centre, located within a National Scenic Area and on a coast protected by SSSI and SAC designations, immediately highlighted the environment as an important factor in the design of any onshore facilities. An environmental scoping study (AURORA Environmental Ltd, Aquatera Ltd and International Centre for Island Technology, 2001) undertaken prior to the project finalization helped to identify the potentially most influential factors: possible loss of navigation due to the physical presence of the test berths; loss of habitat through the construction of the switchgear building and associated cabling; and visual impact from devices and new structures.

This incorporation of environmental considerations early in the project allowed the issues highlighted to be considered in the final design of the facility. The timing of the scoping study ensured that there was sufficient flexibility in the project to allow for changes to be effected which would mitigate against some of the issues identified. The full Environmental Impact Assessment (EIA) (Carlbro, 2002) recommended that the switchgear building be built with as little visual impact as possible (see Figure 20.1). The construction of the switchgear building and installation of cabling involved the development of a pristine site; however, by encompassing the recommendations of the EIA, the building has achieved a negligible visual impact from both onshore and offshore.

Consultation with local stakeholders on the potential loss of navigation/fishing grounds was also conducted at the scoping stage to ensure that all interests were represented. As a direct result of this consultation EMEC commissioned the production of an 'awareness chart'

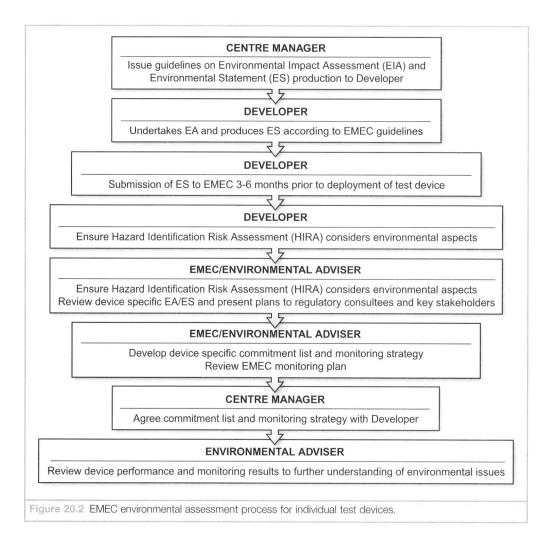

Figure 20.2 EMEC environmental assessment process for individual test devices.

(AURORA Environmental Ltd, 2004). This chart has now been issued to all local sea users (including recreational users) who operate near the wave test site. It includes information on the positions of cardinal buoys (delineating the test site area) and subsea cabling, which can be transferred directly onto an electronic plotter. It was felt that this efficient dissemination of information was vital to maintaining good relations with other sea users.

The wave site EIA also highlighted that device-specific environmental assessment would be necessary due to the unknown characteristics of each individual wave energy converter. EMEC has adopted this recommendation through the production of guidelines on environmental assessment, (AURORA Environmental Ltd and Aquatera Ltd, in prep) which are issued to developers applying for a test berth: the process is summarized in Figure 20.2. Adherence to these guidelines will guarantee that every developer goes through a similar process in assessing the potential environmental effects of their device. This streamlined process will ensure a consistent approach to assessment of devices and development of appropriate environmental monitoring strategies. If required, EMEC is able to impose contractual requirements in order that environmental impacts are avoided or minimized.

Collation of comprehensive data on technical and environmental performance will allow developers to gain a valuable insight into their technologies in full-scale, grid-connected open sea conditions as well as building up a database on potential environmental issues. This information, gained at the prototype stage, will allow the incorporation of environmental considerations into the final design and construction of commercial devices. It may also provide invaluable input into consent applications at other locations for full-scale commercial developments. Furthermore, comparable data will be essential for EMEC in its goal to provide independent verification and testing of marine energy converters.

In order to ensure a good understanding of the environment within which developers will be operating, EMEC undertook the production of an environmental baseline report (AURORA Environmental Ltd, 2005), based on the EIA. This will be issued to each developer to ensure that a similar standard of environmental data is included in each device-specific Environmental Statement (ES). The summary report contains detailed information on the physical and biological conditions at the site prior to the installation of any wave energy devices. This will be continually updated as and when new data become available and can also be used in the development of detailed monitoring strategies.

EMEC further promotes high standards in the prevention of pollution and has developed its own oil spill contingency plan (OSCP) (AURORA Environmental Ltd, in prep). At present there is no statutory requirement for facilities such as EMEC to have such a plan in place, however, the level of uncertainty regarding the types of devices, vessels and operations which may take place at the site increases the need for a clear division of responsibility and system of response, in the unlikely event of a spill.

It is also important that environmental standards are followed through to the decommissioning stage, for which developers are responsible. The EIA guidelines described above will help to ensure that developers consider decommissioning fully when installing their device.

Experience gained from the implementation of the above guidelines and standards at the EMEC facilities will provide an invaluable resource in the long term development of environmental standards for the marine renewables industry. By adopting at the outset principles such as maintaining the comparability of potential effects and monitoring results, information gathered at the centre can also be used to feed into the ongoing development of standards. This method of stewardship through a simple set of guidelines should encourage developers to the site whilst simultaneously ensuring that all devices fulfil the EIA requirements.

The pioneering nature of the technologies tested at EMEC makes accurate prediction of all the environmental impacts which may occur very difficult. It is therefore important that efforts are made at these early stages to take full consideration of siting and design, to minimize any negative environmental impacts that occur, or are predicted.

EMEC aims to use its unique position in the developing industry to identify and encourage the optimization of positive impacts, whilst ensuring adequate consideration of all possible negative effects on the environment at an early stage – or as soon as they become apparent. EMEC is in the process of establishing its research and monitoring programme, through which it aims to help ensure that best practice standards are developed and put in place as the industry develops. Success in this will ensure that the industry maintains its clean, non-polluting and environmentally benign reputation.

References

AURORA Environmental Ltd. (2004). *EMEC Environmental awareness chart.* Prepared by AURORA Environmental Ltd for EMEC.

AURORA Environmental Ltd. (2005). *Environmental description of the EMEC wave test site at Billia Croo, Orkney.* Prepared by AURORA Environmental Ltd for EMEC.

AURORA Environmental Ltd. (in prep). *Oil spill response guidelines for the European Marine Energy Centre wave test site.*

AURORA Environmental Ltd and Aquatera Ltd. (in prep). *Environmental impact assessment (EIA) guidance for developers at the European Marine Energy Centre.*

AURORA Environmental Ltd, Aquatera Ltd and International Centre for Island Technology. (2001). *Environmental scoping for a proposed marine energy test centre, Stromness, Orkney.* Prepared by AURORA Environmental Ltd, Aquatera Ltd and International Centre for Island Technology for Highlands and Islands Enterprise.

Carlbro. (2002). *Marine Energy Test Centre, Environmental Statement.*

Department of Trade and Industry. (2003). *Our Energy Future – Creating a Low Carbon Economy.* DTI Publications.

Garrad Hassan and Partners. (2001). *Scotland Renewable Resource.* Scottish Executive.

International Climate Change Taskforce (ICCT) Report, (25.01.05). Institute for Public Policy Research, Centre for American Progress and the Australia Institute.

Scottish Executive. (2003). *Securing a Renewable Future: Scotland's Renewable Energy.* Scottish Executive.

21 Woodfuel, Rural Development and The Natural Heritage in The Highlands

Fiona Strachan & Cliff Beck – *Highland Birchwoods, Litleburn, Munlochy, Ross-shire IV8 8NN.*

Summary

1. Woodfuel is a viable, sustainable and available alternative to burning fossil fuels for energy production. It is renewable and carbon neutral; efficient, wood burning technology is available, and the Highlands needs local markets for its low grade timber.

2. The available timber resource is in areas of low population; 40% of Scottish electrical demand produces heat and the national grid constrains energy development in peripheral areas, making small scale applications the way ahead.

3. Woodfuel provides more local employment than other renewable energy technologies, particularly for small contractors using tractor based equipment. Local woodfuel markets could encourage thinning, higher initial stocking densities and species mixtures, improving biodiversity, landscape and final crop values.

4. Here we explain the rationale and benefits of woodfuel use in the Highlands, and outline the steps that need to be taken to ensure the development of sustainable woodfuel supply chains in Scotland.

21.1 Introduction

Apart from the sun, wood has always been man's primary energy source, and a log fire is still an icon for relaxation, comfort and security. Nowadays dependence on woodfuel is associated with poverty; increased affluence being accompanied by increased technical sophistication in energy supply. Woodfuel is generally seen as dirty, inconvenient and ineffective in comparison with mains utilities. The tendency towards purely iconographic use of unseasoned logs on open fires only serves to compound such views.

However, this picture has changed dramatically in several parts of Europe. Woodfuel now accounts for 19% of primary energy production in Finland (TEKES, 2002), 22% of rural domestic heating energy in Austria with plans to increase this to 40% by 2010 (Osborn, 2001), and approximately 35% of the Danish timber harvest is for woodfuel (CBT, 1999). As a result of this expansion there are now well tested wood burning technologies suitable for a range of different applications and scales.

Strachan, F. & Beck, C. (2008). Woodfuel, Rural Development & The Natural Heritage in The Highlands. In *Energy and the Natural Heritage*, ed. by C.A. Galbraith and J.M. Baxter. TSO Scotland, Edinburgh. pp. 251-258

Over 40% of Scottish electricity demand is for heat. Unlike other forms of renewable energy, biomass can be used to generate heat directly, rather than as electricity. This could avoid both the grid-imposed limitations on energy generation in peripheral areas, and the transport costs associated with the wide fuel catchment areas required by large combined heat and power developments.

In Scotland, however, the woodfuel industry is still in its infancy. Biomass energy in Scotland has been identified as having the potential to supply as much as 450 MW of electricity from the wood fuel resource while employing over 2,000 people and stimulating other sectors of the economy (FREDS, 2005). Additionally, in rural areas of Scotland in particular, wood is the most plentiful and readily available biomass fuel.

21.2 Advantages of woodfuel use

Woodfuel is regarded as a carbon neutral energy source because the carbon released during combustion is equivalent to that absorbed by the tree while it was growing. Even if CO_2 emissions are analysed on a lifecycle basis a woodfuel powered plant has substantially lower emissions than a fossil fuel burning power station (Figure 21.1).

Small scale woodfuel supply chains, particularly those harvesting early thinnings, represent an opportunity for local contractors, community woodland groups and farmers to

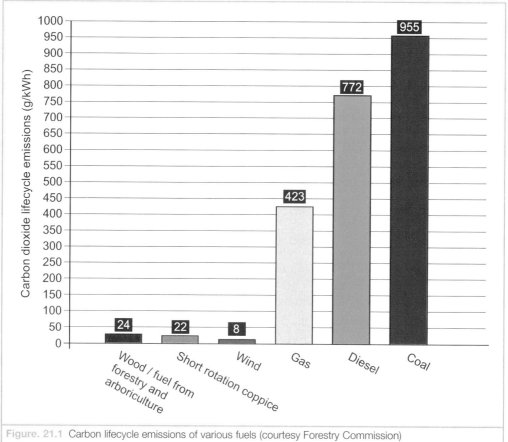

Figure. 21.1 Carbon lifecycle emissions of various fuels (courtesy Forestry Commission)

use non-specialist tractor based equipment to enter the market, as they frequently do in both Austria and Finland. In this way woodfuel has the potential to make a substantial contribution to agricultural diversification and the management of farm woodlands, opening up employment and business opportunities and providing a vital economic boost to rural areas.

21.3 The form of woodfuel

In the developed world, wood is most often used as logs, chips or pellets.

Logs should be felled in winter for burning the next winter. They are used for open fires, stoves and even for some automatic heating systems. They are easily stored and take minimum energy input but they are less convenient than other forms of woodfuel. However, log accumulator boilers are available which are effectively semi-automated log burning systems allowing the advantages of self supply and some of the convenience of automation.

Woodchips can be produced in the forest, at the forest roadside, at a central location such as a fuel supply depot, or at the point of use. Woodchip boilers can be used for individual houses but are more often used in medium to large-scale systems.

Pellets are usually made from timber processing co-products. They are clean, dry and uniform. As such they are suited to both domestic situations and to large automated systems that co-fire with other fuels.

21.4 Utilization

Unlike many forms of energy, wood can be stored and used when needed. It can be used at a variety of scales from individual houses to public buildings or district heating schemes for an entire community.

In general, large boilers have less exacting fuel specifications than their small scale counterparts which require a very consistent chip size and a moisture content of 20-25%. Stemwood chips more consistently than recycled wood or brash, and small dimension trees felled in winter have a lower moisture content than larger trees owing to the high sapwood volume. As a result, chips from small dimension roundwood fetch a premium price in well established woodfuel markets because they are better suited to more exacting boilers. Even so, some drying of the material is still required. This is usually done by covering stacks of roundwood and leaving them for 1-2 years before chipping, but chips can be dried using agricultural grain driers or similar equipment.

Harvesting residues and whole trees from small early thinnings are often used to fuel large boilers. The chips produced are less consistent but adequate for the more robust fuel delivery mechanisms. If used in small auger fed boilers there would be a risk of jamming mechanisms.

Residues and whole trees are often left on the harvesting site until the foliage has fallen away, thus minimizing the damage to the nutrient cycle and reducing the moisture content. However, very large boilers with flue condensers can also burn green woodfuel as the latent heat loss during evaporation is recaptured from the flue gases.

21.5 The resource

Throughout the world, woodfuel is regarded as a local resource for a number of reasons. It has a low bulk density compared to other fuels and is a low value commodity, and thus even

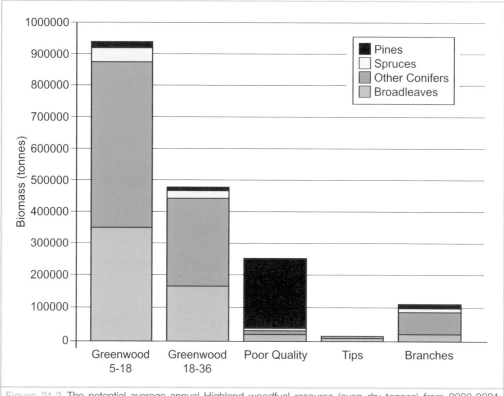

Figure 21.2 The potential average annual Highland woodfuel resource (oven dry tonnes) from 2003-2021 (www.woodfuelresource.org.uk)

over short distances, transport can be a significant proportion of overall costs. This favours small, rather than large woodfuel developments, particularly in peripheral areas with low populations.

The annual Highland timber harvest smaller than 16cm top diameter is shown in Figure 21.2 together with residue and poor quality stems. Some of the roundwood will go into traditional Scottish markets rather than woodfuel. Even so, there is clearly a plentiful resource, some of which is adjacent to major population centres, but the majority is in peripheral areas where haulage costs to other industrial roundwood markets often result in negative returns. Small scale district heating schemes in these areas could greatly improve local timber markets.

Large scale electricity generation schemes are an alternative approach in areas with a low population and a plentiful resource, but two factors mitigate against this.

Firstly, the fuel catchment areas are large, often rendering such plants uneconomic.

Secondly, the National Grid is often unable to accommodate a significant increase in supply in such areas.

21.6 The benefits of woodfuel

The development of small and medium scale wood fuelled district heating would bring both rural development and environmental benefits.

21.6.1 Improved timber incomes

In real terms, timber incomes from forestry are currently poorer than they have been for several decades. Although demand for woodfuel is unlikely to increase timber prices; because it is a local market, haulage costs will decrease and this will improve net incomes in peripheral areas where industrial roundwood markets are not viable at present.

21.6.2 Resumption of thinning

Poor timber incomes mean thinning is often delayed or abandoned resulting in higher proportions of low grade timber that is better suited to industrial processes than to local conversion to meet local needs. The average annual resource available from thinnings in the Highlands (subject to competition from other markets) is over 350,000 oven dry tonnes (www.woodfuelresource.org.uk/). The importance of woodfuel markets to the economics of early thinnings in Finland is shown in Table 21.1.

Table 21.1 Typical Finnish forest management regime (Hakkila P. 2003. Developing technology for large scale production of forest chips)

Treatment	Stand age	Yield of timber	Biomass residues	
	years	m³/ha	m³/ha	toe/ha
Precommercial thinning	10–20	–	15–50	3–9
1st commercial thinning	25–40	30–60	20–50	4–9
2nd commercial thinning	40–55	4–80	15–30	3–6
3rd commercial thinning	5–70	60–90	20–30	4–6
Final harvest	70–100	200–300	60–120	11–22
Total during rotation		330–530	130–280	25–52

Resumption of thinning would increase the value of final crop timber and its suitability for processing at local saw mills. It would also help bring neglected native woodlands under management, encouraging the removal of invasive non-native species.

Resumption of thinning also makes the output from woodlands and forests more constant and therefore provides a more realistic basis for stable local enterprises. Likewise, because local demand for woodfuel is comparatively constant once markets are established, it encourages smaller annual coupes in uniform-aged, poor quality crops which in turn facilitates improved structural diversity, laying foundations for greater continuity of output in the future.

21.6.3 Employment

Apart from the stimulation of more intensive forest management and greater levels of local added value processing, woodfuel use itself creates employment throughout the supply chain. Biomass energy generates approximately six full time jobs per megawatt (FREDS, 2005) which is significantly more than other forms of energy once plant construction is completed.

Moreover the availability of plentiful supplies of heat can stimulate other sectors such as horticulture, and can also help to alleviate fuel poverty. Finally, the biodiversity and landscape improvements referred to below also provide opportunities to improve local employment and incomes.

21.6.4 Improved restocking practices

Danish research indicates that woodfuel harvests are optimized through initial stocking densities as high as 7000 stems/ha (CBT, 2002). This gives far greater flexibility to forest managers, allowing exploitation of silviculturally beneficial mixtures which can be managed in response to changing market conditions.

For example, the improved growth conferred on spruce by silver birch is well documented. Mixed stands of spruce and a predominantly birch native species mix could be planted and then thinned to favour spruce if softwood markets improve, or thinned to favour native species if markets for good quality birch start to pick up. Alternatively, thinning regimes could favour alternate species in different areas creating a patchwork of small stands that will supply commercial timber markets while also maintaining a forest habitat network.

21.6.5 Improved biodiversity

Greater use of mixtures and more frequent thinning and felling will improve the biodiversity of our woodlands and forests (Figure 21.3), which shows a woodland thinned to improve habitat, as part of the LIFE project "Urgent Conservation management for Scottish Capercaillie".

21.6.6 Improved landscape values

Improved structural and species diversity also leads to both improved landscape values and improved opportunities for recreation. This in turn creates opportunities for local businesses and woodland owners.

21.7 Conclusions

Because woodfuel has the potential to improve the economics of clearfelling in low grade stands, thinning in commercial crops and removal of exotics in native woodlands, a well developed small to medium scale woodfuel market could deliver a range of rural development and environmental benefits, particularly in peripheral areas.

This potential economic improvement is greatest in rural areas that are remote from existing industrial roundwood markets. The potential rural development and environmental benefits depend on this economic improvement acting as a stimulus to resume more intensive forest management practices and encourage the structural and species diversification of the existing plantation resource in a way that strengthens the underlying ecology and produces a steady flow of diverse outputs that benefits the local economy.

Further information:

Highland Birchwoods is interested in working with all those promoting woodfuel for the benefit of local communities and the natural heritage. For further information please contact:

Fiona.strachan@highlandbirchwoods.co.uk
cliff@highlandbirchwoods.co.uk

Figure 21.3 Woodland thinned to create capercaillie habitat © Highland Birchwoods

References

Centre for Biomass Technology. (1999). Wood for Energy Production. Technology-Environment-Economy.

FREDS. (2005). Promoting and accelerating the market penetration of biomass technology in Scotland. Scottish Executive.

Osborn, E. (2001). Anglia Woodnet EU Leader II Wood Fuel Study Tour. Summary Report.

TEKES. (2002). Growing Power. Advanced Solutions for Bioenergy Technology from Finland.

22 Familiarity Breeds Content? Public Perceptions of Wind Power in the Scottish Borders

Charles R. Warren & Carolyn Lumsden – *School of Geography and Geosciences, University of St Andrews, St Andrews, Fife KY16 9AL.*

Summary

1. Amongst a sample of 115 people living near an existing or a proposed windfarm in the Scottish Borders, large majorities support the concept of wind power development, both in principle and in (local) practice.

2. Attitudes to windfarms become more positive following personal experience of living near one, such that those with windfarms in their "backyard" are amongst the most supportive of the technology.

3. Aesthetic perceptions, both positive and negative, are the strongest single influence on individuals' reactions to wind power projects.

4. Reasons given for opposing windfarms focus on local environments whereas windfarm supporters highlight global issues.

22.1 Introduction: A 'Green on Green' debate

There is intense debate about the place of wind power in Scotland. Fears about the environmental impacts of windfarms (notably on landscape aesthetics) have generated outspoken opposition to current government policy which strongly encourages renewable energy in general and wind power in particular. Government support for wind energy arises from strategic concerns about energy security and growing worries about climate change (SPECC, 2004). The closure within the next decade of several large power stations could convert Scotland's current energy surplus into a deficit (RSE, 2006). Therefore, to sustain current generating capacity and to achieve the desired low-carbon economy, a substantial expansion of renewables is required, especially if Government chooses not to replace Scotland's nuclear capacity with new nuclear plant (SNH, 2002). These reasons, combined with the facts that Scotland has the best wind resource in Europe and that wind energy is the least costly of the 'new renewables' technologies, explain the enthusiasm for windfarm developments; by mid 2007 the capacity of windfarms in the planning system totalled 11 GW (SNH, 2007), exceeding Scotland's total electricity generating capacity.

Although the current debates over wind power share some of the hallmarks of earlier environmental controversies (Warren, 2002), they differ from them in one key regard. Whereas

Warren, C.R. & Lumsden, C. (2008). Familiarity Breeds Content? Public Perceptions of Wind Power in the Scottish Borders. In *Energy and the Natural Heritage*, ed. by C.A. Galbraith and J.M. Baxter. TSO Scotland, Edinburgh. pp. 259-264 previous conflicts have typically set developers against a largely united environmental lobby, the wind power debate features strong 'green' claims on both sides, with 'clean energy' arguments countered by opposition to the landscape impacts of windfarms. To adopt military terminology, this controversy can thus been characterized as a *'green on green'* debate, just as occurrences of 'friendly fire' are termed *'blue on blue'* incidents. This is perhaps a foretaste of environmental debates to come: society has gone green, but what kind of greenness do we want? Society requires large quantities of energy, and *all* forms of power generation have environmental impacts.

22.2 Aims and research methods

The wind farm debate consists of an exchange of claims and counter-claims which are often long on assertion and short on evidence. Case studies therefore represent important tests of the conflicting arguments. Here we summarize key findings of a case study of public perceptions of wind power in the Scottish Borders. Full results and discussion of this research, are presented by Warren *et al.* (2005). We test three counter-intuitive hypotheses derived from previous attitudinal research:

- **Temporal effects**: the attitudes of local people become more favourable towards windfarms after construction, and opposition is greater at proposed sites than at operational ones.
- **Spatial effects**: attitudes of local people are more favourable with increasing proximity to windfarms.
- **NIMBY-ism**: the NIMBY syndrome does not adequately explain public attitudes to windfarms.

Local attitudes to the development of wind energy at two sites in the Scottish Borders were explored using face-to-face questionnaire surveys conducted at residents' homes during August 2003. One study area was centred on an existing windfarm (Dun Law), the other on a site at which a 22-turbine windfarm had received planning approval but had not been constructed (Black Hill). Attitudes were investigated within two concentric zones, 0-5 km and 5-10 km around each windfarm site (Figure 22.1). Within each zone, 24-32 people participated, totalling 115 respondents.

22.3 Results

At both sites, attitudes towards the concept of wind power in Scotland and towards the local windfarms were strongly positive (Table 22.1) but with significantly greater support amongst those near the existing windfarm. Interestingly, the reasons given to explain this positive perception were predominantly of a global and altruistic kind, concerned primarily with environmental protection and the promotion of renewable energy. Few cited local reasons or personal benefit. Conversely, most of the negative responses arose from local concerns, particularly relating to landscape aesthetics and cumulative impacts. The issues of noise and bird mortality were each raised by just one person.

Following experience of the Dun Law windfarm, 24% of people altered their pre-construction attitudes, all but one becoming more positive. A majority of residents felt that there had been no local impacts, while those perceiving a positive impact greatly outnumbered those who perceived a negative impact (45% v. 18%) (Table 22.2). This

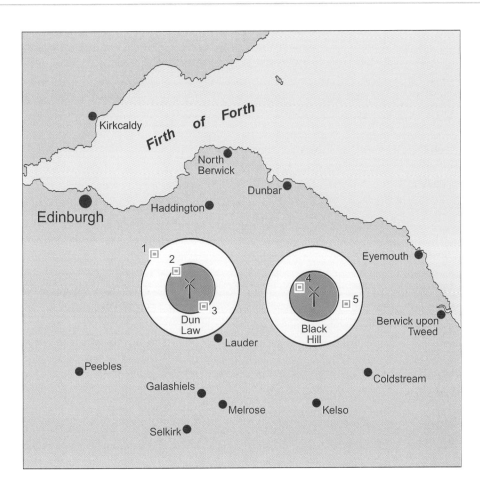

Distance from Wind Farms

Wind farms

Questionnaire survey settlements

Settlements

Survey Locations

Scottish Borders

1 Pathhead

2 Fala

3 Oxton

4 Longformacus

5 Duns

0   20 km

Figure 22.1 The operational and approved windfarm sites in the Scottish Borders, showing the local settlements in which sampling was carried out and the concentric zones around the windfarms. The Dun Law (or Soutra) Windfarm, which is bisected by the A68, was constructed in 2000. It consists of 26 turbines, 42 m high, with a total capacity of 17.2 MW.

Table 22.1 Attitudes of local people in the Scottish Borders site towards:
  A. The development of wind power in Scotland.
  B. The local wind farm (existing or proposed).
  DL = Dun Law, the operational site. BH = Black Hill, the proposed site.

		Strongly support		Support		Neutral		Oppose		Strongly oppose	
		DL	BH	DL	BH	DL	BH	DL	BH	DL	BH
A.	Wind power in Scotland	55%	55%	35%	22%	6%	16%	2%	0	2%	7%
B.	Local wind farm	63%	47%	25%	16%	3%	20%	3%	4%	5%	13%

contrasts with the Black Hill results, where a greater number anticipated negative outcomes (30% v. 25%). Support for the existing windfarms was highest amongst those living in the inner zone, and opposition was slightly greater in the outer zone (10% v. 6%). At Black Hill, by contrast, the inner zone yielded lower support (58% v. 69%) and much greater opposition (33% v. 3%) than the outer zone. When asked where future windfarms should be located, preferences were similar at both sites: uninhabited areas and offshore sites came top of the list, but a significant number also recommended upland areas. Few specifically advocated the avoidance of scenic areas. At both sites, there was a clear preference for windfarms to be modest in size (<25 turbines).

Table 22.2 The perceived positive and negative impacts of the operational windfarm at Dun Law.

	% of responses	Number of responses
Positive impact		
Attractive landscape feature	34	13
Community funding	26	10
Intrinsic value	16	6
A local amenity	13	5
Tourist attraction	11	3
Total	100	38
Negative impact		
Unattractive landscape feature	44	7
Driver distraction	25	4
No local economic benefits	25	4
Noise	6	1
Total	100	16

22.4 Discussion

It appears that opposition to windfarms partly arises from exaggerated perceptions of likely impact, and that the experience of living near a windfarm largely dispels these fears, confirming earlier studies (Braunholtz, 2003; SEI, 2003; Devine-Wright, 2005). Prior to construction, local residents often anticipate negative landscape impacts, whereas, once built, many people regard them as an attractive addition (Table 22.2). For many, then, it seems that 'seeing is believing'. Although elements of typical NIMBY attitudes appear in our survey, especially in relation to the proposed windfarm, the data support Wolsink's (2007) conclusion that the NIMBY concept is too simplistic to capture the wide spectrum of public opinion. Instead, an 'inverse NIMBY' syndrome is apparent whereby those with windfarms in their 'backyard' are amongst the most supportive of the technology. Some of the opposition to windfarms may therefore be a case of NIABY *(Not In Anybody's Backyard)*, a belief that windfarms are inappropriate in the Scottish uplands.

In common with previous studies (Pasqualetti *et al.*, 2002; Wolsink, 2007), our results show that aesthetic perceptions are the strongest single influence on individuals' attitudes towards windfarms. Strikingly, the landscape impact of the Dun Law windfarm was its most frequently cited positive *and* negative attribute, and almost twice as many people found it attractive as found it unattractive (Table 22.2). This highlights the notoriously subjective nature of landscape values and the wide spectrum of perspectives found within society. Some people loathe wind turbines, some love them, and still others are ambivalent about their visual impact but welcome them because they symbolize clean energy (Toke, 2005). Landscape aesthetics clearly lie at the heart of the windfarm debate, with opponents objecting to the speed, scale and uncoordinated nature of windfarm development. Just as opposition to the cumulative impacts of state-sponsored afforestation led local authorities to adopt Indicative Forest Strategies during the 1990s (Warren, 2000), so there is a need for a clear strategic planning framework to guide the siting of windfarms. The introduction of 'Indicative Windfarm Strategies' could be a positive means of imposing some strategic order on the current windfarm 'gold rush'.

This and previous studies (e.g. SEI, 2003) show that an essentially geographical issue lies at the heart of the wind power debate, namely the adoption of contrasting spatial and temporal scales. Arguments in favour of wind power mostly relate to global issues (e.g. climate change), whereas opposition arises primarily from local or regional concerns. Moreover, many people attach greater weight to immediate than to long-term issues. The difficult nature of the global/local balance is exacerbated by the fact that the impacts of climate change are diffuse, large-scale, long term and (so far) largely imperceptible, whereas the impacts of windfarms are localized, immediate and highly visible. In the short term windfarms may be perceived to 'ruin' a local landscape, but if a larger scale, longer term frame of reference is adopted, wind power may be seen as a means of saving landscapes, not destroying them. Such spatio-temporal difficulties are central to this 'green on green' debate and are persistent threads in many sustainability controversies.

22.5 Conclusions

Our results support the three initial hypotheses:

- Large majorities favour wind power development in principle and in (local) practice.

- Those with windfarms in their 'backyard' are amongst the most supportive of the technology.
- Aesthetic perceptions, both positive and negative, are the strongest single influence on individuals' attitudes towards wind power projects.

These conclusions contrast markedly with much media coverage which typically portrays massive grassroots opposition to windfarms. Nevertheless, if the deep concerns of those who fear a rapid industrialization of large swathes of wild land are to be allayed, there is a clear need to introduce a strategic planning framework for wind power development in Scotland.

References

Braunholtz, S. (2003). *Public attitudes to windfarms: a survey of local residents in Scotland.* MORI Scotland, Edinburgh, for Scottish Executive Social Research.

Devine-Wright, P. (2005). Beyond NIMBYism: towards an integrated framework for understanding public perceptions of wind energy. *Wind Energy.* **8**: 125-139.

Pasqualetti, M.J., Gipe, P. and Righter, R.W. (Eds). (2002). *Wind Power in View: energy landscapes in a crowded world.* Academic Press, San Diego.

RSE. (2006). *Inquiry into Energy Issues for Scotland: Final Report.* Royal Society of Edinburgh, Edinburgh.

SEI. (2003). *Attitudes towards the development of windfarms in Ireland.* Sustainable Energy Ireland, Bandon.

SNH. (2002). *Strategic locational guidance for onshore windfarms in respect of the natural heritage.* Scottish Natural Heritage Policy Statement 02/02.

SNH. (2004). *Renewables trends in Scotland: statistics and analysis.* Available at: http://www.snh.org.uk.pdfs.strategy/renewables/sr-rt.pdf

SPECC. (2004). *Renewable Energy in Scotland.* Scottish Parliament enterprise and Culture Committee, Edinburgh.

Toke, D. (2005). Explaining wind power planning outcomes: some findings from a study in England and Wales. *Energy Policy.* **33**(12): 1527-1539.

Warren, C.R. (2000). 'Birds, Bogs and Forestry' revisited: the significance of the Flow Country controversy. *Scottish Geographical Journal.* **116**(4): 315-337.

Warren, C.R. (2002). Of superquarries and mountain railways: recurring themes in Scottish environmental conflict. *Scottish Geographical Journal.* **118**(2): 101-127.

Warren, C.R., Lumsden, C., O'Dowd, S. and Birnie, R.V. (2005). 'Green on green': public perceptions of wind power in Scotland and Ireland. *Journal of Environmental Planning and Management.* **48**: 853-875.

Wolsink, M. (2007). Wind power implementation: the nature of public attitudes - equity and fairness instead of 'backyard motives'. *Renewable and Sustainable Energy Reviews.* **11** (6): 188-1207.

PART 5:

Conclusions

Blanket bog – Claish Moss NNR, Ardnamurchan © Lorne Gill

PART 5:

Conclusions

The two chapters in this part draw together some key issues and present reflections on the energy debate in general.

The chapter by Bill Band and Clive Mitchell provides an overview of energy use and generation in the UK and examines the various strategies for reducing carbon outputs in the years ahead. They examine what impacts these changes may have on the natural heritage, noting that some may have a greater impact than others. They note the real potential that renewable energy offers, whilst stressing the continuing need for the conservation of energy. The need to conserve energy has indeed been a theme running through many of the chapters in this book, and is an approach that appears to be key to developing a balanced energy regime in future.

The final chapter from John Thompson draws all the key issues together. He concludes by stressing the need for everyone involved the energy generation, and in conserving the natural heritage, to work together in order to develop an industry that meets the national demand for energy, and does so in a manner that maintains Scotland's wonderful landscapes, wildlife and habitats.

This spectacular "blue marble" image is the most detailed true-colour image of the entire Earth to date. Using a collection of satellite-based observations, scientists and visualizers stitched together months of observations of the land surface, oceans, sea ice, and clouds into a seamless, true-colour mosaic of every square kilometre (.386 square mile) of our planet. © NASA

23 Energy and the Natural Heritage: Developing an SNH View

Bill Band & Clive Mitchell – *Scottish Natural Heritage, Battleby, Redgorton, Perth PH1 3EW.*

Summary

1. This chapter provides an overview of energy use and generation within the UK, and examines the various strategies for reducing carbon outputs and how these will impact on the natural heritage.

2. Overall, energy use is increasing. It has done so by about 1% a year over the last 20 years and there is no sign of growth slowing down. The UK is still a fossil fuel society – almost 90% of energy use in the UK comes from petroleum, gas or coal. To reduce carbon emissions by 60% by 2050 is no small ambition.

3. Renewable technologies differ in their impacts on the natural heritage. Wave and tidal stream generation, and biomass energy, may be relatively benign, offshore and onshore wind have more significant impacts, while large-scale hydro and tidal barrage have the greatest influence on habitats and landscapes. Scotland has a large renewables resource, and if undertaken wisely, could probably power itself almost entirely from renewables.

4. Coal is bad in emissions terms, and its use should be minimized unless carbon sequestration is developed. Gas stocks have a limited lifetime, and should not be widely used for space heating as at present. Nuclear energy is carbon-free, but has risks which could be very far-reaching in both space and time.

5. In daily life, there are huge opportunities for achieving reductions in energy demand, through energy efficiency, better building design and changes in personal and organizational behaviour. Ways should be found of rewarding low-energy lifestyles. Transport may be most problematic, as society depends on it and enjoys its benefits, and restrictions would bite hard on lifestyles. Public transport, policy-led pricing, and biofuels will all be important.

6. The highest priority should be placed on energy efficiency and demand reduction measures – which can be achieved with few impacts on the natural heritage. In contrast, renewable electricity projects have significant impacts. They should be used only in conjunction with demand reduction - otherwise they will serve only to soak up an unchecked rising demand for electricity.

Band, B. & Mitchell, C. (2008). Energy and the Natural Heritage: Developing an SNH View. In *Energy and the Natural Heritage*, ed. by C.A. Galbraith and J.M. Baxter. TSO Scotland, Edinburgh. pp. 269-280

23.1 Preamble

Other chapters in this volume present ways in which various types of energy use and supply, both past and future, affect the natural heritage. This chapter links these topics together by providing an overview of energy use and generation, and by examining the various strategies for reducing carbon outputs and how these will affect the natural heritage. It addresses the question "In terms of natural heritage interests, which strategies should take priority?"

23.2 Energy trends

The chapter first looks at the major trends in energy consumption and production, and how these contribute to greenhouse gas emissions, drawing on energy statistics available from the Department of Trade and Industry (DTI 2001, 2002 updated 2004, 2004, and 2004 update, and the National Atmospheric Emissions Inventory 1990-2001 (2004)).

Overall, energy use is increasing, and has done so by about 1% a year over the last 20 years (Figure 23.1), and there is no sign of growth slowing down.

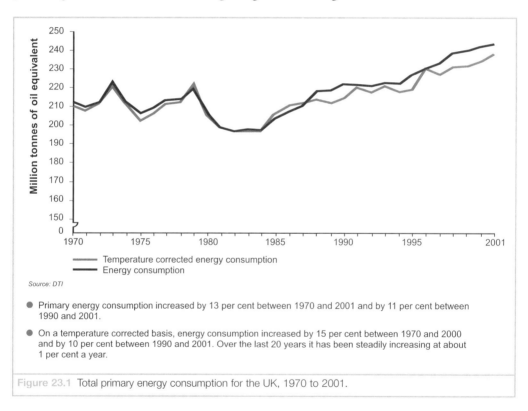

Source: DTI

- Primary energy consumption increased by 13 per cent between 1970 and 2001 and by 11 per cent between 1990 and 2001.

- On a temperature corrected basis, energy consumption increased by 15 per cent between 1970 and 2000 and by 10 per cent between 1990 and 2001. Over the last 20 years it has been steadily increasing at about 1 per cent a year.

Figure 23.1 Total primary energy consumption for the UK, 1970 to 2001.

Figure 23.2 charts the relationship between energy consumption and various kinds of activity. A declining trend is desirable because it means that less energy is used per unit of activity. The ratio between energy use and Gross Domestic Product shows a declining trend for the UK economy overall over the last 30 years, and markedly so for the industry sector. The energy ratio includes both energy efficiency and structural changes in the economy, so sometimes the energy ratio goes down because of efficiency gains – doing more with less – and sometimes it goes down because of underlying changes in the activity – for example the

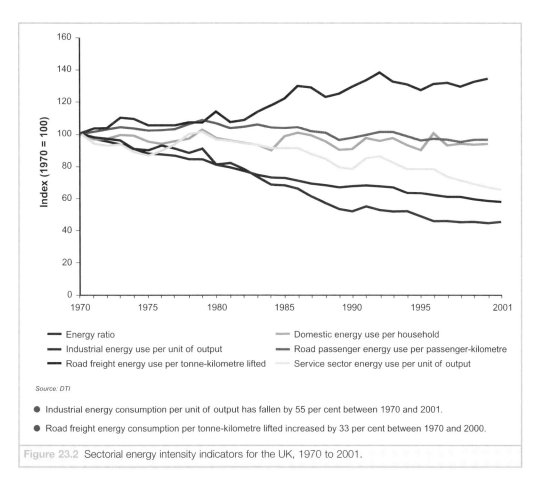

Legend:
- ■ Energy ratio
- ■ Industrial energy use per unit of output
- ■ Road freight energy use per tonne-kilometre lifted
- ■ Domestic energy use per household
- ■ Road passenger energy use per passenger-kilometre
- Service sector energy use per unit of output

Source: DTI

- ● Industrial energy consumption per unit of output has fallen by 55 per cent between 1970 and 2001.
- ● Road freight energy consumption per tonne-kilometre lifted increased by 33 per cent between 1970 and 2000.

Figure 23.2 Sectorial energy intensity indicators for the UK, 1970 to 2001.

shift away from heavy industry in the UK economy. That raises a caution: given that the aim is to reduce global emissions arising from energy use, it needs to be asked whether UK society has stopped using the products of heavy industry (for example), or does it still use them but import them from other countries? In the latter case the UK's footprint would be just as big or bigger than hitherto, but made up of all the little footfalls made around the world – which are not necessarily captured in the energy statistics for the UK.

However, some of the lines are less encouraging. Energy use per household in the domestic sector has shown little change over the last 30 years, and there is little change in energy use per passenger-kilometre for transport, despite substantial improvements in vehicle efficiency. For freight transport the energy use per tonne-kilometre has increased markedly, presumably because of shifts from rail to road and higher transport speeds. So not only are levels of activity increasing alongside growth in GDP; in some sectors like transport, energy consumption per unit of activity is actually increasing. Transport is a particular problem because although there have been many improvements in energy efficiency – doing more with less – much more transport is being used, so overall energy use in the sector is increasing. There has also been a shift away from rail to road for personal transport as well as for freight; with rising incomes private car ownership has increased – although much less so in Scotland where around 66% of households own a car compared with 75% in the rest of the UK.

The point to emphasize is that while the UK economy is using less energy per unit of economic activity, the overall size of the UK economy has grown and continues to grow, and our overall use of energy continues to increase (Figure 23.1). Why all this matters for the natural heritage will become clear.

23.3 Energy flows and emissions

Energy flows in the UK and how they relate to emissions of greenhouse gases drawn from various statistics published by the Department of Trade and Industry (DTI, 2001, 2004, 2004 update) and the National Atmospheric Emissions Inventory 1990-2001 (2004) are shown in Figure 23.3. Some of the key issues are:

- What fuels are used? The UK is still a fossil fuel society: almost 90% of energy used in the UK comes from fossil fuels - petroleum, gas and coal.
- Who uses energy? The four main sectors are transport, domestic, industry and services.

Electricity power stations are kept in a separate category in Figure 23.3, as electricity is not a primary fuel - it may be generated from coal, gas, nuclear, wind or water, and some of those fuels are used to make electricity. Around 50% of overall energy use is accounted for by electricity, but the current overall efficiency factor for power stations in the UK is 38.5% – this is the figure used in the UK Emissions Trading Scheme, (Defra, 2001, 2003). That means that only 40% of that energy is converted into useful electricity: the remaining 60% is waste heat, so for 1 unit of electricity used, 2.5 units of energy are lost. That waste heat shows on the chart as the power station sector, i.e. the energy lost during electricity production, mainly conversion losses and distribution losses, plus energy used by energy industries in the process of transformation e.g. for lighting, compressors, or cooling systems. The useable energy – the electricity used – is included within the energy mix for each of the main sectors which uses it.

Looking at the relationship between what fuels are used and who uses energy (the flows between these two columns in Figure 23.3), it is apparent that transport is almost wholly dependent on petroleum (99%), and conversely most petroleum is used by transport (82%), with only a small proportion (18%) fuelling the other sectors.

In the domestic sector fuel use is dominated by gas (67%); in the domestic, industry, and service sectors around half the energy requirement is for space heating, and more if you include water heating. The dominance of gas reveals something about the importance of price – the price per kilowatt-hour unit to the consumer of gas is 1-2 pence, but electricity is about 7 pence.

Electricity supplies all of the domestic, industry and service sectors. In the UK, electricity is generated from:

- gas (40%)
- coal (32%)
- nuclear (22%), and
- hydro, imports and renewables (all together, 6%).

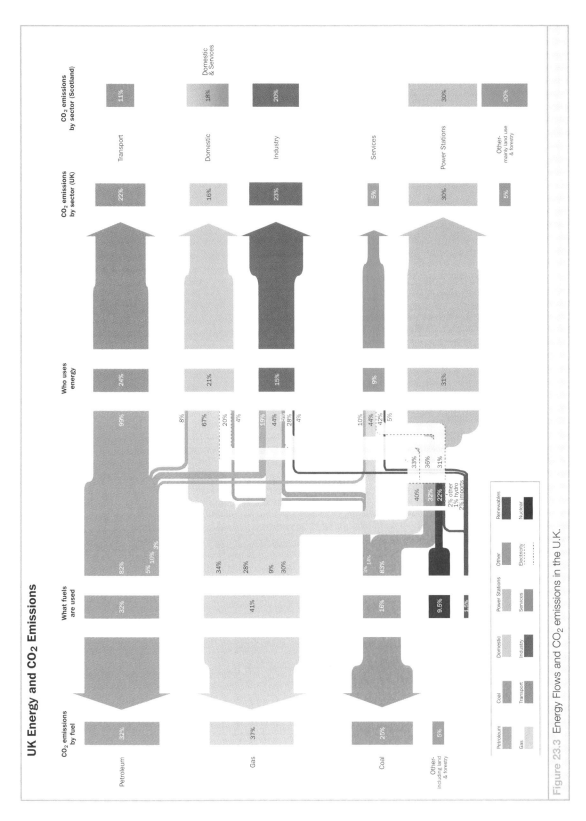

Figure 23.3 Energy Flows and CO₂ emissions in the U.K.

In Scotland the positions of nuclear and gas are reversed, with typically around 40% from nuclear, around 20% from gas, and about the same (30%) for coal. Also the contribution from renewables is greater - around 10% from hydro and about 1.5% for other renewable sources. Coal is almost entirely used by power stations for electricity production (83%).

So what does this mean in terms of emissions of greenhouse gases? The column on the left of Figure 23.3 shows CO_2 emissions by fuel type. (In line with standard UK procedures for reporting emissions of greenhouse gases, the discussion in this paper expresses all emissions in terms of CO_2.) Coal is particularly dirty – it contributes 25% of emissions though it represents only 16% of fuel used – while gas is cleaner. Nuclear fission, of course, does not generate CO_2 emissions.

The fairly even spread of CO_2 emissions across the transport, domestic and industry sectors should be noted (Figure 23.3). Power stations account for nearly one-third of emissions of greenhouse gases by sector, part of this being due to energy wasted as heat during the generation and distribution of electricity, whilst 'services' is the smallest sector in terms of CO_2 emissions producing only around 5% of the total.

Energy use statistics are not as yet available for Scotland alone, but CO_2 emissions by sector in Scotland are shown in Figure 23.3. The emissions from the transport sector are proportionally less than for the UK, while the power station sector produces much the same proportion as for the UK; in these Scottish statistics the domestic and service sectors are combined.

In Scotland the greenhouse gas emissions arising from land management – mainly from agriculture and forestry – represent around 20% of overall emissions. These are largely due to the management of the large volume of carbon-rich soils in Scotland. There is an

Plate 23.1 Ardrossan wind farm © Lorne Gill / SNH

extended timescale underlying many of these emissions, for example where peatland has been afforested, so that it may be difficult to achieve reductions in these emissions. In total, these land-use emissions are about twice those from the transport sector, and this means a high importance must be attached to good stewardship of carbon-rich soils.

In terms of energy use and emissions of greenhouse gases, all sectors and all three main fossil fuel types have an important role to play. As set out by Sprent *et al.* (this volume), a key objective of Government energy policy is to reduce these by 60% by 2050 - and this in the face of a history of growth in energy demand (DTI, 2002 updated 2004). That is no small ambition.

23.4 Impacts on the natural heritage

The possible strategies for emission reduction for each sector and the consequences for the natural heritage are considered.

23.4.1 Electricity

Figure 23.4 shows an assessment of the types of electricity production in terms of their natural heritage impact. Renewable energy is carbon free, but there is a range of direct impacts on the natural heritage from the flooding of valleys to bird strikes.

For marine renewables, SNH has already looked forward to the potential impacts of these and concluded that there is a hierarchy here from wave farms with floating devices moored to the seabed, which may be relatively benign, through tidal stream devices which may be founded in the seabed and have some effect on downstream habitats, through offshore wind farms which require major seabed piling operations, to tidal barrage schemes which would involve complete transformation of the habitat and landscape of an estuary.

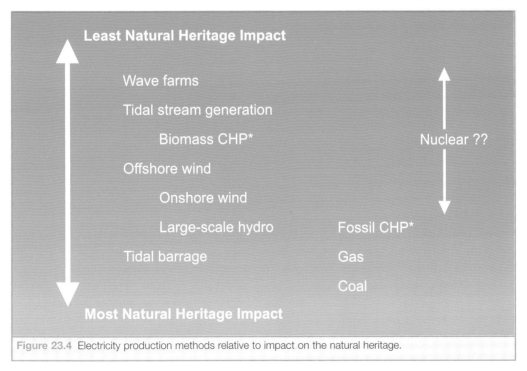

Figure 23.4 Electricity production methods relative to impact on the natural heritage.

Comparing these with land-based renewables, most of the marine devices appear quite favourable. SNH assesses onshore wind as often having greater impacts than offshore, because of their visual and landscape impacts and their effects on bird populations – though much depends on the site chosen. Large-scale hydro has a major influence on habitats and fresh water. In contrast, biomass might be placed high up in this hierarchy – it may be relatively benign, and indeed new crops may bring about some natural heritage benefits, although this depends again on the location, scale and intensity of production. Biomass is most likely to be benign when aligned with a range of land use policy objectives from flood management to biodiversity (Sprent *et al.,* this volume).

There is a large renewables resource in Scotland: if exploited wisely, Scotland could probably power itself almost entirely from renewables. The authors believe that the 2020 targets should be regarded as just a beginning. There are four key, strategic issues:

(i) Cost: objectors to renewables developments are fond of pointing out that renewable electricity costs more to produce than conventionally-generated electricity. That is true, though it is also true that some of the environmental costs of conventional electricity are not accounted for. Overall, however, the argument is a specious one: if it costs more to provide the electricity we need in a sustainable way then so be it.

(ii) Intermittency: some types of renewable sources suffer from intermittency, and there will be a need to look more closely at how this can be overcome. Wind energy derived from installations across the UK is less likely to be vulnerable to becalmed weather conditions than deployment to a few areas. Hydroschemes currently used for baseload generation could be used to make good the gaps from wind or wave generation. Heat storage could be developed on a district heating system scale to smooth out demand on CHP (combined heat and power) systems.

(iii) Major changes in the grid are required to provide connection capacity to those parts of Scotland with the main wind, wave, and tidal resources, and also to facilitate the development of small-scale renewables at a domestic, industrial or district level so that surplus generation can be used on the grid.

(iv) Good strategic planning is needed if the most appropriate technologies are to be encouraged in the areas best able to accommodate them, and investment in a new grid infrastructure channelled in an effective way. It continues to be of concern that the Renewables Obligation – while highly successful at stimulating developer interest in renewables – has led to such an unplanned proliferation in the exploration of windfarm sites around Scotland. Ultimately such a market-led process may be wasteful of both planning authority and developers' resources.

23.4.2 Fossil fuels.

It has been shown, in section 23.3, that coal is bad in CO_2 emission terms, and others (McManus, this volume) have indicated how it is also relatively bad in terms of the scale of the natural heritage impacts associated with extraction. It would seem that from a natural heritage stance, a clear objective should be to minimize its use, unless techniques for carbon sequestration can be developed and proven to be free of any long-term risk of the gases escaping. Even if sequestration is developed and adopted, care should be taken that the availability of such technology does not simply lead to delays in the introduction of cleaner forms of energy supply and production.

Gas is better in emission terms, but the resource is strictly limited. In sustainability terms, the fact that the UK has used up its North Sea gas stocks after only 30 years is not something to be boasted about to our children. Some estimate the lifetime of remaining global gas stocks as perhaps 70-80 years. That is a very short period when measured against the numbers of future generations who potentially could benefit from the availability of gas. Probably, over the coming decades, gas might be best used primarily to make good the intermittency of renewables production, and not as a mainstream means of space heating as it is used at present. Given all the inefficiencies in transformation, it seems particularly wasteful to take a fuel like gas, turn it into electricity and then use that electricity as a fuel for space and water heating. If we do use fossil fuels to generate electricity, then it makes sense to burn them in combined heat and power plants so that none of this heat is wasted, hence more than doubling the efficiency of conversion from fuel into useful energy (Defra, 2004).

Finally comes the difficult issue of where to place nuclear within the hierarchy. It is carbon-free, so it is highly attractive from a greenhouse gas emissions point of view. Most of the risks associated with nuclear power are risks to human health - whether from leakage of wastes or accidental discharges or deliberate acts of vandalism, terrorisim – rather than adverse impacts on the natural heritage *per se*. However, in the unlikely event of another incident of Chernobyl proportions, there could be an impact on species and habitats and upon the ability of people to enjoy the countryside over a period of many generations. The risk may be small but it could be far-reaching in both physical extent and time.

So where is nuclear's place in this indicative hierarchy of natural heritage impacts? It might be placed at the top as carbon-free and, in normal operation, with few impacts on the natural heritage. However, in the light of these small but far-reaching risks, the authors are inclined to position it provisionally mid-way down, and subject to a wide margin of uncertainty; certainly better than burning coal or gas but probably not as good as some of the renewables. There is some further thinking to do on nuclear in the light of other chapters in this volume (Cooper; McSorley, this volume).

This is a very outline hierarchy, based on current and some emergent technologies. The picture could well change if new technologies are developed. If electricity storage becomes practicable on a large scale, then that would mean that small scale and intermittent supplies would become much more manageable. But new technologies bring new uncertainties, so they would need to be embraced with due caution.

23.4.3 Transport

Transport has direct impacts on the natural heritage – damage to the habitat during construction, noise and light pollution, emission of acidic nitrogen oxides (NO_x). But there are also major natural heritage benefits: people can enjoy the natural heritage far more easily as a result of transport, and in turn this leads to better awareness and understanding of its importance. Transport is a problem area – society is dependent on it and enjoys its benefits; any restrictions would bite hard on lifestyles. Yet it is a major contributor to carbon emissions. Improved vehicle efficiency can help, but the long term solution must be more fundamental because the effect of overall growth in the transport sector currently outweighs the efficiency gains by a factor of nine (DTI, 2002 updated 2004). Transport planning and public transport will play an important role, but change in personal and organizational behaviour is also needed. Policy-led pricing is likely to be needed, by which

Plate 23.2 Road, Rail and Shipping – Forth Estuary © Colin Galbraith

is meant deliberately pricing alternatives so that people choose the least polluting forms of transport. The development of biofuels will also be important, and will provide a new market for our farmers at the same time, though care will be needed to ensure that biofuel policies do not unpick the environmental and conservation objectives now built into agricultural policies. Forestry may benefit similarly, if the emerging technologies to derive ethanol from wood sources in Sweden come to fruition (Käberger, this volume).

Air transport is a key issue. If demand continues to rise as predicted, and if 'predict and provide' policies continue, aircraft emissions will jeopardize the UK's ability to meet CO_2 reduction targets. This is an area where rapid progress is needed at an international level to secure agreement on fuel taxation and common principles concerning limitation of growth. It would be helpful to show the way through policies for air transport within the UK and within the EU.

23.4.4 Domestic and industry

In the domestic and industry sectors, by far the main energy use is for space heating and lighting. There is huge scope here for measures to improve energy efficiency by, for example, promoting the use of solar heating, whether passive, active or photovoltaics, facilitating micro-renewables or off-grid renewables to meet local needs, or combining heat and power plants to meet both the electrical and heating requirements of industry or local district housing. And few if any of these measures have an adverse impact on the natural heritage. From a natural heritage perspective, it would seem that these measures should be one of the first priorities in seeking to reduce overall emissions, and introduced in the earliest stages of planning.

SNH's offices at Great Glen House, in Inverness is a good example (discussed further in Chapter 7). Having a sustainable building was placed as a high priority in the building specification, and the results are now available for all to see - a building with a large atrium which draws cool air through the working cells in summer and which provides solar heating in winter. This is an example of building sustainable energy practices into procurement procedures which needs to be extended across the public sector and into the private sector.

Across all the energy use sectors there is a general theme about the importance of changing behaviour, both at a personal and organizational level, towards a lower-energy lifestyle. How does one achieve that? Firstly, good information is important. Just as one can avoid saturated fats by choosing food on the basis of the information provided, it would be helpful to have better information on the energy efficiency of the options available, from appliances to transport systems to housing. The price of energy should at least reflect its social and environmental cost, by building in the £85 per tonne which is the assessed cost of mitigation for carbon emissions. That would not make much difference to transport that is already subject to a high level of fuel taxation, but it would significantly raise the price of electricity, oil and gas for heating. The challenge would be to do so in a way which does not aggravate that other objective of Government energy policy, alleviating fuel poverty, which remains of crucial importance in Scotland. There may even be scope for the prices for some forms of energy use to be increased artificially to encourage more sustainable alternatives. And ways should be found of positively rewarding low-energy lifestyles – providing a positive incentive for people to think more carefully about their energy use.

23.5 Conclusions

Government energy policy is based on reducing greenhouse gas emissions by 60% by 2050. There are substantial uncertainties over the emissions arising from land management and whether anything effective at all can be done to reduce those in the short term; meaning that an even higher level of reduction in the other sectors is required to achieve an overall 60% emissions reduction.

This chapter has outlined the complex matrix of the possible measures which could be taken to reduce carbon emissions, and their direct impacts on the natural heritage. It has demonstrated that the effects are very different in the various sectors. The very general measures presented – like better information on energy consumption – would not affect the natural heritage directly at all. In the domestic, industry and service sectors, addressing energy efficiency, better building design and product labelling will not impact directly on the natural heritage. In the transport sector, there may be some impacts in building more sustainable transport systems and the development of biofuel crops, but there may also be benefits in terms of fewer NO_x emissions and reduced congestion. It is through the production of electricity from renewable resources that the most significant impacts on the natural heritage, both on land and at sea, will arise.

SNH has been - and will continue to be - highly supportive of the drive towards replacement of fossil fuel energy by renewables, though it is recognized that there is a cost in terms of associated natural heritage impacts. But that support is dependent on the highest priority being placed on energy efficiency and demand reduction in the other sectors. If not, there is a risk that renewables are developed only to meet an unchecked rising energy demand, and will still fail to deliver the carbon reductions needed to mitigate climate change. So the overview just set out is important. It provides the context for SNH's stance towards renewables and all other types of energy generation and use, and for SNH's role in relation to transport developments.

Footnote

In April 2006, SNH published a policy statement 'Energy and the Natural Heritage' (SNH 2006). This statement was informed by the papers submitted to this Energy and the Natural Heritage conference, and the considerable discussion which these papers triggered.

References

Department of Environment, Food and Rural Affairs. (2001). Climate Change Agreements: Guidance on converting electricity from dedicated supplies to primary energy. CCA09, December 2001.

Department of Environment, Food and Rural Affairs. (2003). Guidelines for the measurement and reporting of emissions by direct participants in the UK Emissions Trading Scheme Protocol.

Department of Environment, Food and Rural Affairs. (2004). The UK Government's Strategy for Combined Heat and Power to 2010.

Department of Trade and Industry. (2001). Energy flowchart.

Department of Trade and Industry. (2004). Energy in Brief.

Department of Trade and Industry. (2004 update). Energy – its impact on the Environment and Society.

Department of Trade and Industry. (2002 updated 2004). Energy Consumption in the United Kingdom.

National Atmospheric Emissions Inventory (AEAT/ENV/R/1481). (2004). Greenhouse gas inventories for England, Scotland, Wales and Northern Ireland: 1990-2001.

Scottish Natural Heritage. (2006). Energy and the Natural Heritage. SNH Website http://www.snh.org.uk/strategy/enh.asp

Plate 15.2 Windfarm at sunset © Des Thompson

24 Concluding Remarks

John Thomson – *Scottish Natural Heritage, Caspian House, Clydebank Business Park, Clydebank G81 2NR.*

The wealth of material presented over the two days of this conference has proved that it is addressing the right topic at the right time. Speakers have repeatedly stressed both the gravity and the urgency of the underlying issues, and especially of the threat posed by global climate change. It was argued that society has no more than perhaps a 20 year window in which to address these challenges. There is a crying need for a wider, better informed public debate about them and all public bodies with a stake in the outcome have a responsibility to promote one.

Several of the talks, notably those by John McManus and Terry Langford, underlined the centrality of energy to human life. They strikingly mapped current concentrations of population against past energy sources. Energy is, of course, a means to an end, not an end in itself, but it is the key to a wide range of important human activities. John McManus' talk brought out just what pain and privation people in the past were prepared to endure to gain access to energy. Terry Langford's picture of a Highland cottage reminded us just how much ready access to a flexible source of energy can contribute to the quality of life, wherever people may be.

Moreover, the human appetite for energy clearly extends well beyond the desire for a basic sufficiency. Many luxuries are energy intensive, including optional travel. Janet Sprent described the social composition of those using cheap flights, highlighting the fact that they were predominantly the better-off taking the opportunity to further enhance their quality of life.

What the world faces, therefore, is a combination of very high energy consumption in the developed countries and entirely understandable aspirations in less affluent societies elsewhere to boost living standards to something even vaguely approaching the same level – with inevitable consequences for rising energy use.

It is evident that all energy sources – fossil fuels, nuclear, renewables, even biofuels – have environmental impacts. The range of these impacts is very wide: direct and indirect, short-term and long-term, ecological and aesthetic.

How significant these impacts are depends critically on how and where things are done, as Bill Band made clear. The issues raised include matters of equity and social justice, as exemplified by the effects of opencast coal mining on adjacent communities – and even of vapour trails on people who will never see the inside of an aircraft.

The problems to which our insatiable appetite for energy gives rise are not purely ones of greenhouse gases and climate change. This conference has highlighted some of the others, including oceanic acidification, which could be at least as grave. Whilst even now there remain some climate change sceptics, the whole picture presents an irresistible argument for action.

Thomson, J. (2008). Concluding Remarks. In *Energy and the Natural Heritage*, ed. by C.A. Galbraith and J.M. Baxter. TSO Scotland, Edinburgh. pp. 281-286

What form should such action take? The answer seems to be many different kinds. Clearly there is a need for action at a policy level. Encouragingly some aspirational, and even brave, decisions have been taken in Government. But the scope and requirement for action extends right down to the individual level. And whilst some of the decisions involved are relatively short-term, others are very long-term indeed. The paybacks for these decisions will often be inter-generational, in some cases extending beyond even our children's generation and far into the future.

First of all, though, we must recognize the scale of the problems that we face and accept personal responsibility for doing something about them. Chairing one of the sessions James Curran reminded us that we can't blame everything on the politicians and accuse them of not being brave enough. We get the politicians that we deserve. But if we are to take on responsibility personally then we have to know in practical terms what we can do: the issues must be made real.

What are the key requirements? Perhaps the strongest single message from the conference is that we have to grasp the pricing nettle. It isn't just that it is theoretically right to internalize environmental costs; it is that so much flows from the responses that price signals can trigger. The degree of innovation that they can stimulate is much harder to achieve by other means. So the decision to raise prices is a critical one. One area where it is particularly needed is aviation fuel – where the current absence of taxes for such an environmentally damaging activity is a glaring anomaly. But we know from past experience of fuel price protests just how controversial such increases in energy costs are likely to prove.

Given the cross-cutting nature of these issues integrated action is essential. Some speakers have pointed out how difficult it is to secure joined-up Government. It is an easy criticism to make - blame the politicians again! In fairness one can see how narrowly-focused approaches develop and why they are so hard to avoid, especially in an era of intense specialization. But it has repeatedly been pointed out that there is scope for win-win outcomes if you can make the connections. A good example lies in what Tomas Käberger had to say about opportunities in the field of biofuels. He remarked, for example, that Scottish sawmills would be competitive with Scandinavian ones if only they had a market for the co-products or by-products of their primary products, such as wood pellets for space heating. But that requires secure supply chains and the coordinated action needed to create and maintain them.

It is vital to look ahead. So many of the problems that have been presented to us have flowed from not looking far enough ahead. It may be true that all we learn from history is that it doesn't repeat itself, but nevertheless we have to try to learn from the past. James Curran produced the rather enigmatic phrase "late lessons from early warnings". Baffling though it may be, I am sure that it contains a fundamental truth.

Equally, it seems essential to, in some shape or form, "strategize". As Tony Cooper stressed, there are dangers in having strategies. They can lock you into approaches that really ought to be reconsidered and abandoned. But realistically there seems to be no alternative to having some form of strategy, which starts by asking what you want to achieve, how you can deliver it, what the timescales are and how you can mobilize the effort needed to achieve it. Whether or not we have a UK – or a Scotland – Energy Strategy, we need to think strategically and tackle the issues strategically.

What are the options? One was summarized very neatly by Fred Dinning: energy conservation and demand management. From a natural heritage standpoint these are likely to be extremely attractive options; Ian Todd pointed out that they were also likely to be the cheapest ones in most instances. Once again, though, however obvious they may appear, they will not be easily implemented. They involve changing people's behaviour and whilst some of that behaviour may be quite responsive to price signals, other aspects of it may be strongly resistant to them. Travel may well be an example of the latter.

Other possibilities include carbon sequestration. Initially, CO_2 injection could be viewed simply as a means of boosting oil output but ultimately the point was made that it also had the benefit of locking away the greenhouse gas. Given this double attraction economically, it has surely to be a serious runner.

Nuclear likewise has to be considered, and Tony Cooper presented a passionate case on its behalf. If any credible solution to the challenges that we face on the energy front has to have many components, as seems to be inevitable, then politically the thorniest question of all must be whether that mix includes a nuclear element.

Next on the list are renewables, and much of the conference was devoted to detailed analyses of the natural heritage impacts of a variety of different renewables technologies. Behind these clearly lay a desire to mitigate these adverse impacts and thereby to find a way of reconciling two potentially conflicting sets of environmental objectives.

The first characteristic of the renewables industry seems to be a multiplicity of technologies at very different stages of development. Marine technologies are clearly well behind wind. Similarly hydrogen, although it may be practical in certain limited respects quite quickly, is manifestly a long way off as a major part of an overall solution.

A second characteristic is the comparatively small output of most of these installations. Even the very large offshore windfarms that Sandy Downie described, with 250 to 300 turbines, would have an output that was no more than a small fraction of a very large thermal power station like Drax, especially when you take account of the intermittency of output.

The differing technologies also have varying siting requirements. Put this together with the modest output of individual installations and you are looking at a geographically very widely dispersed system of electricity generation. In some respects this may be desirable and a welcome move away from the traditional, concentrated model. But it would have very significant implications for the natural heritage and, I suspect, from a wider public perception and political perspective. Energy developments will affect very many people and this is likely to present an even bigger problem than the technical challenges involved.

The overall picture, therefore, is a very complex one: radically varying technologies, with very different environmental impacts, spread widely across the country.

The industry itself is also, on the evidence of the audience at this conference, quite diverse. At one extreme there are the big established energy suppliers; at the other quite small-scale concerns, even (perhaps especially in the biofuel sector) individual entrepreneurs. And whilst overall the industry is in my judgement very environmentally committed – hence some of the tensions between conflicting environmental perspectives – there are some more opportunistic elements. As the economic incentives have increased, so too has the risk that such purely commercial motives will become more pronounced. This need not even be on the part of the industry itself; very often it will reflect the aspirations of landowners, seeking a new source of income for their business.

Similarly, different operators can and do differ markedly in their familiarity with environmental issues and requirements. Some are very well-versed, extremely competent and have access to excellent professional advice. Others are much less so, and indeed a good few have little knowledge of Scotland as a place.

So what is needed to reconcile renewables and natural heritage objectives? Bill Band hit the nail on the head: "location, location and location". The single biggest trick is to get the right scheme in the right place. As part of that there is a design issue. In the case of windfarms a major factor is the size of the turbines. Technological and financial considerations are pushing people towards larger, more efficient turbines, to the point where, as I understand it, smaller ones are becoming unobtainable. Yet quite frequently turbine size is critical to determining the acceptability of a windfarm development in a particular location. As part of the reconciliation that we are seeking, shouldn't we be seeking flexibility in turbine size? Maybe there is even an economic opportunity here for a manufacturing company in Scotland to exploit – serving a market created by an environmentally-sensitive regulatory framework.

SNH has long believed that Scotland needs a stronger planning framework for the development of renewables. One possibility is some system of regional targets, which would give local authorities – as the key planning bodies – a clear context within which to do their job.

Some interesting questions have also been raised about Strategic Environmental Assessment and Environmental Impact Assessment at the project level. These include the idea that EIAs should be commissioned by the decision-making body, rather then the developer, although in accordance with the 'polluter pays' principle the latter would fund them. These issues go wider than energy developments but at the moment they are perhaps arising most acutely in relation to renewables developments.

One intriguing question is what the planning framework should be for types of renewable development other than wind. The Water Framework Directive was mentioned in relation to hydroelectricity schemes, of whatever scale. What should be the framework for future marine technologies? The issue is attracting some debate at present; it is very important that this leads to some satisfactory conclusions before too long.

Then, as several speakers have emphasized, there is a need for monitoring and for a feedback loop that enables us to apply the lessons from earlier generations of development to later ones. We remain very short of both baseline data and of evidence about interactions, which always presents a challenge to environmental bodies of how precautionary we should be in circumstances of considerable uncertainty. It is in my view incumbent on the industry to accept that we need to improve our knowledge and to exercise, in the meantime, a degree of precaution. But equally, environmental interests need to recognize that they should not hide behind a very rigid and rigorous application of the precautionary principle; for developments with an environmental objective, a degree more flexibility and pragmatism is entirely appropriate.

Some people have made it clear that they are pretty frustrated at the amount of information that SNH and other environmental bodies seek when assessing proposals. On occasions we may indeed ask far too much. But I hope that the industry will recognize that in order to make as good an assessment as possible of uncertain environmental effects, we do need a good deal of information. That material can, moreover, often be used to find ways of modifying an initially problematic proposal to keep its adverse natural heritage effects within tolerable bounds.

Plate 24.1 Wind turbine on South Ronaldsay, Orkney © Lorne Gill/SNH

In circumstances where we all recognize that we know less than we would like, there is a compelling argument for sharing whatever information we have. Here is one instance where market-based solutions, relying on carbon taxes and other such instruments, can be less satisfactory. They could easily encourage a culture of secrecy, defended on the basis of commercial confidentiality. Such hoarding of information would severely impede the growth in shared understanding that is so crucial if society is to make the right judgements about renewables – and indeed other energy-related developments.

Underlying this issue there is a yet broader and more fundamental one about honesty and trust. In this complex and tricky arena everybody must be prepared to work together. This applies particularly to industry and environmental interests. Already there is substantial cooperation in the preparation of guidance on, for example, the assessment of the risks to birds from windfarms. We need to proceed further down that road, even whilst recognizing that in some respects we are starting from different places. We shall not agree about everything but we should try to work together. The challenge for all of us is to find ways of engaging effectively with the public, and their concern for their surroundings, so well described by Laura Campbell. Public acceptance is crucial to any successful strategy for tackling the energy problems that we face; it is thus vital that the public are not offended by the renewables developments that they encounter.

Hitherto I have focused heavily on electricity generation. But before I finish, I should stress that to succeed in curbing the adverse effects of excessive energy consumption we need to address a much broader range of uses. Both Janet Sprent and Ian Todd have highlighted the fact that electricity generation only accounts for a relatively small proportion of total consumption.

We must look at heating; we must look at transport. We have heard a good deal about the scope from improving energy conservation through improved building design, for example. It would be good if such messages could get out more widely. Above all, perhaps, we should prize flexibility and adaptability. We must not shackle ourselves to particular favoured solutions: we need a multiplicity of actions and of approaches and we need to stimulate innovation.

We shall have to prepare ourselves, too, to contemplate and accept some pretty radical changes. That is quite a challenge for conservation interests, as well as for others. And it lies at the heart of the question of public acceptance. The public will only accept change if it is really convinced that it is necessary. But equally if people are persuaded, they will be prepared to go along with quite far-reaching measures.

Sometimes it takes a real shock to shift attitudes. A good case in point is the oil price hikes in the 1970s, which as we have heard triggered much of the previous effort to improve energy efficiency, especially in countries, such as Sweden, that were dependent on imported fossil fuels. There is thus a place in any credible policy approach both for progressive incremental change and for the sudden jolt, however uncomfortable the latter may be.

As part of this process we must be prepared to discard some of our preconceptions and prejudices and we have all had plenty of those. We must be prepared to learn from elsewhere. This conference has heard a good deal about how much has been achieved in continental Europe. There was much interesting information, for instance, about Sweden. And the point was strikingly made that Germany has already accomplished virtually the increase in renewables output that the UK is currently seeking. So it can be done, and we have to learn from other peoples' experience.

Despite this encouraging example, we are manifestly all feeling our way forward in this field. We have some idea of where we want to get to but we are by no means sure how we can get there. Surely this makes it all the more important that we work together in finding a way through. I conclude, therefore, by wishing us collectively good luck; we shall need it.

Glossary

AGLV – Area of Great Landscape Value
AGR – Advanced Gas-cooled Reactor
AFC – alkaline fuel cell

BACI – Before – After – Control – Impact
bar – a unit of pressure
BHA – British Hydropower Association
BOD – Biological Oxygen Demand
BPEO – Best Practicable Environmental Option
BRE – Building Research Establishment
BREEAM – British Research Establishment Environmental Assessment Method

CAA – Civil Aviation Authority
CABE – Commission for Architecture and Built Environment
CAP – Common Agricultural Policy
CAR – Controlled Activities Regulations
CBD – Convention on Biological Diversity
CCS – Carbon Capture and Storage
CCW – Countryside Council for Wales
CEGB – Central Electricity Generating Board
CHP – Combined Heat and Power
cm^2/sec – square centimetres per second
CMACS – Centre for Marine and Coastal Studies
COWRIE – Collaborative Offshore Wind Research into Environment

DBERR – The Department for Business and Regulatory Reform
DDGS – Distillers Dried Grains with Solubles
DfT – Department for Transport
DMPEM – Direct Methanol Proton Exchange Membrane fuel cell
DTI – Department of Trade and Industry

EHS – Enivironment and Heritage Service (Northern Ireland)
EIA – Environmental Impact Assessment
EMEC – European Marine Energy Centre
EMF – Electromagnetic Field
EOR – Enhanced Oil Recovery
EPS – European Protected Species
ETS – Emissions Trading Scheme
EU – European Union

FETA – Forth Estuary Transportation Authority
FREDS – Forum for Renewable Energy Development in Scotland

g/kg – gram per kilogram (a unit of mass concentration)
G TNT/kJ – grams of TNT per kilojoule a measure of explosion energy

GDP – Gross Domestic Product
GJ – gigajoule, a unit of energy
GWh – Gigawatt hour, a unit of energy
HHV – Higher Heating Value
HIE – Highlands and Islands Enterprise
HLOS – High Level Output Specification
HLW – High Level Waste
HSE – Health and Safety Executive

ICIT – International Centre for Island Technology
IEA – International Energy Agency
IEEM – Institute of Ecology and Environmental Management
ILW – Intermediate Level Waste
IMS – Integrated Management System
IPCC – International Panel on Climate Change
ISO – International Standards Organization

JNCC – Joint Nature Conservation Committee

kg/m^3 - kilograms per metre cubed
kJ/litre – kilojoules per litre
km^2 – kilometres squared
kW – kilowatt
kWh – kilowatt-hour
kWh/kg – kilowatt-hour per kilogram

LHV – Lower Heating Value
LIFE – The EU's financial instrument supporting environmental and nature conservation projects
LIIEMA – Landscape Institute and the Institute of Environmental Management and Assessment
LIMPET – Land Installed Marine Powered Energy Transformer
LLW – Low Level Waste

m^3 – cubic metres
Magnox – A now obsolete type of nuclear power reactor
MarLIN – Marine Life Information Network
MCFC – Molten Carbonate Fuel Cell
MCS – Marine Conservation Society
MEG – Marine Energy Group
MJ/litre – megajoules per litre
MSW – Multi sea winter salmon
mSv – millisieverts – a unit of radiation dose
MTR – Materials Test Reactor
MW – magawatts
MWh – megawatt hours

NAEI – National Atmospheric Emissions Inventory
NDA – Nuclear Decommissioning Authority
NE – Natural England
NFLA – Nuclear Free Local Authorities
NGO – Non-Governmental Organization
NIABY – Not in Anyone's Backyard
NIMBY – Not in My Backyard
NNR – National Nature Reserve
NOK – Norwegian Kroner
NO_x - an oxide of nitrogen
NSA – National Scenic Area

OfGem – The Office of Gas and Electricity Markets
OLF – The Norwegian Oil Industry Association
OSCP – Oil Spill Contingency Plan
OSPARCOM – Oslo and Paris Commission

PAFC – Phosphoric Acid fuel cell
PCM – plutonium contaminated material
PEM – Proton Exchange Membrane fuel cell
PFR – Prototype Fast Reactor

QHSE – Quality, Health, Safety and the Environment

RCEP – Royal Commission on Environmental Pollution
RME – Rape Methyl Ester
RO – Renewables Obligation
ROC – Renewables Obligation Certificate
RWMAC – Radioactive Waste Management Advisory Committee

SAC – Special Area of Conservation
SACTRA – Standing Advisory Committee of Trunk Road Assessment
SEA – Strategic Environmental Assessment
SEERAD – Scottish Executive Environment and Rural Affairs Department
SEPA – Scottish Environment Protection Agency
SNH – Scottish Natural Heritage
SNIFFER – Scotland and Northern Ireland Forum for Environmental Research
SO_x - oxide of sulphur
SOFC – Solid Oxide fuel cell
SPA – Special Protection Area
SRC – Short Rotation Coppices
SSSI –Site of Special Scientific Interest
STAG – Scottish Transport Appraisal Guidance
SUD – Sustainable Urban Drainage
SVEBIO – Swedish Bioenergy Association

TAPCHAN – Tapered Channel wave energy device
THORP – Thermal Oxide Reprocessing Plant
toe/ha – ton oil equivalent per hectare

UKAEA – UK Atomic Energy Authority
UKBAP – UK Biodiversity Action Plan

Index

Note: page references in **bold** indicate chapters. Those in *italics* indicate illustrations.